CYBER SECURITY
FOR
CRITICAL INFRASTRUCTURE

Redefining National Security Concepts

K S MANOJ

INDIA · SINGAPORE · MALAYSIA

Notion Press Media Pvt Ltd

No. 50, Chettiyar Agaram Main Road,
Vanagaram, Chennai, Tamil Nadu – 600 095

First Published by Notion Press 2022
Copyright © K S Manoj 2022
All Rights Reserved.

ISBN 979-8-88503-639-9

Dedicated to

Late Gen.Bipin Rawatji,
(First Chief of Defence Staff of the
Indian Armed Forces.)

"Manjari"
Temple Road, Sasthamangalam
Thiruvananthapuram - 695 010
Ph: 0471-2720941, email: gmnairg@gmail.com
Mobile: 9446523700

G. MadhavanNair
Past President
International Academy of Astronautics (IAA)
Former Chairman, ISRO

Foreword

In modern world computers, software's and connectivity has become the main stay for life. These technologies have matured and evolved into systems providing various kinds of services. In early days standalone computers were performing various data acquisition, control and command functions in manufacturing plants, in scientific research and managing power system, telecom and automated functioning of transportation.Software and data play very major role in providing efficient services. In such standalone system ensuring the security and safety was relatively simple affair. It could be implemented by controlled entry to such installations and protection by password and encryption so that authorized persons only can get access to the system and make any corrections or modifications. With the advent of Internet and fast connectivity across the globe the situation has completely changed. Cyber networks are no more contained within the four walls of the institutions. Creation of large common database, cloud computing sharing the hardware resources and passing on knowledge has been facilitated. At the same time there is a risk of misuse of such resources. It is a common experience that any technology developed for peaceful application are modified or misused for causing damage to others especially in the fully automated world this is really becoming a real menace.

In the early days we have seen various forms of viruses which can affect the software, hardware in a computer and virtually cripple. Of course immediately R & D teams swing into action to find antivirus, software which can to a great extend protect the system. Multiple firewalls access control using passwords and encryption had also been modified suitably. Notwithstanding his there is virtually a war going on between the hackers and the software development community provide adequate protection.

In this book the author addresses to how the critical infrastructure facility can be protected from cyber-attacks. His main experience in the field of electric power generation and distribution has been exploited to demonstrate the vulnerability and possible solutions. The large manufacturing plants, power grids, power plants, digital communication, networks, highways, air traffic, marine cargo movements was some of the examples of the critical infrastructure for any country. In all the systems computer software and interface hardware make use of advanced capabilities of digital systems. Most of these systems are configured and controlled remotely using advanced software techniques. Any interruption on interference with these can virtually paralyzed the life in metros or commercial activities. The recent example quoted there was a total out age of power in several cities like USA and China are examples of this catastrophe. It could be due to inherent limitation in the operating system or by deliberate action by hostile groups. Day by day the hackers are finding new techniques by which they can penetrate even the strongest firewall or initiate attacks using techniques like Trojan Horse.

The textbook is well organized and renowned the final aspects of ensuring security 2 critical infrastructure the various security protocols and standards to be followed.

The author Shri. K S Manoj with his Engineering and Physics as well as first hand knowledge about Industrial control systems has done an excellent work in researching most advanced field of cyber security aspects of critical infrastructure earlier he had authored four titles Industrial automation with SCADA, cyber security in industrial automation power system of commercial, smart grid concept to design the present document namely cyber security for critical infrastructure is meant for students and teachers and researchers working on advanced studies related to cyber security. I am sure the author will continue his research and the most advanced field which is very much needed by the society. May God bless him with long life and energy to bring out more such document for the benefit of young generation.

G. Madhavan Nair
Former Chairman ISRO.

Contents

List of Figures

List of Tables

Preface

MESSAGE FROM THE AUTHOR

Industrial Control Systems (ICS) are ubiquitous in many areas of Critical Infrastructure (CI), controlling everything from nuclear power plants to Water Purification Plants. As it continuously innovates and appropriately amalgamates Information and Communications Technology (ICT), sophistication of cyber-attacks also increases. Today almost in every month, in every day, in every hour and in every minute, the security researchers encounter hundreds and thousands of cyber-attacks on ICS with new worms and viruses.

The present cyber security counter-measures are inadequate and chaotic as the astuteness of cyber-attacks grow exponentially. Multiple *Stuxnet* attacks on Iran's nuclear facility has demonstrated it. Hence comprehending and contributing to defend the national critical infrastructure is an obligatory challenge for all loyal security adepts of all nations.

Careful attention is given to providing the reader with clear and comprehensive background and pertinent to CI infrastructure and its security. This book also provides information regarding specific operating and security issues and methods which are suitable to monitor and protect the CI and design strategies to reduce threats. It also offers chapters on CI cyber threats, attacks, metrics, risk, intrusion detection and security testing for current system owners who wish to securely configure and operate their CI.

There are very few books available in the market on the cyber-security of Critical Infrastructure. Hence this book may be a worthy addition.

It is written in such a manner that most of its contents are quite readable even by novices in OT cyber security. Also written with an imagination that it can be used for teaching a course on the industrial cyber-security.

TARGET AUDIENCE

This book is intended for a specific range of readers who want to secure the environment of CI systems will indeed benefit from an understanding of CI physical-cyber security concepts, challenges, mitigation strategies, ICS security standards, secure communication, attack vectors, risk assessment etc. This includes professionals who are engaged with design and implementation of CI-ICS, its security auditing, evolving Smart Grid etc. and the Electronics and Automation Engineering students. Security solution architects and technocrats who conduct research in CI security may also be interested in addition to CI-automation project managers, national security agencies, cyber security analysts and auditors, cyber security consultants and industrial cyber security policy makers.

SALIENT FEATURES

Critical infrastructure describes the physical and cyber systems & assets that are so vital to any nation that their incapacity or destruction would have a debilitating impact on our physical or economic security or public health or safety. This book explains the current cyber threat landscape and discusses the strategies being used by governments and corporate sectors to protect against these threats. Initially the book provides a historical reference with concept of critical infrastructure, cyber space, documented cyber-attacks, and description of viruses, worms, malware, and other cyber threats that created the need for the cyber security for critical infrastructure. It then discusses the vulnerabilities of critical infrastructures especially in the power system, the broad arsenal of cyber-attack tools, and the various mitigation strategy issues involved in protecting the infrastructures. It goes on to cover cyber intelligence tactics, recent examples of cyber conflict and warfare, and the key issues in formulating a national strategy to defend power grid against cyber terrorism.

- Presents a mixture of theoretical work and real-world implementation of cyber security in critical Infrastructure.

- It discusses the potential impact of industry-wide transformational changes, such as virtualization, social media, cloud computing, structured and unstructured data, big data, and data analytics.

- Provides the reader with a good understanding of both physical-cyber-securities in detail.

- Discusses a detailed description of the cyber-vulnerabilities and mitigation techniques for Critical Infrastructure of a Nation.

- Presents many real-world documented examples of attacks against Critical Infrastructure of various Nations.

- Provides information about industrial cyber security standards presently used.

- Explores defense-in-depth strategy of ICS from conceptualisation to materialisation.

- Is a suitable material for automation engineers and OT cyber security professionals to learn the OT security for Critical Infrastructure.

Organization of the Book

This book is mainly intended for practicing industrial cyber security engineers and post graduate students of Computer Science and Automation who wish to be the part of implementation of cyber security of critical infrastructure of any nation. Every action is a depended variable of energy and it is an accepted fact that there is a revolutionary change taking place in the automation of industrial sector and one of them is the automation of Critical Infrastructure which is the most important infrastructure of any nation. This book has been arranged in nine chapters beginning with the introduction of critical infrastructure concepts.

Chapter 1: CRITICAL NATIONAL INFRASTRUCTURE: Critical Information Infrastructure (CII) is generally believed as those computer resource, the destruction of which, shall have debilitating impact on national security, economy, public health or safety. Ensuring seamless operation of critical infrastructure requires safeguarding the availability and integrity of machinery. This means that organizations overseeing critical infrastructure must foresee any possible risks and implement systems, procedures, and technologies that mitigate or remove these risks so as to keep their operations running. This chapter gives brief description of Information Infrastructure, critical infrastructure of a nation, its criticality, interdependencies, National and Global Information Infrastructure, etc. It also explains the asset identification, critical assets and determining its criticality.

Chapter 2: CYBER SPACE AND ATTACKS: The word *cyber* has become one of the most omnipresent and powerful concepts in contemporary security studies. Today, cyberspace has emerged as a domain of its own, in many ways like land, sea and air. Even if a nation whether it is small in land area, low in GDP, low in resources, less important in geopolitics, low in strength of armed forces, it can be a military super power if that nation is capable of launching a cyber-attack on critical infrastructures of any nation including superpowers and crumble the nation. This chapter begins with a brief concept of cyber space and the security definitions in cyber space. Various threat sources to ICS, its vulnerabilities, dreadful ICS malwares and the documented incidents.

Chapter 3: OPERATIONAL TECHNOLOGY AND SCADA: Chapter begins with explaining Operational Technology (OT) and its difference with Information Technology (IT). Then this chapter describes the Industrial Control Systems, its various types, functioning, control and network components. It then move on to explaining the communication architecture of basic SCADA. Then moves on to describing the common communication philosophies adopted in DCS. As the reliability and availability of DCS functions are the most important, they are briefly introduced, but cater the necessary understanding to industrial security professionals. It then explains the concepts of Fault Tolerant Systems, Fail Safe redundant systems, High Availability, etc.

Chapter 4: CRITICAL INFRASTRUCTURE COMPONENTS: This chapter gives an introduction to SCADA with an emphasis on Data Acquisition Systems (DAS) and its components. The objectives and advantages as well as the evolution of SCADA are briefly discussed but with clarity. A brief discussion of the various components of DAS such as Sensors, Signal conditioners, Sample and Hold circuits, Analog to Digital Converters, etc. are also given in this chapter. A brief discussion regarding the selection criteria of the DAS is then given before moving to give a comprehensive description of Remote Terminal Units (RTU), Programmable Logic Controller (PLC) and the different modern components of Power System SCADA such as Intelligent Electronic Devices, Data Concentrator Units, Merging Units, Human Machine Interface, etc. The brief introduction of Data Concentrators and Merging Units are presented in such a manner that how digital substations can be designed. This chapter then gives an introduction of architecture of SCADA Master Stations and its hardware and software components. It concludes with a brief description of Geographical Positioning

System (GPS) and the network components generally deployed in the automation.

Chapter 5: COMMUNICATION IN CRITICAL INFRSTRUCTURE: This chapter has focused on various communication aspects of the industrial SCADA with an emphasis on DCS and Smart Grid. It begin with discussing various types of transmission technology in very modest way so that it is very apt and most essential for a power engineer who engaged in the design and implementation of SCADA and Smart Grid. The chapter then discusses the guided and unguided media used today for communication in such a manner that it is very useful for a practicing communication professional, which includes the various cabling issues as well. The various but most relevant communication technologies which find space not only in industrial SCADA but also in other smart automation technologies today are discussed comprehensively. Finally the chapter focused on the security issues of the wireless communication technology.

Chapter 6: RISK ASSESSMENT AND MITIGATION STRATEGIES: Risk assessment are very important issues in ICS and SCADA systems. Unless security flaws are not properly identified, they cannot be fixed. For this computer professionals and automation engineers have to have an in-depth knowledge of industrial networking to guide and implement right solutions to fix the security holes. This chapter begins with describing Risk Calculation, Risk Assessment Steps such as Asset Identification, System Characterization, Threat Modelling and Mitigation Strategies. Chapter concludes with a short description about PenTest.

Chapter 7: MITIGATION WITH DEFENSE IN DEPTH ARCHITECTURE: It can seem as a difficult task to keep track of all the ICS security threats those are out there, and the new ones that just keep emerging. Whether the media is creating a culture of fear out of being online and placing trust in leaving the information out for all to see and manipulate, or whether the threats that wait in the dark corners of the internet are truly serious and can happen to anyone. The best thing one can all do is to be prepared to mitigate with preventive and counter measures. There is no way to be completely sure that a system is impenetrable by cyber threats. The responsibility of the computer professionals and automation engineers is to ensure that the ICS systems are secure as much as possible. This chapter gives the modern aspects of ICS security based on the *Defence-in-Depth architecture* describing all the five levels of security *viz.* Physical Security, Network Security, Computer Security, Application Security and Device Security.

Chapter 8: PROTOCOLS, STANDARDS AND GUIDELINES: In ICS whatever data is gathered in the field, has to be send to the control room for processing and decision making. Being an industrial process, which is to be controlled in real-time mostly from a remote control room, the data and the control information have to be exchanged in a most secure manner. In computer science, this is achieved by encrypting the data and using proper protocols. Hence an essential and appropriate knowledge of various relevant protocols adopted and developed for ICS are required for a security engineer to get a proper control over the security process. This chapter briefly describes the various ICS Protocols, the various security standards such as IEC 62443, NIST 800, NERC CIP and ISO 27001 and their selection requirements.

Chapter 9: INVESTIGATIONS AND LITIGATIONS OF CYBERCRIMES IN CII: Cyber-attacks on CI are in increase day by day. As the attackers gain the complex ICS technology which governs the CI, the attacks will become successful. The world witnessing this today with successful cyber-attacks on CI (power grid, oil & gas pipeline, etc.)of many nations including super powers. Though the CERT could block some of these attacks by configuring the firewalls, or blocking the data flow independently this is not a right solution **in** industrial world as seamless functionality has to be ensured. Hence a proper investigation of the cyber incidents have to be carried out to identify the real cause and patch up the holes appropriately. Unfortunately the present system in any many nations are not capable to carry out this because of the lack of team work comprising of domain experts, techno savvy judges and lawyers. This chapter explains various cybercrimes, terrorist attacks, incident response process, complexities in cybercrimes, cyber law for cyber terrorism, digital evidence gatherings, etc.

About the Author

K S Manoj an automation engineer and physicist with research interest in physical-cyber security of Industrial Control Systems (ICS) who continues to explore the adoption of new security strategies in order to promote safer and more reliable automation infrastructures. Initially he specialized in design and development of ICS, by focusing on monitoring and control of SCADA and DCS networks. However after realizing the importance of the industrial cyber security, he later focused towards the threat vectors of advanced attacks in these complex interdependent critical infrastructure environments and framing mitigation strategies. He holds an M.Tech (*Communication Electronics*) from Department of Electronics, CUSAT, India and has over 30 years of experience in Automation and Energy Engineering specializing in power system automation and critical infrastructure security. He has authored four more titles viz. Industrial Automation with SCADA, Cyber Security in Industrial Automation, Power System Automation and Smart Grid-Concepts to Design. He may be contacted *ksmanoj321@gmail.com*.

Acknowledgements

First and foremost, let me contemplate over the compassion of Sree Narayana Gurudev and the 51 Akshara deities of Wisdom at Pournamikavu for giving me the ambience and mindset to write this complex technical book. A relaxed mind and inspiring friends are most essential to have a tireless body to write a technical book. Hence the availability of technically cognizant colleagues and friends who are willing to spend time both to discuss complex technical matters and suggest remarks on the structure and sections of this book, are of great advantage to the author. Else it would have been a fretting bustle. I also remember my parents with respect and sincerely thank to all my friends, colleagues and classmates who helped me with many technical debates and especially for reading and commenting on presentation of particular sections of this book.

I express my profound gratitude for the spiritual support of Rithambarananda Swamiji of Sivagiri Mutt without which this attempt would not be materialized. I remember my dear professors with great respect especially *Prof. S. Sooryadas, Dr. G.S. Bhuvaneshwer, Dr. C.S. Sridhar, Prof. P. Saraswathy, Dr. M.S. Valiyathan, Dr. M. Harisankar, Dr. K.G. Nair, Dr. P. Mohanan, Dr. Tessamma Thomas, Dr. R. Gopikakumari and Dr. P. Sethumadhavan* for their support and blessings. I also remember my cousins especially Saji Natarajan, R. Ranjith, and K.S. Jayamohan, for their genuine love and support which have also been very crucial in non-academic aspects. Finally I dedicate this work to Late Gen. Bipin Rawatji, the first Chief of Defence Staff of the Indian Armed Forces.

In spite of all my efforts, there may be quite a few errors remaining in the book, and there would have been many more. Without the help of the expert reviewers, they may not be corrected and any suggestions for improvement of this book are always welcome. The author will be definitely privileged, if the readers get the intended sense which is the sole aim of this effort.

My sincere thanks to the publishers for their support and co-operation on this project.

– **K S Manoj**

Critical Infrastructure of a Nation

1.1 INTRODUCTION

Critical Information Infrastructure (CII) of a nation is usually considered as those computer resources and networks, the destruction of which, shall have debilitating impact on national security, economy, public health or safety. Ensuring continuous operation of critical infrastructure requires safeguarding the availability and integrity of machinery. This means that organizations overseeing critical infrastructure must foresee any possible risks and implement systems, procedures, and technologies that mitigate or remove these risks so as to keep their operations running. This chapter gives brief description of Information Infrastructure, critical infrastructure of a nation, its criticality, interdependencies, National and Global Information Infrastructures, etc. It also explains the asset identification, critical assets, determining criticality, etc.

1.2 INFORMATION INFRASTRUCTURE

Information systems infrastructure refers to a range of devices and technologies, applications and systems, standards and conventions that the individual user or the collective rely on to work on different organizational tasks and processes. This technological advancement led to generation of huge data which, in turn, required IT for management, storage, processing and dissemination of data or information to different stakeholders, partners and vendors.

Initially, the applications and programmes were developed for standalone functions, but as the reliance on IT grew, the industrial and business processes began to get integrated. Hence, an information system was initially understood to be just an application of computers developed to help large organizations to process the vast amount of data in order to improve their management of information. Evolving from mainframe computing to the client/server networks and enterprise computing or the cloud computing of today, information systems do not just perform auxiliary functions such as payroll processing but also underpin almost every vital function, be it human resource management, production, project management or business analytics. As the computer technologies have developed and matured over time, their potential applications areas also have increased manifold, and accordingly the role of an information system and the scope of the discipline has widened both horizontally and vertically.

There are many stakeholders involved in the design, development and maintenance of information infrastructure. No single body, or organization or government can perform all these tasks individually or muster the resources to develop such a massive infrastructure. Therefore, keeping the information infrastructure up and running is a collective effort of multiple actors. Small to large segments of independent infrastructure, when woven into a web of network, manifest in the form of national information infrastructure (NII) and global information infrastructure (GII).

The term *critical* refers to infrastructure that provides an essential support for economic and social well-being, for public safety and for the functioning of key government responsibilities, such that disruption or destruction of the infrastructure would result in catastrophic and far-reaching damage. Therefore, critical infrastructure is composed of the basic services on which nation states have developed dependency, and they are necessary to support the society, economy and to ensure national stability. The loss, damage, unavailability, though for a short duration, can have significant consequences and cascading effects far beyond the targeted sector and physical location of the incident.

1.3 TOPOGRAPHIES OF INFORMATION INFRASTRUCTURE

To be able to meet the challenges embedded in the new role for IT, it is imperative that new IT infrastructure has certain basic features that improve its capabilities. Some of the important features are described below:

1. The new IT infrastructure shall cover a wider geographical area and support a variety of access methods and diverse protocols for communication. Local Area Networks (LANs), Wider Area Networks (WANs) and the Internet shall be integral parts of IT infrastructures of reasonably moderate sized companies.

2. IT infrastructure shall focus on global operations and resources. It shall have to be supported by a well-established communication plan. Such a plan shall cover whole gamut of users, in and outside the organisation, and shall have multi-level access controls and security features.

3. IT infrastructure shall isolate the technology from the end user environment, providing flexibility to change technology without the need to reorient the end user environment. The end user need not know where and how information is stored and being made accessible. This will ensure security.

4. The new IT infrastructure must have facilities to accept data in unstructured form. Outputs of electronic spreadsheets that are becoming so popular these days shall have to be acceptable for integration. Interface of data with other standard software tools shall become absolute necessity and facilities for data exchange shall be essential in the new IT infrastructure.

5. Quick adaptability to the changes in operating environment shall be an important feature of new systems. Ability of the systems to cope up with changes in product lines, packing sizes/trading lets, clubbing of related products and services shall have to be very quick and quite natural to the systems.

Similarly, systems shall accept a variety of combination of information needs and external data shall flow in them. Exception reporting shall be a regular feature for the systems. Policy changes shall be easy to implement on new systems and policy implications on various parameters of the business shall be easily traceable.

1.4 NATIONAL INFORMATION INFRASTRUCTURE (NII)

The National Information Infrastructure (NII) is a high-priority national initiative to combine communications networks, computers, databases, and consumer electronics to deliver information services to all citizens of a nation. It includes both public and private networks, the internet, the public switched network, and cable, wireless, and satellite communications. National Information Infrastructure (NII) includes more than just the physical facilities used to transmit, store, process and display voice, data and images, rather it includes:

➤ A wide range of equipment including cameras, scanners, key boards, telephones, fax machines, computers, switches, compact disks, video and audio tape, cable, wire, satellite, optical fiber transmission lines, micro wave nets, televisions, monitors, printers and much more.

➤ NII requires building foundations for living in the Information Age and for making these technological advances useful to the public including libraries.

➤ The information itself, which may be in the form of video programming, scientific or business databases, images, sound recordings, library archives and other media.

➤ Applications and software that allow users to access, manipulate, organize and digest the proliferating mass of information that the NII will facilitate to put their fingertips.

➤ The network standards and transmission codes that facilitate interconnection and interoperation between networks and, ensure the privacy of persons and the security of the information carried, as well as the security and reliability of networks.

➤ NII will enable to develop new electronic communities and share knowledge and experiences thereby leading to economic growth of a nation.

Technical Features

Both the capability and the demand for National Information Infrastructure (CII) depend much on technological advancements in microelectronics and fiber optical communication and have become the major drivers. However National Information Infrastructure (NII) would have the following technological characteristics.

Speed: Data transmission speed will be substantially faster e.g. hundreds of thousands, millions, or billions of bits per second. That is why optical fiber is fast replacing the traditional copper wires in certain segments of communications because of its extremely high data carrying capacity.

Information and Communication Technology: computer and communication technologies are being inseparably amalgamated. Distributed computing applications are finding increasing demands on the capacity of the communication systems, and computing and presently embedded in the network.

Digital technology: Information in digital format could be transmitted more reliably and quickly, but it is in a form directly usable by computers. That means information can be stored, manipulated and displayed in many ways it can also be recognized and interpreted within the transmission system, which is itself, computer controlled. Digital information can also be made more secure. All the security system algorithms are designed for digital information only.

Portability: Digital radio, digital mobile phone, laptops have the facility of connectivity anywhere, any time.

ISDN: In digital encoding, all forms of information, sound, computer data, images, or text could be handled for, transmission or processing.

Flexibility: The system will be far more flexible and able to support a wide variety of services beyond imagination. Of course much of the capability will reside in its computer software and databases rather than hardware.

ICT is the key to growth and development of NII and GII. The NII's telecommunication system should exhibit the following characteristics.

    a.   A sufficiently broad bandwidth to enable both existing and future digital systems and services,

    b.   Universal connectivity among homes, business etc.

c. User friendly seamless interaction and interoperability within both the NII and GII,

d. Network security, user privacy and protection of intellectual property rights.

e. Accessibility to mobile users through fully functional wireless systems.

Components of NII

Broadly speaking, the National Information infrastructure consists of four parts:

Hardware: Microelectronics and the related technologies of satellites, fiber optics, all form of digital networks, coaxial cable system, along with all the mainframe, mini and microcomputers, terminals and workstations that store and access information

Software: Software comprises the information systems and computer programmes that enable end users to operate hardware efficiently and effectively by telling it what to do, how to do it and when to do it.

Supporting physical and human resources: This component is composed of all the physical plant and facilities and the supporting human resources.

Data, Information and Awareness: The fourth component is the actual data, information and knowledge in whatever media or format, (electronic, optical, hard copy) in the digital form in computer data centers, or in archival repositories, or in literature in libraries.

1.5 GLOBAL INFORMATION INFRASTRUCTURE (GII)

The Global Information Infrastructure (GII) can be defined as a seamless web of interactive communications being deployed world-wide to provide the infrastructure for new services and activities based on the strategic use of all types and formats of information.

The GII will depend upon an ever-expanding range of technology and products, including telephones, fax machines, computers, switches, compact discs, video and audio tape, coaxial cable, wire, satellites, optical fiber transmission lines, microwave networks, televisions, scanners, cameras, and printers as well as advances in computing, information, and networking technologies.

But the GII extends beyond hardware and software, it is also a system of applications, activities, and relationships. There is the information itself, whatever its purpose or form. There are also standards, interfaces, and transmission codes that facilitate interoperability between networks and ensure the privacy and security of the information carried over them, as well as the security and reliability of the networks themselves. Most importantly, the GII includes the people involved in the creation and use of information, development of applications and services, construction of the facilities, and training necessary to realize the potential of the GII.

The development of a Global Information Infrastructure offers many new opportunities and poses many new challenges. Properly used, new computer and communications technologies can foster democracy, open new markets, create high-paying jobs, promote peace and international understanding, promote freedom of expression and freedom of information, and foster sustainable development. Global Information Infrastructure should not be used by governments to monitor their citizens, commit acts of terrorism, or fight an information war in cyberspace.

Computer and communications technologies are advancing so quickly and are being used in so many new and unexpected ways that it is hard for policy-making to keep pace. This has been particularly true in the area of national security and international relations where many of the consequences of the development of the GII can often only be guessed at. The task is made even harder because relatively little serious study has been done on these questions.

1.6 CRITICAL INFRASTRUCTURE OF A NATION

An infrastructure of a nation is a system, made up of several facilities to enable a specific set of activity for the benefit of society. The surface, air and water transportation enable the movement of people, goods and freight, interconnected banking operations, network of ATMs and other financial services over Internet enable delivery of banking services round the clock in every corner of the world etc. are typical examples of infrastructure. These infrastructures are dependent on other infrastructure to dispense their core functions. Banking system uses telecommunication network to deliver mobile banking or security functions. Energy sector (electricity generation) depends the transportation infrastructure for bringing the fuel (coal, LSHS, naphtha etc.) to the generation site. The seamless functioning of these facilities are most essential for a nation for the normal function of societies. Hence they are considered as critical. In fact the term the term *critical* refers to infrastructure that provides an essential support for economic and social well-being, for public safety and for the functioning of key government responsibilities, such that disruption or destruction of the infrastructure would result in catastrophic and far-reaching damage. Different nations defines critical infrastructure in different manner.

The Australian government defines critical infrastructure as physical facilities, supply chains, information technologies and communication networks are deemed critical for the functioning of a nation state, because, if destroyed or degraded, they would impact social and economic well-being or affect the ability to ensure national security.

The US government has defined critical infrastructure as physical and cyber-based systems essential to the minimum operations of the economy and government, whose incapacitation or destruction would have debilitating impact on the national security and the economic and social welfare of a state.

The EU has defined critical infrastructure as an asset, system or part thereof located in Member States which is essential for the maintenance of vital societal functions, health, safety, security, economic or social well-being of people, and the disruption or destruction of which would have a significant impact in a Member State as a result of the failure to maintain those functions.

The critical national infrastructure has been defined by the Government of United Kingdom (UK) as those critical elements of infrastructure (namely assets, facilities, systems, networks or processes and the essential workers that operate and facilitate them), the loss or compromise of which could result in:

- Major detrimental impact on the availability, integrity or delivery of essential services—including those services, whose integrity, if compromised, could result in significant loss of life or casualties—taking into account significant economic or social impacts and/or

- Significant impact on national security, national defence, or the functioning of the state.

Through an executive order in 1996, the President of the US declared the following as their critical Infrastructure.

- Telecommunications,
- Electrical power systems,
- Gas and oil storage and transportation,
- Banking and finance,
- Transportation,
- Water supply systems,
- Emergency services (including medical, police, fire and rescue) and
- Continuity of governance.

So the definitions and scope of critical infrastructure vary from country to country, so does the degree of dependency of different sectors on information infrastructure. However, maintaining social and economic well-being and ensuring national security and public safety remain the underlying principles or core of the concept of critical infrastructure. As mentioned earlier, critical infrastructures, in their respective country and capacity, have certain degree of dependency on the information infrastructure. The critical infrastructures rely on a range of ICT based control systems or information systems for continuous and reliable operations. Therefore, ICT has not just become omnipresent but it also connects infrastructure systems, subsystems and constituents in such a manner that they have subsequently become highly interrelated and interdependent.

1.7 CRITICAL INFORMATION INFRASTRUCTURE (CII)

Within the last two decades, advances in information and communications technologies have revolutionized Government, scientific, educational, and commercial infrastructures. Higher processing power of end devices, miniaturization, reducing memory storage cost, wireless networking technologies capable of supporting high bandwidth and widespread use of internet have transformed stand-alone systems and predominantly closed networks into a virtually seamless fabric of interconnectivity. ICT or information infrastructure enables large scale processes throughout the economy, facilitating complex interactions among systems across global networks. Their interactions propel innovation in industrial design and manufacturing, e-commerce, e-governance, communications, and many other economic sectors. The information infrastructure provides for processing, transmission, and storage of vast amounts of vital information used in every domain of society, and it enables Government agencies to rapidly interact with each other as well as with industry, citizens, state and local governments, and the Governments of other Nations.

Information technology, itself as an infrastructure and has become an integral part of the critical infrastructure of a nation. It encompass interconnected computers, servers, storage devices, routers, switches and other related equipments increasingly support the functioning of such critical national capabilities. Hence, the part of the information infrastructure that is essential for the continuity of critical infrastructure services is known as Critical Information Infrastructure (CII) and the ICT has become a vital part of the CII as well and need to be protected from cyber-attacks.

In essence, there are certain common criteria which reflect across the different definitions or varying perspectives on the constituents of critical infrastructure. First, there exists a computer resource, upon which other physical systems or processes are dependent, and this computer resource, if compromised or incapacitated, would cause widespread damage, which might have severe consequences. This control system, which takes care of a critical process in the plant, has a computer resource which monitors the gauged physical parameters and executes a predefined or programmed industrial function. In India the following sectors are declared as CII by the National Critical Information Infrastructure Protection Centre (NCIIPC).

Critical Infrastructure Sectors in India

1. Transportation:
    a. Civil Aviation
    b. Railways and
    c. Shipping,

2. Power and Energy:
    a. Thermal Power,
    b. Hydroelectric Power,
    c. Nuclear Power,
    d. Oil and Natural Gas,
    e. Power Grid,
    f. Oil Refineries and
    g. All type of Renewable Energy,

3. Information and Communications Technology:
    a. PSTN Network,
    b. Satellite Communication,
    c. Network Backbone,
    d. Mobile Telephony and
    e. Broadcasting,

4. Defence:
    a. Indian Army,
    b. Indian Navy,
    c. Indian Air Force and
    d. Indian Coast Guard,

5. Banking, Financial Services and Insurance:

  a. Reserve Bank of India,

  b. Stock Exchanges,

  c. Banking Sector,

  d. Clearing Houses and

  e. Payment Gateways.

6. e-Governance and Strategic Public Enterprises:

  a. NIC and

  b. e-Governance Infrastructure.

Critical Infrastructure Protection (CIP)

As explained the operational stability and security of Critical Infrastructure is vital for economic security of a Nation and hence its protection must be given paramount importance. Many Nations consider power sector as Super/Crucial Critical Infrastructure (SCI) as it is the back bone of almost all industry. One of the purposes of Critical Infrastructure protection is to establish a real-time ability for all sectors of the critical infrastructure community to share information on the current status of infrastructure elements. Ultimately, the goal is to protect the Critical Infrastructure by eliminating the known vulnerabilities and develop a proactive defence mechanism to counter cyber-attacks to Critical Infrastructure. Thus the need of the hour is to chalk out a national policy for Critical Infrastructure Protection (CIP), created through a partnership between the government and private industry

1.8 CRITICALITY IN CII

By definition, criticality assessment of an asset is the estimation of its relative importance as compared to other assets, and in concept, it is based upon a wide variety of factors, such as the significance, mission or function it performs; the extent to which Criticality assessment is important because it aids the practitioners, based on the factors, in prioritizing the security of those assets that require elevated protection, given the finite resources and budgetary constraints.

Critical infrastructure, by virtue of its structural evolution, is a highly complex, heterogeneous and interdependent infusion of facilities, systems and functions that are extremely vulnerable to a wide variety of threats. Given the immense size and scope of this vast potential target set, it is absolutely infeasible to completely protect all the assets at all times, against all conceivable threats, through all probable threat vectors. It is essential to define between critical assets and noncritical assets in order to gain a clear picture of the impact of failures, disruptions and analysis of risk with respect to the business functions, depending on the importance of the asset to the core mission of the enterprise. In other words, if called as criticality assessment, the purpose of the exercise is to compute the relative importance of the assets, as a derivative of various factors such as their function, risk exposure and significance in terms of enterprise security, economic security, public safety or any other criterion laid out.

The process of determining the criticality of an asset is usually done in four stages and they are:

1. In this step dependency of core mission or key business processes on the asset and the difficulty in restoring the services in the case of damage or disablement has to be evaluated.

2. The second step envelopes vulnerability of the asset and deliberates on redundancy built up with the asset and its access.

3. In the third step criticality assessment, the attractiveness to the adversary, given the importance and vulnerability of the assets are to be evaluated, based on the apparent value of the asset to the adversary.

4. The fourth step, and the most difficult to assess, is the public reaction when public safety is endangered and the adverse effect on society, either in the form of deteriorating public confidence, the behavior of stock markets or financial sector and the open issues of liability have to be evaluated.

In principle, criticality assessment is generally carried out in every department or unit of an organization in some way or the other, though it may or may not be in detail. However, when the organization is part of the critical infrastructure of a nation, either perceived or designated as, its critical assets need to be assessed in a conscientious manner. While figuring out the answers to the process of determining the criticality, the analysts have to assess under a defined framework or a set of parameters. Defining and drawing on these parameters could be the jurisdiction of the organization or the sector it belongs to, or there could be nationally agreed upon parameters to conduct the criticality assessment as part of a regulatory framework.

Criticality Parameters

The criticality of an asset or an industrial function is dependent upon a range of factors, such as the duration of loss of service or equipment, availability of alternatives to execute the same function or the time taken to bring back the service into functioning. Therefore, the resilience of an industrial function, or a business process or an asset, to the instances of disruption and degradation increases when the substitutes which can promptly restore the services to normalcy are readily available.

Service disruptions or equipment degradation can culminate into cascades of failure if other business functions are highly dependent on the outputs of the given system. This is the characteristic which brings in the element of criticality. Industrial functions, at the micro level, have certain degrees of dependence on other functions, whether they are upstream or downstream in the chain. Owing to certain characteristics, and to the specific functions they perform, their degree or magnitude of criticality varies. The parameters given in Table 1.1 contribute towards the criticality of an asset, an industrial function or probably for an infrastructure. However, this list is indicative, and there may be additional parameters subjective to the specific case under consideration. In addition, the moment of failure, the criticality of an infrastructure could vary with time as at a specific time of the day or under specific circumstances, its criticality can be high.

Criticality	Redundancy
	Restoration Time
	Impact Severity
	Probability
	Impact Type
	Interdependency
	ICT Dependency

Table 1.1: Criticality Parameters

The key principle to ensure availability of a function or asset is incorporating *redundancy*. A redundant function or asset, even if disrupted, is less likely to impact the mission-critical processes, while a function without redundancy becomes critical and, at the same time, vulnerable. Redundancy, must be incorporated as the part of the design has become the key principle to ensure availability of the mission critical services under all circumstances. Moving forward, the assets or services with high duration of failure or higher mean time to restore are undoubtedly critical as they require more time for total recovery. Their higher downtime between service restoration, or time required for reinstating business continuity, make them a point of vulnerability. The assets or services which have high degree of impact or severity also contribute more towards criticality.

An asset whose disruption, loss or unavailability could significantly disrupt, or for that matter even cease, the operations of the entire facility/ industry/infrastructure gains higher on criticality as the consequences could be catastrophic. While assessing the criticality of infrastructure, this parameter could also be quantified in terms of percentage of population affected or percentage of services impacted, or the number of causalities or the number of users impacted. As a parameter, impact could be further segregated into factors based upon the definitions of CII laid down by various governments, where emphasis is on the impact over societal functions, public health and safety, national security and economic or social well-being of the people.

Probability or the likelihood of disruption is also a determining factor, but the assessment would require several experts to assess the impact and probability of failure of core business functions. The approach is quite similar to risk assessment where probability/likelihood for an accident or failure is combined with the estimation of negative consequences. The dependence of various business functions on ICT increases their vulnerability and exposure to the threats hovering in cyberspace. The disruption of information infrastructure and related services can have catastrophic consequences on the very execution of core business functions of critical infrastructure, and the higher dependence on such services and assets adds to the criticality. The complex interactions among various industrial functions of critical infrastructure and the exchange of information leads to interdependencies, which is the most significant and yet the most complicated parameter of criticality. These interdependencies vary from geographical to physical and cyber to logical. A minor disruption at one point could have a rippling effect across multiple infrastructures.

In addition to these parameters, while comprehending the parameters of criticality for infrastructure at large, there are certain observations from definitions which need attention. It is evident from the definitions that critical infrastructures, as entities, have clear implications for national, economic and environmental security. These dimensions must be understood and reflected upon when the assessments for designating critical infrastructure are made. In principle, national security could encompass economic security, energy security, food security, political security, military security, environmental security and so on.

It must be noted that the parameters defined here are indicative and not definitive. Moreover, it is not necessary that all of them are applicable to the case under consideration. There may be more parameters which are relevant for certain organizations. The basic aim of defining the criticality parameters is to facilitate or present the broader principles which have utility in undertaking an organization-wide exercise to identify the assets vital to the critical business or industrial processes or nationwide exercises for critical infrastructure/CII assessment. However, at the organizational level, the exercise begins with identification of cyber assets before computing their relative importance in terms of criticality.

1.9 INTERDEPENDENCIES IN CII

The fact that critical infrastructures of a nation are interconnected and mutually dependent in an intricate way, both physically and logically through a host of information and communications technologies. A given infrastructure can contain numerous linear and complex interactions. Imagine a natural gas pipeline supplying gas to a number of consumes at a remote location. When examined in isolation from other infrastructures and the environment, the flow of gas in the pipeline may appear to be a linear process with predominantly linear interactions. Gas flows from a source, passes through a gas conditioning plant and many compressor stations to finally reach the consumer premises. However, in a broader context this process includes couplings to other infrastructures makes this linear process a complex one. Here the gas conditioning plants and compressors need electricity for their operations and the electricity generation may need natural gas as fuel. Hence both are mutually dependant and interconnected. In fact the electrical grid and pipeline grid are coupled in an intricate and complex manner.

In California, electric power disruptions affected oil and natural gas production, refinery operations, pipeline transport of gasoline and jet fuel within California and to its neighbouring states, and the pumping of water from northern to central and southern regions of the state for crop irrigation. Many industries including transportation, the disruptions affected and led to loss of billions of dollars due to productivity loss. Further it stressed the Western power grid, causing extensive security and reliability concerns. Same was the case in India during the 2012 North Eastern black out.

So in the present scenario, critical infrastructure is increasingly interlinked with nearly all other infrastructures, which includes both critical and non-critical infrastructure, where isolating or segregating critical segments from non-critical infrastructure in the dynamic ecosystem still remains an intimidating task. Complexity of infrastructures and their interdependency leads to elevated risk exposure. The potential vulnerabilities of an integrated infrastructure system are compounded by the interdependence of various constituents. As the complexity of networks increases, and the number of attacks on these networks surge, an impact even due to a small disruption could be severe.

The defence and mitigation strategy warrants the authorities to have credible and sufficient knowledge or awareness of their critical infrastructure, and the ICT infrastructure which is the game changer today helps to function these critical infrastructures and their interdependencies. This poses significant challenges before authorities in terms of identifying, understanding and analysing such interdependencies, which are interweaved through intricate topologies. As the interactions among the critical infrastructure increase, the interdependency between various elements is an important factor in criticality analysis.

Critical infrastructures depend on inputs/outputs of each other for physical commodities, data, information, energy and so on. Disruption or degradation of cyber elements can also have impact on physical world. In the context of critical infrastructure, interdependency could be defined as a bidirectional relationship between two infrastructures through which the state of each infrastructure influences or is correlated to the state of the other. In other words, two infrastructures are interdependent when each is dependent on the other. Mathematically,

$$x=f(y) \text{ and } y=f(x)$$

Figure 1.1 Interdependency of critical infrastructure with power which is also a critical infrastructure

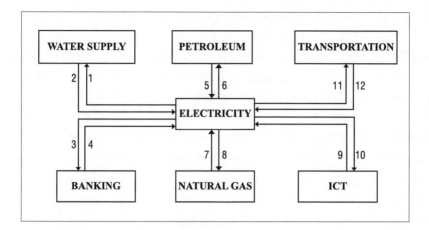

1. *Power for pumping and control systems*
2. *Cooling*
3. *Power for control systems*
4. *Financial transactions insurance*
5. *Fuel for generators*
6. *Power for pumping and control systems*
7. *Fuel for generators*
8. *Power for compressors*
9. *Monitoring, control and communication*
10. *Power for network devices*
11. *Power for signalling*
12. *Fuel transport*

Figure 1.1: Representing Interdependency between Critical Sectors

Interdependency among critical infrastructure sectors is depicted in Figure 1.2. All the critical sectors, such as transportation, communications and government services, depend upon the power/ electricity sector for their basic requirement of electricity supply, which powers the railways, airports and communication systems such as switching centres or telephone exchanges. In an interdependent function, the power/electricity sector itself depends on transportation for fuel supplies and communications for its data transmission or to maintain health of the transmission/distribution networks. Similarly, governments depend on the banking and financial services for all monetary needs. The banking sector is technology driven, and communications sector plays a pivotal role in seamless banking operations. The depiction in the figure is just indicative and does not represent the complexity of the relationship. It does represent the direct relationship between two sectors, such as transportation and the power/electricity sector, but it is inadequate to define the characteristics of the relationship. For analysis, interdependency could only be expressed in the form of mathematical models, which can identify all the linkages, as well as assign a degree or measure of dependency to assess the characteristics of the interdependent business function.

The real-world networks are continuously evolving. The networks can expand and evolve very quickly, and this phenomenon is based upon the mathematical concept of power functions, an amplification mechanism where small ranges accelerate changes logarithmically. The networks grow organically as well as the growth owes to the migration of nodes to the network. As nodes increase in size, they eventually become hubs, which link numerous nodes. The network of critical infrastructure is unceasingly growing with the inclusion of new industries and facilities and increasing links among the segments and industries.

Detangling Interdependencies

The challenge of complexity in the study of critical infrastructure, as a result of the underlying interdependencies, is fundamentally derived from both organizational and technical complexities. It is fact that there is shortage of specialized tools and techniques to model these complex infrastructures, comprehend their interdependencies, analyse their vulnerabilities and find the optimal means of their protection. OT security experts stresses the need of quantitative methods to scientifically compute the optimal allocation of limited resources to the most important assets of each sector of critical infrastructures. Such tools must operate at the local, state, regional and national levels. Due to the intricacies of interdependence, so far this field has been studied from an organizational perspective, analysing critical infrastructures as physical assets and not as a stratified web or network of interdependent and closely knit system of systems.

Most of the studies are carried out at the organizational level for risk assessment, which provides credible inputs to the decision makers, but is futile for the policymakers whose task is to enhance preparedness and infrastructure resilience at national level. The efforts are primarily concentrated in the area of dependency analysis to understand the intricate web of dependencies between cyber assets and physical infrastructures. The interdependence between the infrastructures is fundamental to the propagation of threats among them. Some of the analysts have focused upon the coupling between different sectors of critical infrastructure, such as physical coupling, logical and information coupling, inter-regional economic coupling and inter-sector economic coupling, which broadly explains the interdependence of infrastructure when they behave as a network.

For the purpose of simplification, the interdependencies can be divided into four principle categories viz. physical, cyber (information), geographic, and logical. Although each has distinct characteristics, these categories of interdependencies are not mutually exclusive.

Physical Interdependency

Two infrastructures are physically interdependent if the state of each is dependent on the physical outputs of the other. As its name implies, a physical interdependency arises from a physical linkage between the inputs and outputs of two agents. A commodity produced or modified by one infrastructure (output) is required by another infrastructure for its operation (input). Here any disturbances in one infrastructure can ripple over to other infrastructures. Thus, the risk of failure in one infrastructure can be a function of risk in a second infrastructure as the two are interdependent.

Cyber (Information) Interdependency

If the state of a function depends on information transmitted through information infrastructure, the relationship can be classified as information dependency. In this case, the commodity passed on is information. These interdependencies occur due to the connection between infrastructures via electronic/digital or informational links. Going forward, nation states will be more dependent upon their NII and it will become too difficult to assess the risk associated due to the breadth and complexity of the networks. Cyber interdependencies are relatively new and a result of the universal computerization and automation of infrastructures over the last several decades. Cyber interdependencies connect infrastructures to one another via electronic, informational links; the outputs of the information infrastructure are inputs to the other infrastructure, and the commodity passed between the infrastructures is information.

Geographical Interdependency

Infrastructures are geographically interdependent if a local environmental event can create state changes in all of them. A geographic interdependency occurs when elements of multiple infrastructures are in close spatial proximity. For instance, a case of fire in one infrastructure can have negative consequences for geographically interdependent infrastructures. Such correlated changes are not due to physical or cyber connections between infrastructures; rather, they arise from the influence the event exerts on all the infrastructures simultaneously. Note that more than two infrastructures can be geographically interdependent based on their physical proximity. Implicit in our discussion is the fact that some interdependencies and their effects on infrastructure operations are caused by physical phenomena, whereas others result from human intervention and decisions.

Logical Interdependency

Two infrastructures are logically interdependent if the state of each depends on the state of the other via a mechanism that is not a physical, cyber, or geographic connection. Logical interdependencies may be more closely likened to a control plan that links an agent in one infrastructure to an agent in another infrastructure without any direct physical, cyber, or geographic connection. Consider the power crisis that emerged in California in late 2000 and the logical interdependency between the electric power and financial infrastructures.

Given the interplay of dependencies and interdependencies, the infrastructures are bound to interact with each other, and these interactions may take the shape of linearity or complexity. In a mesh or network of infrastructures, a set of two infrastructures could either be directly connected or there could be an indirect coupling between the two through single or multiple intervening infrastructures. Linear interactions are quite visible, expected and known or apparent, and subsequently their sequences or linkages are familiar. Complex interactions, on the other hand, are outcomes of unexpected sequences, unfamiliar therefore invisible and unplanned, and at the worst, they may not be visible or immediately comprehensible.

1.10 NETWORK ANALYSIS OF CRITICAL INFRASTRUCTURE

The behavioural characteristics of critical infrastructure have paradoxical evidences, an architectural or structural challenge from a technical perspective. Such as, a robust system is often not resilient to failures or disruptions. A technically dependable or hardened system may not have optimal operational efficiency. Optimization has its own trade-off; either the system could be designed optimally for security or performance.

A hierarchical network is fundamentally most efficient, but it lacks redundancy, and a single-point failure at the top can break the network down and therefore, it is most vulnerable. Larger networks, such as social networks, Internet or electricity grids, are not hierarchical, rather they behave as random networks, which are more resilient to random failures.

The network of critical infrastructure displays the characteristics of a complex system. In a complex system, there is a network which defines the interactions between and among the components. In order to understand the complex systems, understanding or detangling of network behind the complex systems is very important. Certainly, critical infrastructures are networked systems, leading to complex relationships due to varying degrees of interdependence and interconnectedness. The critical infrastructure network can be analysed using the principles of graph/network theory.

This approach can help establish the relationships between objects which, in normal assessment, appear to be discreet. A complex system is represented by components which are the nodes or vertices of the network, the interaction signified by the links and edges; and the system which is denoted by the network or graph. The real-world networks are continuously evolving. The networks can expand and evolve very quickly, and this phenomenon is based upon the mathematical concept of power functions, an amplification mechanism where small ranges accelerate changes logarithmically. The networks grow organically as well as the growth owes to the migration of nodes to the network. As nodes increase in size, they eventually become hubs, which link numerous nodes. For instance, the transportation network is evolving continuously with the construction of new highways between the cities, the railways networks are also expanding and so is the case of aviation. Some of the airports are hubs of activity. Therefore, networks continue to emerge as their size and scope expands. The network of critical infrastructure is continuously expanding with the inclusion of new industries and services and the growing linkages among the sectors and industries.

1.11 IDENTIFYING ASSETS AND DETERMINING CRITICALITY

The infrastructure of a facility, a company, or an economic sector, consists of an array of assets which are necessary for the production and/or delivery of a good or service. Similarly, the infrastructure of a city, state, or nation consists of an array of assets necessary for the economic and social activity of the city and region, and the public health and welfare of its citizens. The first step in the process is to determine which infrastructure assets to include in the study.

The methodologies reviewed do not provide a definitive list of such assets but suggest which ones might be considered. For example, people assets may include employees, customers, and/or the surrounding community. Property usually includes a long list of physical assets like buildings, vehicles, production equipment, storage tanks, control equipment, raw materials, power, water, communication systems, information systems, office equipment, supplies, etc. Information could include product designs, formulae, process data, operational data, business strategies, financial data, employee data, etc. Roper's examples of activities and operations assets include such things as intelligence gathering and special training programs. Many methodologies suggest considering, initially, as broad a set of assets as is reasonable.

However, not every asset is as important as another. In order to focus assessment resources, all of the methodologies reviewed suggest that the assessment should focus on those assets judged to be most critical.

Criticality is typically defined as a measure of the consequences associated with the loss or degradation of a particular asset. The more the loss of an asset threatens the survival or viability of its owners, of those located nearby, or of others who depend on it (including the nation as a whole), the more critical it becomes.

Consequences can be categorized in a number of ways viz. economic, financial, environmental, health and safety, technological, operational, and time. For example, a process control centre may be essential for the safe production of a particular product. Its loss, or inability to function properly, could result not only in a disruption of production (with its concomitant loss of revenue and additional costs associated with replacing the lost capability), but it might also result in the loss of life, property damage, or environmental damage, if the process being controlled involves hazardous materials. The loss of an asset might also reduce a firm's competitive advantage, not only because of the financial costs associated with its loss, but also because of the loss of technological advantage or loss of unique knowledge or information that would be difficult to replace or reproduce. Individual firms, too, have to worry about loss of reputation.

While the immediate impact is important, so, too, is the amount of time and resources required to replace the lost capability. If losing the asset results in a large immediate disruption, but the asset can be replaced quickly and cheaply, or there are cost-effective substitutes, the total consequence may not be so great. Alternatively, the loss of an asset resulting in a small immediate consequence, but which continues for a long period of time because of the difficulty in reconstituting the lost capability, may result in a much greater total loss.

Another issue which decision makers may consider is if the loss of a particular asset could lead to cascading effects, not only within the facility or the company, but also cascading effects that might affect other infrastructures. For example, the loss of electric power can lead to problems in the supply of safe drinking water. The loss of a key communications node can impair the function of ATM machines.

The initial set of assets are categorized by their degree of criticality. Typically the degree of criticality is assessed qualitatively as high, medium, or low, or some variation of this type of measure. However, even if assessed qualitatively, a number of methodologies suggest being specific about what kind of consequence qualifies an asset to be placed in each category. For example, the electric utility sector methodology suggests that a highly critical asset might be one whose loss would require an immediate response by a company's board of directors, or whose loss carries with it the possibility of off-site fatalities, property damage in excess of a specified amount of dollars, or the interruption of operations for more than a specified amount of time. Alternatively, an asset whose loss results in no injuries, or shuts down operations for only a few days, may be designated as having low criticality.

For those sectors not vertically integrated, ownership of infrastructure assets may span a number of firms, or industries. Whoever is doing the analysis may feel constrained to consider only those assets owned and operated by the analyst or analyst's client. For example, transmission assets (whether pipeline, electric, or communication) may not be owned or operated by the same firms that produce the commodity being transmitted. Both the production assets and the transmission assets, however, are key elements of the overall infrastructure. Also, a firm may rely on the output from a specific asset owned and operated by someone else. The user may consider that asset critical, but the owner and operator may not. Some of the methodologies reviewed encourage the analyst to also consider (or at least account for) the vulnerability of those assets owned or operated by someone else that provide critical input into the system being analysed. These interdependency problems are often characterized in terms of inter-sector dependencies (e.g., the reliance of water systems on electric power), but they may also exist intra-sector. The interdependency issue is both a technical one (i.e., identifying them) and a political/legal one (i.e., how can entity A induce entity B to protect an asset).

Cyber assets could be part of either the control systems, SCADA or the networking equipment used by any of the control or SCADA. Control systems primarily comprise of the devices or sets of devices that manage, command or regulate the parameters of processes, devices or other systems. SCADA systems are a collection of sensing, monitoring and controlling devices and communication links for sampling, collecting and storing data from the designated system to a centralized Servers kept in the Master Control Center or a HMI. The networking equipment includes devices such as routers, hubs, switches, bridges, firewalls, data diodes, networks interface cards and modems.

To identify cyber assets within the perimeters, a proper review and assessment is made to measure the impact on the essential business or industrial functions, which could be one or a combination of the following:

1. The asset may provide operational information in the real time.

2. The asset controls parameters of industrial processes, which could either be manual intervention or through an automated function.

3. It performs some critical functions such as it prompts errors, raises alarms, flags or alerts for further action or human intervention.

4. The asset may provide data connectivity between cyber assets within the electronic security perimeter.

5. The asset supports the operations or the business continuity plans.

Once the exercise of identifying cyber assets is complete, the next step is to identify those cyber assets which underpin or support the critical assets/business processes/industrial functions, known as critical cyber assets. Again, the criteria could be subjective, but in broader terms, they could be:

1. The cyber asset is involved in or capable of or executes supervisory or autonomous control that enables an essential function of a critical asset.

2. The cyber asset displays, transfers, processes or contains/stores information, which is used to make operational decisions in real time, regarding an essential function of a critical asset.

3. The cyber asset, if lost/compromised/unavailable, would severely degrade/disable/incapacitate the critical asset to deliver its essential functions.

In general in a utility, the critical asset elements are categorised as four groups which are mentioned below.

1. Human Resources: Includes staff, management and executives who are deemed to be necessary to plan, organize, acquire, deliver, support and monitor mission critical/core services, information systems and facilities.

2. Automated Information and Control Systems: This category encompasses entire electronic and communications equipment, hardware, and software

3. Data: Entire data belonging to the organization (both in electronic and print form) and information that is part of or which supports critical assets and mission-critical services.

4. Facilities and Equipment: All facilities and equipment that form part of or support critical assets/mission critical services, especially those that house and support IT assets.

Every organization conduct similar exercises as part of their risk assessment activities. However, it becomes vital for organizations that are part of the national critical infrastructure to proactively and periodically conduct this exercise. However, few organizations have understood the mesh of interdependencies, which unconsciously shape their risk exposure. The disruptions in one of the sectors might have unforeseen impact on other sectors, and therefore it is essential to detangle the mesh of interdependencies for better readiness.

1.12 CRITICAL AND NONCRITICAL INDUSTRIAL NETWORKS

The security practices recommended within this book aim for securing the CI which is presently a nerve-wrecking task. In fact go above and beyond the existing standards is preferred by many government and regulatory groups. The requirement of the security standard depends upon the nature of the industrial system being protected. The consequences of a cyber-attack on CI are very crucial. The production of energy is very important in modern society. The proper manufacture and distribution of electricity can directly impact our safety by providing heat in winter or by powering our irrigation pumps during a drought.

Regardless of an ICS's classification, however, most industrial control systems are by their nature important, and any risk to their reliability holds industrial-scale consequences. However, while not all manufacturing systems hold fatal consequences, that doesn't mean that they aren't potential targets for a cyber-attacks. The likelihood of an incident diminishes as the sophistication of the attack and its consequences grow. By implementing security practices to address these uncommon and unlikely attacks, there is a greater possibility of avoiding the devastating consequences that correspond to them.

The goal of this book is to secure Critical Infrastructure, it stresses electric energy sector, but reference various standards, recommendations, and directives. Regardless of the nature of the control system that needs to be secured, it is important to understand these directives, especially NERC CIP, IEC 62443, ISO/IEC 27002, CEA guidelines for power sector and the control system security recommendations of National Institute of Standards and Technology (NIST). Each has its own strengths and weaknesses, but all provide a good baseline of best practices for industrial network security (each is explored in more detail in Chapter 8, Protocols, Standards and Guidelines. The industrial networks that control critical information infrastructures (CII) mandate the strongest controls and regulations around the physical-cyber security and there are many organizations helping to achieve it.

1.13 CRITICAL CYBER ASSETS

At an organizational level, the physical elements of the information infrastructure include the location and disposition of network equipment (such as servers, routers and storage media), documents and physical storage devices associated with the organization's own data elements. The logical elements of the Cyber Assets are inclusive of electronic information assets, such as the data and information stored across the systems, the operating systems and the various applications an organization has developed and deployed. Second, the operational stability and security of Critical Information Infrastructure (CII) is vital for national and economic security of the nation state. The IT infrastructure provides the processing, transmission and storage of vital information, and also enables government agencies to rapidly interact with each other as well as with industry, citizens, state and local governments and the governments of other nations. Many of the critical services that are essential to the well-being of the economy are increasingly becoming dependent on IT.

Governmental institutions across the globe have been making efforts to identify the core services that need to be protected. In this regard, they have been consistently working with organizations responsible for operationalizing, maintaining and operating critical infrastructure. The primary focus of these efforts has been to secure the information resources belonging to the government as well as those key organizations which are an integral part of the nation states' critical sectors. The unprecedented dependence of modern societies and nation states on CIIs, their interconnectedness and interdependencies with other infrastructure, sometimes across the physical or political borders, as well as the underlying vulnerabilities and the threats of exploitation they face elevates the requisites to strengthen the security of Critical Information Infrastructure and inculcate resilience. In both conceptual and operational terms, Critical Infrastructure and Critical Information Infrastructure are embedded to each other.

Operationally there may not be such distinctions, and the figure is just indicative to explain the concepts governing the identification of CI and CII. As the critical infrastructures of a nation state are becoming integrated and gaining strategic advantage, there is a growing insecurity among the nation states on the issues pertaining to the protection and defence of these infrastructures. There has been a significant increase in the number of cyber-attacks, and this has been established from reports published by security agencies and private security firms.

The cyber threats, particularly categorized as cyber-crime, cyber terrorism, cyber espionage and cyber warfare, exploit numerous vulnerabilities in the software and hardware design, human resources and physical systems. This concern has gained significant traction among governmental agencies, computer/network security firms and the scientific and strategic community. There is an awful need to evolve a comprehensive security policy to address the physical, legal, cyber and human dimensions of security. Nation states across the globe have realized the growing challenges in preventing and containing the attacks on critical infrastructure, while embedding resiliency in the critical infrastructure and the corresponding information infrastructure.

Summary

Critical Information Infrastructure (CII) is generally believed as those computer resource, the destruction of which, shall have debilitating impact on national security, economy, public health or safety. Ensuring seamless operation of critical infrastructure requires safeguarding the availability and integrity of machinery. This means that organizations overseeing critical infrastructure must foresee any possible risks and implement systems, procedures, and technologies that mitigate or remove these risks so as to keep their operations running. This chapter gives brief description of Information Infrastructure, critical infrastructure of a nation, its criticality, interdependencies, National and Global Information Infrastructure, etc. It also explains the asset identification, critical assets and determining its criticality.

Cyber Space and Threats

2.1 INTRODUCTION

The word *cyber* has become one of the most omnipresent and powerful concepts in contemporary security studies. The increasing cyber-attacks are seriously drawing attention today because of their enormous potential to challenge our security assumptions. Today, cyberspace has emerged as a domain of its own, in many ways like land, sea and air. Even if a nation whether it is small in land area, low in GDP per capita, low in resources, less important in geopolitics, low in strength of armed forces, it can be a military super power if that nation is capable of launching a cyber-attack on critical infrastructures of any nation including superpowers and crumble the nation. The microprocessors and the smartphones are the instruments of the present age and cyberspace is its oxygen. The interconnected, interdependent, globalised, and technologically advancing world depends so much on cyberspace. From social media to high priority financial services, communications, transport, oil and gas, and maybe most important, our military organizations, the sophisticated weapons and the power sector, all increasingly place reliance on the internet and everything connected to it. This chapter gives a brief description about the cyber space, cyber security definitions, different types of attacks on CI which today an automation security professional must be aware of.

2.2 CYBER SPACE

The word *cyber,* originating from the Greek word meaning *skilled steering or guidance,* has taken on the modern meaning of using digital communications within and among intelligent devices to perform information gathering and commanded control. Cyberspace refers to the virtual computer world, and more specifically, is an electronic medium used to form a global computer network to facilitate online communication. It is a large computer network made up of many worldwide computer networks that employ TCP/IP protocol to aid in communication and data exchange activities. In fact, it is a digital medium with an interactive world but not a copy of the physical world. It is dynamic, undefined, and growing exponentially. It is as vast as human imagination and has no fixed shape.

It is expected that in the second decade of the twenty-first century, cyberspace is probably the place where most of us spend a major part of our lives. It has become an inseparable element of our existence. Cyberspace refers to the virtual computer world, and more specifically, is an electronic medium used to form a global computer network to facilitate online communication. It is a large computer network made up of many worldwide computer networks that employ TCP/IP protocol to aid in communication and data exchange activities.

In fact, cyberspace is a digital medium with an interactive world but not a copy of the physical world. It is dynamic, undefined, and exponential. It is as vast as human imagination and has no fixed shape.

2.3 SECURITY DEFINITIONS

Automation engineers often use the cyber security terms vulnerability, threat, risk, etc. However very few use those terms in the right sense by comprehending the correct meaning and their relationships between them. Some of the important cyber security terms of importance are briefly explained below.

Vulnerability: It is a weakness in a SCADA system for a countermeasure and could be exploited by a threat. It can be a software, hardware, procedural, or human weakness that can be exploited.

Threat: It is any potential to destructively impact a SCADA system that is associated with the exploitation of vulnerability. The threat is that someone, or something, will identify a specific vulnerability and use it against the company or individual. The entity that takes advantage of a vulnerability is referred to as a *threat agent*. A threat agent could be an intruder accessing the network through a port on the firewall, a process accessing data in a way that violates the security policy, or an employee making an accidental mistake that could expose confidential information.

Risk: It is the probability that a specific threat exploiting a vulnerability and the consequent impact or harm to the SCADA system. If a firewall has several ports open, there is a higher probability that an intruder will access the network in an unauthorized method.

Exposure: It is an instance of being exposed to losses. Vulnerability exposes an organization to possible damages. If password management is lax and password rules are not enforced, the company is exposed to the possibility of having users' passwords captured and used in an unauthorized manner. If a company does not have its wiring inspected and does not put proactive fire prevention steps into place, it exposes itself to potentially devastating fires.

Control or countermeasure: It is put into place to mitigate (reduce) the potential risk. A countermeasure may be a software configuration, a hardware device, or a procedure that eliminates vulnerability or that reduces the likelihood a threat agent will be able to exploit a vulnerability. Examples of countermeasures include strong password management, firewalls, a security guard, access control mechanisms, encryption, and security-awareness training.

Safeguard: A countermeasure or security control designed to reduce the risk associated with a specific threat.

Impact: The effect or consequence of a threat realized against a SCADA system.

If users are not aware of the processes and procedures, there are chances that an employee will make an unintentional mistake that may destroy data. If an Intrusion Detection System (IDS) is absent on a network, the attack probability is very high. Risk ties the vulnerability, threat, and likelihood of exploitation to the resulting business impact.

Cyber War: the unauthorized invasion by a government into the systems or networks of another, aiming to disrupt those systems, to damage them partially, or to destroy them entirely. A specific target is to slow down if not curtail the military systems of the target state, there is no point having excellent missiles and weapons if the delivery systems can be paralyzed. And as our military establishments become more and more dependent on sophisticated technologies, the risk of equally sophisticated attacks on them grows. The Stuxnet attack on Iran nuclear facility and Blackenergy attack on Ukraine power sector are typical examples to Nation sponsored cyber-attacks.

Cyber Espionage: Governments can invade the systems of their rivals to steal sensitive information that would be useful for their own purposes. These attacks are usually hard to discover and the case of Operation Shady RAT, the world's biggest hacking ever, is rather phenomenal. For five whole years hackers had access to 70 government and private agencies around the world as they secreted away gigabytes of confidential information, unbeknownst to those at the receiving end. By the time Shady RAT was spotted, 49 networks had been infected in the United States alone along with several others in India, South Korea, Taiwan and elsewhere.

Cyber Crime: is the kind of threat which is the most familiar. While this also has military and political implications, it affects the lives of ordinary Internet users more closely. Just the other day, for instance, a domestic aide of mine, recently introduced to the world of email, came up to me looking rather dazed. He had, he said, just received an email that some lady in Kenya had left him a substantial amount of money. In order to access that money he needed to deposit a relatively small but still significant sum (Rs.40,000 to be exact) at a local bank account here, so that the transfer could be facilitated. Such messages come in daily and there are many who fall prey to them. Cyber Crime also includes pornography, Internet stalking, and personality imitation.

Cyber Terrorism: This includes websites spreading extremist propaganda, recruiting terrorists, planning attacks, and otherwise promoting terrorists' political and social objectives. It also involves the use of hackers by terrorists to debilitate states and governments, much like in Cyber War, with the only difference that this involves a non-State actor. Cyberspace offers a great advantage for the shrouded business of terrorists, making their work murkier than ever to those outside.

2.4 MOTIVATION FOR ATTACKS

Hackers attacking ICS have different motives, may be mostly not the financial gain but political reasons or military objectives. Attacks may be state-sponsored or they could also come from competitors, insiders with a malicious goal, and even hacktivists.

2.5 THREAT SOURCES TO ICS

A threat can be defined as any person, circumstance or event with the potential to cause loss or damage. A vulnerability can be defined as any weakness that can be exploited by an opponent. Both are evaluated based on the consequences and the amount of loss or damage occurred from a successful attack. Distributed Control System (DCS) is a typical Cyber Physical Systems (CPS), which tightly integrates a physical power transmission system with the cyber process of network computing and communication at all scales and levels. Obviously it is susceptible to cyber threats and vulnerabilities and can be exploited by different attack groups. They are mainly classified as described below.

> ➢ Threat from crackers: who break into computers for profit or bragging rights. internet increases availability of hacker tools along with information about infrastructures and control systems,

> ➢ Ransomware threats: who breaks into computers with a strong financial motive for cyber-crime to exploit vulnerabilities,

> ➢ Threat from insiders: who disrupt their corporate network, sometimes an accident, often for revenge, Threat from terrorists: who attack systems for cause or ideology and

> ➢ Threat from hostile countries: countries which attack computers and servers of the enemy countries.

2.6 ICS VULNERABILITIES AND ATTACKS

With the integration of ICT, transition to a smarter electrical grid is very much optimistic and promising. However it introduces cyber vulnerabilities to the Grid. The major points which lead DCS vulnerable to cyber-attacks are described briefly below.

➢ *Bi-directional communication:* Though bi-directional communication provides great benefits to the utility and the customer with the capability to communicate and share information, it makes the system vulnerable to cyber-attacks.

➢ *Customer data privacy:* The information shared over the DCS is intrinsically sensitive, requires high level privacy and personal security.

➢ *Device Security: Device Security* of various manufactures roll out devices with different security features with different security levels built in, making it a challenge to standardize security practices.

➢ *Distributed connectivity:* Smart Meters are part of the Neighborhood Area Network (NAN) in DCS which is not confined to a specific geographic area. Hence the boundaries of the network will expand and become more difficult to secure.

➢ *Authentication and access controls:* As the number of customers, suppliers and contractors increases, it becomes difficult to gain access to the network resulting in identity theft.

➢ *Proper employee training and awareness*: Without proper training and awareness, there are chances of increasing the insider threats and lapses.

➢ *Guidelines, standards and interoperability:* This may pose the potential for gaps in visibility, defense and recovery. These threats are real that many Nations have declared its digital infrastructure as strategic asset and made cyber-security a national agenda with highest priority. They are setting up security policies to force power utilities responsible for protecting the critical electrical infrastructure. Many Nations entrusted their secret agencies to monitor for hackers attempting to infiltrate the power sector. But government regulation and pressure won't be enough to safeguard the Critical Infrastructure. Hence utilities have to take spontaneous and significant steps to secure their networks. The techniques which attackers use to gain control of an ICS or cause different levels of damage are mostly similar to those in case of IT. But they also possess certain explicit techniques and some of the techniques used are briefly described below.

- *Backdoor entry through communication devices:* A cyber-attacker may compromise some of the communication devices such as modems, routers, etc. and infiltrate the system using it as a backdoor to launch attacks.

- *Spreading of malwares:* Malwares developed by an attacker can infect the AMI, RTU, PLC or control center servers or utility's corporate servers. Malwares can replace or alter the device functions or a system including sending false commands and sensitive information.

- *DoS attacks network availability:* DoS attacks might attempt to delay, block, or corrupt information transmission in order to make DCS resources unavailable. As the DCS uses IP protocol and TCP/IP stack, it becomes subject to all the vulnerabilities inherent in the TCP/IP stack and hence the DoS attacks.

- *Accessing and manipulating the database:* ICS events and data are stored in a database on the control center server network and then mirror the logs into the business network. If the database management systems are not properly configured, an adroit cyber-attacker can gain access to the business network database, and then exploit the control system network.

- *False Data Injection:* An attacker can send false packets of information into the network, such as wrong Smart Meter data, false price tariffs, fake emergency event, etc. Fake information can cause huge financial impact on the electricity markets. This type of attacking technologies are advancing much faster than security patch ups to control it. Hence it is very essential that the end node security aspects of DCS especially the Smart Meter should ensure that it has communication capabilities that meet all basic integrity and confidentiality criterions. Unfortunately the Smart Meters today do not meet the required protection against false data injection. These facts highlight a much larger potential issues with data integrity throughout the DCS infrastructure.

- *Modbus security issue:* Modbus protocol is widely used in Power System SCADA especially for the communication between the IEDs and RTUs. Hence all Modbus security issues are applicable to the SCADA system or all the facility-based processes such as DCS processes.

- *Eavesdropping and traffic analysis:* An enemy can obtain sensitive information by monitoring network traffic. It can be the utilities business strategy, future price information, control structure of the grid, and power usage. Later these data can be used for hostile deeds.

2.7 ALARMING ICS THREATS

The present day ICS threats are much advanced technically and the implemented ICS and DCS are secured just because of *security through obscurity*. A brief description of the technically advanced lethal threats and vulnerabilities are explained in the following sections.

➤ Zero Day Vulnerabilities

The term zero day implies that the developer does not get enough time to develop and deploy a patch to overcome the flaw. Before that, an attacker exploits the flaw and/or creates and deploy malwares to attack the SCADA system. There are many zero-day flaws that may affect a SCADA system. Stack overflow is one of them. This attack can occur on the field devices as well as the servers. The stack buffer in the memory can be corrupted by a malicious player, leading to injection of dangerous executable code into the running program and thus usurping the control of the industrial process. The vulnerability reported in China is a well-known example. Zero Day Attacks can also occur in the form of DoS attacks that overload computer resources. Stuxnet is a lethal computer worm which uses four zero-day Windows vulnerabilities. It was primarily written to target Iranian nuclear centrifuges. Its final goal is to disrupt ICSs by modifying programs implemented on PLCs to make them work in a manner that the attacker intended and to hide those changes from system operators. It is believed that Stuxnet is introduced to a computer network through an infected removable drive. To hide itself while spreading across the network and realizing the final target, the virus installs a Windows rootkit by exploiting four zero-day vulnerabilities. The success of this virus in penetrating the PLC environment shows that traditional security measures are not sufficient for the complete protection of safety-critical infrastructures.

➢ Non-prioritization of Tasks

This is a serious flaw in real-time operating systems of many Industrial Control Systems (ICS). In certain embedded operating systems, there may not have the feature of prioritization of tasks. Memory sharing between the equally privileged tasks lead to serious security issues. The features such as the accessibility to create Object Entry Point (OEP) in the kernel domain can lead to loopholes in security. Non-kernel tasks maybe protected from overflows using guard pages. But the guard pages may be small and cannot provide stringent protection.

➢ Database Injection

Detrimental query statements can be injected to exploit the vulnerabilities in a ICS especially when the client inputs are not properly filtered. This is widely reported for SQL-based databases. Here the attacker sends a command to SQL server through the web server and attempt to reveal critical authentication information.

➢ Communication Protocol Issues

Today with the developments in encryption and authentication, IT security is capable of encountering the sophisticated cyber-attacks and threats.

But they are not adopted in an adequate manner in ICS and DCS especially when the process is controlled with the client server architecture.

Earlier SCADA security was not a major concern and hence communication protocols did not give sufficient importance to authentication. This does not mean that authentication and encryption methods cannot be used with these systems. It should be noted that encryption is effective only in an authenticated communication between entities. To have a secure TCP/IP communication, internet Protocol Security (IPsec) framework has to be employed. It will help to create a secure channel of communication for ICS. IPsec uses two protocols for authentication and encryption viz. Encapsulating Security Payload (ESP) and Authentication Header (AH). Advanced Persistent Threat (APT) attacks which monitor network activity and steal data for a future attack, can be effectively dealt with protocols like Syslog that keeps security logs which provide a means for detecting stealthy attempts to gather information prior to building sophisticated attacks by malicious players.

➢ **Stealthy Integrity Attack**

Stealth attacks are targeted to disrupt the service integrity, and make the networks to accept false data value. Security experts reports that powerful adversaries equipped with in-depth knowledge, disclosure resources, and disruption capabilities who are capable to perform stealthy attacks which partially or totally bypass traditional anomaly detectors. The detectability of an attack strategy depends on the capabilities of adversaries to coordinate attack vectors on control signals and sensor measurements.

➢ **Replay Attack**

These are the network attacks in which an attacker spies the communication between the sender and receiver and takes the authenticated information e.g. stealing the key and then contact the receiver with that key. In replay attack the attacker gives the proof of his identity and authenticity. The negative effect of a replay attack on a feedback control system has been found that this attack strategy is carried out in two steps which are mentioned below.

➢ The hacker records sensor measurements for a certain window of time before performing the attack.

➢ The hacker replaces actual sensor measurements with previously recorded signals while modifying control signals to drive system states out of their normal values.

A replay attack is capable of bypassing the classical detectors.

➢ False Data Injection Attack

DCS may operate in very hostile environments. AMI components lacking tamper-resistance hardware increases the possibility to be compromised. The attacker may inject false measurement reports to disrupt the DCS operation through the compromised meters and sensors. The objective of the attacker is to fool the state estimator by carefully injecting a certain amount of false data into sensor measurements. Those attacks are denoted as false data injection attacks. It can upset the grid system and lead to a false state estimation resulting to the disruption of the energy distribution. Security experts are of the opinion that the false data injection attack is a discrete-time state-space model driven by Gaussian noises. A Kalman filter is generally used to perform state estimation, and a failure detector is employed to detect abnormal situations.

➢ Zero-Dynamics Attack

In ICS Zero-Dynamics Attack (ZDA) is one of the hardest attacks to defend, especially in closed-loop feedback system which possesses an unstable zero, such as an unbounded actuator or sensor. These attacks cannot be observed by the monitoring data. The ZDA can be easily implemented in the cyber space or injected into the communication links by an attacker who has a proper understanding of Data Acquisition System (DAS). As modern control systems are implemented on digital computers using sample and hold mechanisms, where the controllers can be dealt with in a Sampled Data (SD) framework, can generate vulnerability to stealthy attacks due to the unstable sampling zeros in the SD system.

➢ Covert Attack

This attack is a targeted attack, but it is constructed and deployed using public tools. These are custom-made and minimally equipped. The strategy of covert attack consists of coordinating control signals and sensor measurements into a concerted malicious attack. This attack is executed in two steps as described below.

➢ The state attack vector can be chosen freely based on malicious targets and available resources.

➢ The sensor attack vector is designed in such a way that it can compensate for the effects of the state attack vector on the sensor measurements. The covert attack strategy can be considered as the worst case attack because it has the capaability to bypass traditional anomaly detectors. However, the covert attack needs to compromise numerous sensors to assure its stealth. Therefore, ICS defenders can remove a covert attack by protecting some critical sensors or deploying secure sensors.

> **Surge Attack, Bias Attack, and Geometric Attack**

The three types of stealthy attacks, viz. the surge attack, the bias attack, and the geometric attack are also important and is to be addressed by a cyber-security expert. The surge attack seeks to maximize the damage as soon as possible, while the bias attack tries to modify the system by small perturbations over a long period. The geometric attack integrates the surge attack and the bias attack by shifting the system behavior gradually at the beginning and maximizing the damage at the end.

2.8 DREADFUL ICS MALWARES

As ICS and DCS improve the efficiency and performance of the power grid, they also increase the grid vulnerability to potential cyber-attacks. Black Energy, Stuxnet, Havex, Duqu, and Sandworm are all recent examples of malwares targeting ICS. The AMI components especially the Smart Meters and increase in External Access Points (EAP) added with the integration of Renewable Energy Sources (RES) introduced new additional areas through which a potential cyber-attack may be launched on the grid. The present malware intrusions have resulted in a significant disruption of grid operations like what it had occurred to Ukraine by the dreadful malware BlackEnergy. The following sections are dedicated to describe some of the SCADA malwares.

> **BlackEnergy**

BlackEnergy is a Trojan horse malware program which infects the SCADA systems. Though it has been detected in 2007, the vehemence of destruction is realized only in 2015 with the Ukraine power sector attack. Till the Ukraine power sector attack, it has been believed that BlackEnergy was designed only for nuisance spam attacks and not targeted ICS or critical energy infrastructure. Today, BlackEnergy is a special concern for Critical Infrastructure companies especially to ICS because the software being used is in an Advanced Persistent Threat (APT) form, apparently to gather information. BlackEnergy specifically targets HMI software which is typically running 24/7, with the provision of remote access. It is rarely updated, thus making it a favorite target for opportunistic hackers. While no attempts to damage, modify, or otherwise disrupt the victim systems' control processes immediately after infection of BlackEnergy, indicates that the APT variant of BlackEnergy is a special concern as it is a modular malware capable moving through network files.

➤ Ukraine Incident

The December 23rd 2015, a cyber-attack has been carried out by the BlackEnergy malware which resulted in disrupting the ICS network almost completely in a brilliant sabotage operation which is briefly described below.

The hackers penetrated the ICS networks through the hijacked VPNs and sent commands to disable the UPS systems they had already reconfigured. Then they issued commands to open breakers. But before they did, they launched a Denial-of-Service (DoS) attack against customer call centers to prevent customers from calling in to report the outage. DoS attacks sent a flood of data to the web servers and as a result, the phone systems of the control center were flooded with thousands of bogus calls, in order to prevent genuine callers from getting through. This clearly demonstrates a high level of complexity, cleverness and organization of the attackers. Expert cybercriminals and even Nation sponsored attackers often fail to anticipate in all likelihoods. However, regarding BlackEnergy attack, it has been observed that the attackers put very concentrated effort to make sure that they are covering all aspects without any lapse so that nothing could go wrong. The move certainly required considerable time to the attackers to complete their operation. But by the time the operators realized this adverse situation that their machine has been hijacked, a number of substations had already been taken down and the situation had been totally slipped out of their control. In fact the operators become silent witness of this attack.

By gaining the remote control and opening the breakers, the attackers switched off a series of substations from the grid. They carried out these most clever operations in fact paralyzed the grid. They overwrote the firmware of the substation serial-to-Ethernet converters, replacing genuine firmware with their malicious firmware and rendering the converters thereafter inoperable and unrecoverable, unable to receive commands. As a result, these gateways are blown and cannot be recovered until they got new devices and integrate them.

Once the attackers have completed all of these, they used a malware called KillDisk to wipe out files from operator stations to make them inoperable. KillDisk wiped or overwrote the data in essential system files, causing computers to crash. Because it also overwrote the master boot record, the infected computers could not reboot. All these happened during the beginning of night peak, and the power utilities posted a note to their web sites acknowledging that power was out in certain regions and reassuring that they are working vehemently to identify the cause of the crisis. But within half an hour, the KillDisk completed its dirty action and left power operators without any doubt what caused the blackout. The utilities then posted another note to customers intimating the cause of the outage was hackers.

In effect, up to 95% of daily electricity consumption in Ukraine was not supplied. Though the cyber-attacks on the energy distribution companies has been attributed to the Russian APT group, the Black – Energy cyber-attack on Ukrainian power sector not only wrecked the Nation economically, but also worsened the energy customers confidence in the Ukrainian power companies and government.

➢ Stuxnet

Stuxnet, the Nation sponsored world's first lethal digital weapon, was unlike any other virus or worm that came before. Rather than simply hijacking targeted computers or stealing information from them, it escaped the digital realm to wreak physical destruction of equipments which are controlled by the computers. Initially it designed specifically to infect the Siemens SIMATIC WinCC and S7 PLC products, either installed as part of a PCS 7 system, or operating on their own. It starts operation by taking advantage of vulnerabilities in the Windows operating systems and Siemens products. Once it detects a suitable victim, it modifies control logic in of PLCs or RTUs. Undoubtedly the objective is to sabotage a specific industrial process using the vendors' variable-frequency drive controllers, along with a supervising safety system for the overall process. Though there has been much speculation on Stuxnet's intended target, recent information suggests it was Iran's nuclear program and more specifically, its uranium enrichment process. Stuxnet is capable of infecting both unsupported/legacy and current versions of Windows including Windows 2000, Windows XP, Windows Server 2003, Windows Vista, Windows Server 2008 and Windows 7. It also infects the Siemens STEP 7 which is one of the world's best known and most widely used engineering software in ICS in such a way that it automatically executes when the STEP 7 project is loaded by an uninfected Siemens system. Some of the important characteristics of the worm are,

1. It propagates cleverly between targets, typically via USB flash drives and other removable media,

2. Once migrated the target, it propagates quickly within the target via multiple network pathways,

3. It very cunningly searches for numerous vendors' anti-virus technologies installed on machines and modifies its behavior to avoid the detection,

4. It contacts a command and control server on the internet for instructions and updates,

5. It establishes a peer-to-peer network to propagate instructions and updates within a target, even to equipments without direct internet connectivity,

6. It modifies PLC or RTU program logic, causing physical processes to malfunction,

7. It hides the modified PLC or RTU programs from control engineers and system administrators who are trying to understand the reason for the malfunctioning of the system,

8. It is signed with certificates stolen from major hardware manufacturers, so that no warnings are raised when the worm is installed and

9. If a particular machine is not the intended target, the worm removes itself from the machine after it has replicated itself to other vulnerable media and machines.

➢ Iranian Experience

In 2012 it has been confirmed that the Iranian nuclear facilities were attacked and infiltrated by the first *cyber-weapon* or the *digital missile* of the world known as the Stuxnet. It is believed that this attack was initiated by a random worker's USB drive. One of the affected nuclear facilities was the Natanz nuclear facility. The first signs that an issue existed in the nuclear facility's computer system was in 2010. Inspectors from the International Atomic Energy Agency (IAEA) visited the Natanz facility and observed that a strange number of uranium enriching centrifuges were breaking. The cause of these failures was unknown at that time. Later Iranian technicians contacted computer security specialists in Belarus for examining their server and network systems which control the facilities. This security firm eventually discovered multiple malicious files on the Iranian computer systems. It has subsequently revealed that these malicious files were the Stuxnet worm. Although Iran has not released specific details regarding the effects of the attack, it is currently estimated that the Stuxnet worm destroyed 984 uranium enriching centrifuges. By current estimations this constituted a 30% decrease in enrichment efficiency.

➢ Spreading of Stuxnet

As already explained Stuxnet is one of the most complex, lethal and well engineered 500kilobyte computer worms the world has ever seen. It took advantage of at least four Zero Day Vulnerabilities (ZDV) with remarkable sophistication. The worm propagates using three totally diverse mechanisms as described below.

➢ Via infected removable drives (such as USB flash drives and external portable hard disks)

➢ Via Local Area Network communications (such as shared network drives and print spooler services) and

➢ Via infected Siemens project files (including both WinCC and STEP 7 files).

Within these three, it uses the following vulnerability exploitation techniques for spreading to new computers in a system. The worm initially exploits a Zero Day Vulnerability in Windows Shell handling of LNK files which is a vulnerability present in all versions of Windows since at least Windows NT 4.0. Then uses several techniques to copy itself to all accessible network and spread from there to all possible locations. It also copies itself to printer servers using a zero-day vulnerability, The Conficker RPC vulnerability is also used to propagate through computers which are not properly patched up. If any Siemens WinCCSQLServer database servers are present, then the worm installs itself on those servers via database calls and puts copies of itself into Siemens STEP 7 project files to auto-execute whenever the files are loaded. Certain versions of the worm used a variant of the old *autorun. inf* trick to propagate via USB drives.

In addition to the propagation techniques described above, the worm uses two ZDVs to escalate privilege on targeted machines. This provided the worm with system access privileges so that it could copy itself into system processes on compromised machines. When first installed on a computer with any software, Stuxnet attempts to locate Siemens STEP 7 programming stations and infect these. If it succeeds, it replaces the Dynamic Link Library(DLL). Mostly Stuxnet spreads through the infected removable devices especially the USB. However it is a misconception that it spreads through only removable devices and an effective disabling of the storage device access can prevent the spreading of Stuxnet.

➢ **Havex**

The modified version of Havex malware mainly targets the energy sector. Originally, Havex was distributed via spam email or spear-phishing attacks. The new version of Havex appears to have been designed as a Trojan horse specifically to infiltrate and modify legitimate software from ICS and SCADA suppliers, adding an instruction to run, code containing the Havex malware. In the instance discovered, Havex malware was used as a Remote Access Tool (RAT) to extract data from Industrial Control System (ICS) related software used for remote access. The cyber-attack leaves the company's system in what appears to be a normal operating condition, but a backdoor has been opened by the attacker to access and control the utilities ICS or SCADA operations. The Havex malware possibly enter the control systems of targeted utilities using one or multiple levels of attack as described below.

1. Top level management are targeted with malicious PDF attachments.

2. Websites are likely to be visited by people working in the energy sector. Such websites can be infected and visitors are redirected to another compromised legitimate website hosting an exploit kit.

   Using this exploit kit, the RAT may be installed.

3. Through software downloads from ICS related vendors which they include the RAT malware.

Havex is also called as *Backdoor. Oldrea* or the *Energetic Bear RAT* as it contains the malware known as *Kragany*. Havex is a product of the Dragonfly group, which appears to be a state-sponsored undertaking focused on espionage with sabotage as a definite secondary capability. The malware allows attackers to upload and download files from the infected computer and run executable files. It was also reported to be capable of collecting passwords, taking screenshots and cataloguing documents.

➢ Sandworm

Sandworm is a type of Trojan horse, focused on exploiting vulnerability in the Windows operating system. USB storage devices with automatically run files, carrying the malware is used for the attack. The primary mode of Sandworm attack is spear phishing. Using well written emails with topics of interest has been sent to the target. The malware contains an attachment that exploits the vulnerability to deliver variants of the BlackEnergy Trojan.

Various reports released regarding the Sandworm team and investigations of the malware samples and domains, realized that Sandworm team is targeting SCADA centric victims especially who are using GE Intelligent Platform's CIMPLICITY HMI solution suite. The HMI can be viewed as an operator console that is used to monitor and control devices in an industrial environment. Sandworm can potentially have greater impacts on an enterprise, as the malware could be transferred to other corporate business systems.

It is important to note that CIMPLICITY is mainly used as an attack vector by Sandworm. However, there is no sign that this malware is manipulating any actual SCADA systems or data. Since HMIs are located in both the corporate and control networks, this attack could be used to target either network segment, or used to cross from the corporate to the control network.

➢ **Duqu and Flame**

Duqu and Flame are computer malwares that were discovered on 1st September 2011 and 28th May 2012, respectively. Duqu is almost identical to Stuxnet but with a different tenacity. Flame is also known as Flamer or Sky-wiper. The goal of Duqu is to collect information that could be useful in launching an ICS attack later. Flame like Stuxnet and Duqu, uses rootkit functionality to evade information security methods. Unlike Stuxnet, which was designed to sabotage ICSs, the target of Flame is to gather technical diagrams such as AutoCAD drawings, PDFs, and text files. Though Duqu and Flame were not designed to target ICSs directly, their penetration and acquiring information about the systems, is an indication of a targeted stealthy attacks in the future.

2.9 FLASH DRIVE USAGE AND END NODE SECURITY (ENS)

USB attacks are becoming more sophisticated, affecting all classes of USB device instead of just storage. As USBs have become a common method for easily sharing information locally between devices, they have become a common source of information system cyber-compromise. As per NERC CIP guidelines, use of USB or USB type ports are strongly discouraged because a USB port is not immune to protection from *unauthorized access*.

It would be helpless against connecting modems, network cables that bridge networks or insertion of an infected USB pen drive. Cyber protection for USB ports can be enforced, however, it is often cost prohibitive and is not one hundred percent effective. There is no essential requirement for using a USB instead of other standard and more secure interfaces such as Ethernet and serial ports. Some of the common methods to protect the USB ports are,

> disabling (via software) the physical ports,

> prominent physical port usage discouragement such as, a port cover plate or tamper tape and

> physical port obstruction using removable locks.

These measures are examples of defense-in-depth methods, but the CIP guidelines acknowledge that these control approaches can be easily circumvented. It is also not uncommon for an employee or authorized contractor to inadvertently compromise a device simply by plugging in an infected smart phone to charge the battery. USB flash drives pose two major challenges to critical infrastructure cyber-security viz.

> ease of data theft owing to their small size and transportability, and

> system compromise through infections from computer viruses, malware and spyware.

It is a well-accepted fact that a USB supported portable peripheral device can trigger a massive cyber-attack, even when the computer system targeted is isolated and protected from the outside with firewalls and other types of security devices.

> BadUSB

BadUSB is an USB which includes firmware in addition to disk space. It is inherently a microcontroller with writable storage memory registers. This firmware however can be embedded with executable codes which cannot be verified by third party security software applications since the firmware is not an open source. This flaw in USBs opens the door to modification of USB firmware, which can easily be done from inside the operating system, and hide the malware in a way that it becomes almost impossible to detect. The flaw is even more potent because complete formatting or deleting the content of a USB device won't eliminate the malicious code, since it is embedded in the firmware. Patches made for BadUSB have been largely ineffective and a fix is years away.

BadUSB can act like different input/output devices like physical keyboard, mouse, network adapter, phone, tablet, webcam, or authentication token. For example, if it pretends it is a keyboard or mouse, the malicious software can inject keystrokes and mouse clicks, performing multiple actions on the computer, like launching Microsoft Outlook and sending an e-mail to a certain address, with attached files from the user's computer. If it pretends it is an authentication token, a BadUSB would force the computer to prompt a token password, which can then be stored on the flash drive and retrieved at a later date.

In fact till date, there has been no fool proof defensive solution against BadUSB attacks and it exposes the fundamental vulnerabilities of unconstrained privileges in USB devices. This being the situation, ICS and DCS design and implementation must be in such a manner that it completely eliminates the need for a USB port which is advised and recommended in the interest of reliable and safe operations.

➤ **Cyber Incidents using USB**

- ▪ Two US based power plants were infected with malware after using USB drives in their ICS. At one of the plants this resulted in downtime and delayed the plant's restart by three weeks. This caused considerable financial loss.

- ▪ Another cyber incident of malware wreaking havoc includes the recent widespread infections at Saudi Aramco and Ras-Gas, where malware were planted by USB drives. At Saudi Aramco approximately 40,000 computer hard drives were completely wiped off. As none of the infected power plants had updated anti-malware softwares, the infected computers were totally incapable of detecting the malware on the inserted USB drives.

Usually, almost every vendors or implementation agencies offer or sign the contract stating that the control system shall be protected by an automatically updated antivirus system. The agreement is reasonable, but it may be very difficult to comply with. The ICS industry is very much aware of this problem. Different solutions have been tried, including the use of glue guns to disable USB ports and physical USB locks.

2.10 OTHER DOCUMENTED POWER SYSTEM CYBER INCIDENTS

➢ Crashed Ohio Nuke Plant Network by Slammer Worm (2003)

In January 2003, a Slammer worm penetrated a private computer network at Ohio's Davis-Besse nuclear power plant and disabled a safety monitoring system for more than 5 hours, despite a belief by plant personnel that the network was protected by a firewall. The Slammer worm spread from the enterprise network to the ICS network by exploiting the vulnerabilities of the MS-SQL. It was reported that process computers had crashed for hours, aggravating the system operators.

• Taum Sauk Hydroelectric Power Station Failure (2005)

The Taum Sauk incident on December 14, 2005, was not an attack but instead a failure of a hydroelectric power station. Various explanations, including design or construction flaws, instrumentation malfunction, and human error, have been attributed to the catastrophic failure of an upper reservoir. Investigation revealed that the sensors failed to indicate that the reservoir was full and the pumps were not shut down until the water overflew for about 5 to 6 min. This overflow damaged the parapet wall, resulting in the collapse of the reservoir. Apparently this incident was (apparently) not an attack, but the idea behind it could be exploited to perform undetectable attacks in safety-critical infrastructures. This can be a means for a stealthy attack on a SCADA by sending compromised sensor measurements to the control center.

➢ Cyber Incident on Georgia Nuclear Power Plant (2008)

In July 2008, a nuclear power plant in Georgia was forced into an emergency shutdown for 48 hours because a computer used to monitor chemical and diagnostic data from the corporate network rebooted after a software update. When the updated computer restarted, it reset the data on the control system. The safety systems interpreted the lack of data as lowering of the levels in the water reservoirs that cool the plant's radioactive nuclear fuel rods, and triggering a system shutdown.

- ### *PSS Giant Telvent Compromised in Canada (2013)*

A breach on the internal firewall and security systems of Telvent, Canada, one of the most reliable company which supplies remote monitoring and control tools to the energy sector, was discovered on September 10, 2012. After penetrating the network, the intruders stole project files related to the OASyS SCADA product, a highly sophisticated remote administration tool allowing companies to combine older IT equipment with modern Smart Grid technology. It is very likely that the adversaries gathered information about this new product to find its vulnerabilities and to prepare for future stealthy attacks against PSS.

- ### *Ukraine Power Grid Cyber-attack December(2015)*

The Ukraine power grid Cyber-attack took place on 23 December 2015 and is considered to be the first known successful cyber-attack on a power grid. Hackers were able to successfully compromise information systems of three energy distribution companies in Ukraine and temporarily disrupt electricity supply to the end consumers. The cyber-attack was complex and comprised of the following steps,

- prior compromise of corporate networks using spear fishing emails with BlackEnergy malware, seized the ICS under control, and switched off substations remotely,

- disabled IT infrastructure components such as uninterruptable power supplies, modems, RTUs, commutators,

- destroyed files stored on servers and workstations with the KillDisk malware, and

- denial-of-service attack on call-center to deny consumers up-to-date information on the blackout.

A brief account on the Ukraine attack has been already described earlier in this chapter.

- ### Stuxnet attack on Iran's Natanz nuclear facility (2012 & 2017)

In 2012 Iranian nuclear facilities were attacked and infiltrated by the first *cyber-weapon* or the *digital missile* of the world known as the Stuxnet. It is believed that this Natanz nuclear facility attack was initiated by a random worker's USB drive. By current estimations this attack results in 30% decrease in enrichment efficiency. It is reported that in 2017, once again Iranian critical infrastructures and networks have been vehemently attacked by a new variant of the lethal Stuxnet which is many fold sophisticated than its former variant leaving extreme concerns to the security of the industrial automation world. A brief account on the Iranian nuclear facility attack has been described earlier in this chapter.

➢ ICS CYBER-ATTACKS ON US

It has been reported by IBM X-Force that the number of events targeting the ICS assets in 2019 increased over 2000 percent since 2018. In fact, the number of events targeting OT assets in 2019 was greater than the activity volume observed in the past three years combined. As the US is the most cyber targeted nation they have stepped up security measures by strictly implementing the mandatory standards in ICSs. In 2019 June US grid regulator NERC issued a warning that major hacking group with suspected Russian ties was conducting reconnaissance into the networks of electrical utilities. Some of the significant successful attacks are described below.

- *Penetration of Electricity Grid of US by Spies (2009)*

On August 14, 2003, the Northeast and Midwest regions of the United States and some provinces in Canada suffered a serious blackout because of a software bug. These incidents have raised concerns about the security of electric power grids, because disrupting national power systems might cause catastrophic damage. *The Wall Street Journal* reported that on April 8, 2009, Cyber-attackers have penetrated the US electric power grid and left behind a software program that can be used to disrupt the system.

- **Water Tower Decoy in US (2012)**

In December 2012, a malicious computer virus concealed in an MS Word document sent from Chinese hacking group, APT1, successfully took over a water tower control system in the US. Fortunately for anyone nearby, the tower was actually a trap set up to attract such would-be industrial attacks. So, while nothing was hurt or destroyed in this incident, it did demonstrate the frightening reality of these attacks.

- **US Wind farm attack (2019)**

The largest renewable energy developer in US located at Utah was hit by a cyber-attack that briefly break contact of a number of wind and solar farms. Later it has been reported that it was a DoS attack that left grid operators temporary blinded generation sites totalling a loss of 500MW. The cyber-attack took advantage of a known weakness in Cisco firewalls to trigger a series of a five minute communication outage over a span of about 12 hours.

➤ CYBER THREATS TO INDIAN ICS

The US was the most cyber targeted nation in the world in 2019 for power sector cyber-attacks. However India surpassed US and topped in the list for three months and remained within the top 5 cyber targeted countries in 2019 leaving extreme concerns to India's power sector automation and Smart Grid projects which are struggling to comply the relevant physical-cyber security standards. If any cyber security flaws are introduced by chance to the Indian power grid by the implementation agencies, likelihood of exploiting these vulnerabilities by our enemy nations are very high. Government of India (GoI) and Central Electricity Authority (CEA) are giving directions to implement the proper cyber security measures without any lapse to the various power Transmission and Distribution utilities while moving to digital energy. Realising the possibility supply chain attacks, the GoI recently cautioned the power utilities to test all the Chinese products especially the industrial networking products used in power sector automation.

- **Indian North-Eastern Grid Blackout (2012)**

In 2012 one of the world's worst blackout has occurred in India. The exact cause for this blackout is yet to be confirmed as many speculations/reports of a cyber-attack from enemy nations are live though official explanation denies it. But the Nation has realised the consequences of a blackout if it happens due to a cyber-attack. The security experts point out it may occur at any times as India is facing 30 cyber-attacks daily on its power sector mostly from China, Slovania, Mexico, Ukraine and Pakistan unless India identify and fix the flaws of the imported industrial networking and automation products. The 2012 blackout left almost 710 million people without power. The noted other impacts due to this blackout are briefly described below.

More than 700 million people in India have been left without power in the world's worst blackout of recent times, leading to fears that protests and even riots could follow if the country's electricity supply continues to fail to meet growing demand. First to fail was India's northern grid, leaving an estimated 350 million people in the dark for up to 14 hours. It was quickly followed by the eastern grid, which includes Kolkata, then the north-eastern grid. Twenty of India's 28 states were hit by power cuts, along with the capital, New Delhi, when three of the country's five electricity grids failed at lunchtime.

As engineers struggled for hours to fix the problem, hundreds of trains failed, leaving passengers stranded along thousands of miles of track from Kashmir in the north to Nagaland on the eastern border with Burma. Traffic lights went out, causing jams in New Delhi, Kolkata and other cities. Surgical operations were cancelled across the country, with nurses at one hospital just outside Delhi having to operate life-saving equipment manually when back-up generators failed. Electric crematoriums stopped operating; some with bodies left half burnt before wood was brought in to stoke the furnaces. As Delhiites sweated in 89% humidity and drivers honked their horns even more impatiently than usual, in West Bengal the power cut left hundreds of miners trapped underground for hours when their lifts broke down. All the state's government workers were sent home after the chief minister announced it would take 10 to 12 hours for the power to return. There were some agitations, riots and protests in urban areas which were very reliant on electricity. TVs and computers were not worked for a week and one-third of India's households do not even have electricity to power a light bulb. By early evening, 50 of the trapped miners in West Bengal had been rescued and power had been restored to the north-east of the country, as well the most affluent areas of Delhi.

India has five electricity grids viz. northern, eastern, north-eastern, southern and western. All are interconnected. The blackout and its impacts were an eye opener to the Indian energy engineers that the present power grid of India needs to be cyber secured in every respect with appropriate architecture with approved standards as the all the five regional grids are interconnected, operated and controlled by NLDC, New Delhi. It also given a lesson to the grid security to engineers on the need of PMU based power system monitoring and control when national grids integrates and operates as a single grid.

- *Breach at the Kudankulam Nuclear Power Plant (2019)*

Towards the end of October 2019, reports were spreading in social media regarding a cyber-attack at Kudankulam Nuclear Power Plant. On October 29, the Plant authorities, denied such an attack and informed that both the reactors (1000MW and 600MW) were running without any operational or safety concerns. But unexpectedly, Nuclear Power Corporation of India Limited (NPCIL) within 24 hours admitted that there indeed was an incident and Dtrack RAT has been located within the plant. Source code included hard coded credentials to KNPP indicating that it was a targeted attack. It also contains methods to collect browser history, passwords, host IPs, running processes and all files on disk volumes.

The matter was conveyed to Computer Emergency Response Team (CERT-In) as soon as it was noticed. CERT-In said that they had identified a malware attack that breached India's largest nuclear power facility's administrative network on September 4. They further emphasised that the nuclear plant's operational systems were safe they are air gapped and the administrative network was not connected to it. Hence there was nothing to be panic.

This clearly exposed the lack of the technical awareness of the plant authorities regarding the air gap jumpers. Further the malware, DTRACK, was developed by a North Korean hacker group called LAZARUS who specialised in stealing information from a system. It is suspected that a large amount of data was stolen during the breach. This data could be used to plan the next attack more efficiently. As per the cyber security experts and ethical hackers, Domain Controller level access has been gained by the hackers at KNPP.

In the modern environment, most of the ICS networks are air gapped/ stand-alone having no connectivity to cyber-space to make it secure.

Hence the ICS threat actors usually carried out the attacks to ICS in two stages as explained in previous chapters. Hence it can be observed that the stage I attack has been carried out successfully by the threat actors. The chances of the stage II attack which will be the real objective behind the ICS attack cannot be ruled out. The CERT-In and the NPCIL authorities might have taken all necessary actions without any compromise to prevent such attack else it will be extremely disastrous.

Summary

The word *cyber* has become one of the most omnipresent and powerful concepts in contemporary security studies. Today, cyberspace has emerged as a domain of its own, in many ways like land, sea and air. Even if a nation whether it is small in land area, low in GDP, low in resources, less important in geopolitics, low in strength of armed forces, it can be a military super power if that nation is capable of launching a cyber-attack on critical infrastructures of any nation including superpowers and crumble the nation. This chapter begins with a brief concept of cyber space and the security definitions in cyber space. Various threat sources to ICS, its vulnerabilities, dreadful ICS malwares and the documented incidents.

Chapter Three

Operational Technology and SCADA

3.1 INTRODUCTION

The operating environment of ICS control a physical process which is a real time control and having unique network configurations and protocols. The data can become stale in a fraction of few seconds, resulting in loss of process efficiency, damage or shut down. As a result, ICS reliability is crucial and continues to operate even during a cyber-attack. Process inefficiencies and shutdowns are often very expensive, with millions of dollars or much more for large process. In critical infrastructure, loss of the ICS can have significant, detrimental impact in the health and functionality of society. Earlier, ICS were physically isolated or air gapped from the outside world. Now systems are linked into the corporate WAN and internet to allow process monitoring and maintenance for off-site groups. Control engineers, technicians, operators are usually not skilled in cyber security. Conversely, the IT professionals are not skilled in process control. They have sometimes conflicting goals and management in the corporate structure. This chapter briefly explains the Operational Technology (OT), its difference from the IT and ICS.

Various SCADA architectures are adapted today depending on the requirements. It starts with the basic single channel Data Acquisition and Control architecture to the complex multi-channel, real-time, fault tolerant, fail safe system which utilizes many secure communication methodologies with proper End Node Security (ENS). A Standalone ICS architecture is relatively simple as it has PLCs, RTUs, Servers, and HMI segmented into two or three zones viz. Enterprise Security Zone, Industrial Demilitarised Zone and Process Security Zone. However when comes to Distributed SCADA, the system architecture becomes complex and needs stringent physical-cyber security measures. The following sections elaborate the various ICS architectures with emphasis on Distributed SCADA.

3.2 OPERATIONAL TECHNOLOGY (OT)

Present and the next generation of operational technology demands that decision-makers understand OT in its traditional sense *and* as the area of exciting innovation. At very fundamental level, OT refers to a technology which monitors and controls specific devices and processes within industrial workflows.

When compared with IT, OT is unique with its hardware and software and is usually designed to do specific things such as control physical parameters like heat, pressure, humidity etc. and monitor mechanical performance, issue emergency shut offs, etc. on proper decisions. Typically, this is done through Industrial Control Systems (ICS) and Supervisory Control and Data Acquisition (SCADA).

3.3 INFORMATION TECHNOLOGY (IT) VS OPERATIONAL TECHNOLOGY (OT)

In the simplest sense, IT deals with information, while OT deals with machines. The former manages the flow of digital information such as CRM, ERP, Email, etc, while the latter manages the operation of physical processes and the machinery used to carry them out. Some examples of OTs are SCADA, PLCs, HMIs, etc.

From power plants and oil rigs to manufacturing assembly lines and inventory management processes, OT is an essential part of some incredibly complex physical processes. Some of the IT systems invented to manage are now being applied to operational technology to manage the flow of information flow of water, lubricating oil, heat, packing peanuts, and breakfast cereals. In fact, OT and IT now work hand-in-hand to monitor and regulate essential industrial processes outside of regular IT workflows. Although these processes will differ from one industry to industry, ICS has a central role to play in the success of many modern enterprises – and manufacturers in particular.

For these kinds of enterprises, whether public or private, it's of vital importance that key decision-makers understand how IT and OT differ-in addition to how each discipline can and should interact. Given the rise of the internet of Things and its successful application across nearly every industry, now is the time for organizations with a stake in IT and OT systems and networks to invest in next-generation solutions that can bring these two distinct disciplines into ever-tighter partnership.

Function	Information Technologies (IT)	Operational Technologies (OT)
Objective	Information Technology focuses on the storage, recovery, transmission, manipulation and protection of data.	OT is more oriented to the control of processes or their change through the monitoring and control of devices
Application domain	Business-oriented	Process-oriented
Access	Connected with the external world	Very restricted access and limited to people with role based access.
Assets Vs workers	The number of assets is usually equal (or close) to the number of professionals	More automated and having more devices than operating personals.
Frequency change	Constantly changing with new employees joining the company and former employees leaving the company	Slow changing environment and there may be no changes for months to years.
Main priority	Confidentiality, Integrity and Availability	Uptime is essential. Availability, Integrity and Confidentiality.

Continued...

Updates	Constant due to software updates. Service interruptions are tolerable and, in some cases, programmable outside of working hours	Updates must be tested carefully in advance and, usually involve restarting or stopping the machines.
Life cycle	Shorter life cycles (3-5 years)	OT systems have longer life cycles (15-20 years). As a result, legacy systems and no longer supported ones are frequent.
Latency	Minutes-days	Milliseconds-Seconds
Security	Logical security. The objective is to protect confidential information from any potential risk such as human error, natural disasters, cyber-attacks, etc. No lives at risk.	The objective is to protect the environment, people and infrastructures.
Operating System	Standard Operating Systems	Specific purpose equipment with Custom-developed software and Operating Systems.

Table 3.1: Comparison of Information Technology (IT) and Operational Technology (OT)

3.4 INDUSTRIAL CONTROL SYSTEMS (ICS)

An industrial control system is a combination of a variety of systems like computers, electrical and mechanical devices. It can be considered as the combination of several control systems such as Supervisory Control and Data Acquisition (SCADA) systems, Distributed Control Systems (DCS), and Programmable Logic Controllers. They are used to provide automated or partially automated control of the equipment in manufacturing and chemical plants, electric utilities, distribution and transportation systems, and many other industries. It can also be described as the automatic regulation of unit operations and their associated equipment as well as the integration and coordination of the unit operations into the larger production system. ICS is used in manufacturing operations and it can also be applied to material handling.

3.5 TYPES OF INDUSTRIAL CONTROL SYSTEMS

ICSs are classified based on their uses and the separation between the controller and the supervisory components and they are,

1. *Process control system:* This system does the automation function in a manufacturing unit, process control systems are mostly seen in factories.

2. *Safety instrumented system:* These systems are used in the automation process it will check the process and it prevents unsafe operation processes. They have sensors which will send signals to the controller which can prevent any fault operation

3. *Distributed control system:* DCS can handle multiple automation processes in a factory, it can control all the automation or it can monitor or supervise the factory process.

4. *Building Automation System:* Building automation system controls and monitor the whole building process such as air-conditioning, ventilation, energy management, and fire protection. So we can control the whole building from a control room with the help of BAS.

5. *Energy management system:* An energy management system can control and monitor the transmission and generation of electricity. It can be considered as a type of SCADA which can control the power generation and transmission.

6. *Supervisory control and data acquisition:* SCADA is a type of industrial control system which can observe the automation process across geographical areas which will be miles away.

SCADA system can control and monitor remote field controllers, and the result will be given to operators by a human-machine interface. SCADA system can control one or more distributed or process control systems at distant locations.

3.6 FUNCTIONING OF AN INDUSTRIAL CONTROL SYSTEM

The basic units and its operation of an ICS are:

> *Control loop:* control loop has sensors for measurement and they have controller hardware like PLC, actuators, control valves, breakers, switches, and motors. The controlled variable is transmitted to the controller from the sensors.

> *Human-machine interface:* operators and engineers do the configuration of set points control algorithms and establish parameters in the controller. The HMI displays the process status information.

> *Remote diagnostics and maintenance utilities:* These devices are used to prevent failure, and to identify and recover from failure.

3.7 CONTROL COMPONENTS OF ICS

Control server: This provides the control software for DCS or PLC which is designed to communicate with lower-level control devices

SCADA server or master control unit: SCADA server acts as the master In the SCADA system, remote terminal units and PLC devises which are located at remote field sites act as slaves.

Remote terminal unit: These are designed to support SCADA remote stations, it is a special-purpose data acquisition and control unit. RTU's are used to support remote situations where wire-based communications are unavailable

Programmable logic controller: PLC is a small industrial computer that is designed to perform the logic functions executed by electrical hardware. PLC has the ability to control complex process and they are used in SCADA systems and DCS. PLC's can be used as a field device because they are more economical and flexible.

Intelligent electronic device: IED is a smart sensor that has the intelligence to acquire data, communicate to other devices, and it performs local processing and control. Automatic control is possible with the help of IED

Human-machine interface: It can be considered as the combination of the software and hardware which allows operators to check the state of a process if it is under control or not. HMI can be used to modify control settings to change the control objective and it can be used to manually override automatic control operations in case of emergencies. Operators can configure set points or control algorithms with the help of HMI. It can display process, status information, historical information and other information to operators.

Data historian: It is a centralized database for logging all process information within an ICS information that is stored in a database that can be accessed to support various analyses.

Communications gateways: Two dissimilar devices can be communicated by this, it transforms data from a sending system to match the protocol and transmission medium of a destination host

Field devices: FIeld devices are sensors transducers and actuators and machinery which directly interface with a controller through a digital or analog input/output module.

Input/output server (I/O server): it is a control component that does the collecting, buffering, and providing access to process information from control sub-components such as PLC, RTU... it can be used to interface with the third party control components such as an HMI and a control server.

3.8 NETWORK COMPONENTS OF INDUSTRIAL CONTROL SYSTEM

Fieldbus network: This device can link sensors and other devices to a PLC or other controller. With the help of this, the need for point to point wiring between the controller and the device is eliminated.

Control network: It connects the supervisory control level to lower-level control modules.

Communication routers: It is a device that can transfer messages between two networks. LAN and WAN are examples of routers, it can be used as a long-distance network medium.

Firewall: Devices on a network are protected by a firewall, it can protect the network by monitoring and controlling communication packets.

Remote access points: They are distinct devices, we can control the control system remotely by the help of this.

MODEMS: Modems are used for long-distance serial communications, digital data can be converted by modem and it can transmit data over a telephone line to allow devices to communicate. Remote communication is possible through the help of MODEMS.

3.9 DIFFERENT OPERATIONAL ZONES IN ICS

Industrial control systems are very complex, they can be used to control the complex processes in real-time with the help of many components. In order to control the operation process, ICSs are divided into three operational zones they are:

Enterprise zone: This zone comprises of business network and enterprise systems, it has many endpoint devices that evolve rapidly and are upgraded continuously. The business network is commonly based on the IP protocols and it will be connected to external networks and the internet. These networks are usually kept separate from the operational networks used in other zones.

Control zones: In this zone, it has a distributed control system like the SCADA systems. This zone includes the control room environments. This zone has a network-based IP protocol just like the enterprise zone. The devices in this zone are not often updated and the network has some time constraints and because of this only a few cyber-security uses this zone.

Field zone: This zone is also called an operational zone it has many devices and networks in charge of control and automation. The field zone devices and networks are comprised of high reliability and safety.

3.10 ICS ATTACK PHASES

In the modern environment, most of the ICS networks are air gapped/ stand-alone having no connectivity to cyber-space to make it secure. Hence the threat actors usually carried out the attacks to ICS in two phases viz.

➢ In the first stage the ICS attacker gain access to the ICS network by all means possible, to launch the stage II attack. Here, hackers may try their best to find a foothold into the administrative or business network of the organization, so that a pivot point can be found to jump into the ICS network.

➢ The main objective of this stage of attack may be sabotage of the production process or plant functionality. This stage attack includes gaining the access of ICS network, identifying the ICS network topology, creating the backdoors in the applications and devices to infiltrate the data, and finally carry out the sabotage the plant process.

3.11 SUPERVISORY CONTROL AND DATA ACQUISITION (SCADA)

Supervisory Control and Data Acquisition (SCADA) is a system that operates with coded signals over communication channels so as to provide control of remote equipment (using typically at least one communication channel per remote station). In SCADA, the control system is combined with the data acquisition system by fetching the coded signals over communication channels to acquire information about the status of the remote equipment's for displaying or for recording or controlling equipment functions. SCADA systems historically distinguish themselves from other ICS systems by being large-scale processes that can include multiple sites, spread out over large areas. These processes can be industrial, infrastructure, and facility-based processes.

Industrial processes include those of manufacturing, production, power generation, fabrication, and refining. The process can be run in continuous, batch, repetitive, or discrete modes. Infrastructure processes may be public or private, and include water treatment and distribution, wastewater collection and treatment, oil and gas pipelines, electrical power transmission and distribution, wind farms, civil defense siren systems, and large communication systems. Facility processes occur both in public facilities and private ones, including buildings, airports, ships, and space stations. They monitor and control heating, ventilation, and air conditioning systems (HVAC), access, and energy consumption.

Evolution of SCADA

SCADA systems have been evolved through the following four generations.

- *Monolithic SCADA:* These SCADA systems were in use before the revolution of computer networking. They were stand-alone systems having no connectivity to other systems and developed as local SCADA. These mostly used guided communication with proprietary protocols. Further these systems did not envisage the fail safe and fault tolerant design aspects seriously. Hence these SCADA systems faced reliability issues considerably. The hardware used was mainly minicomputers capable of large computing capabilities.

- *Distributed SCADA:* This generation came into existence when the computer networking technology has been developed and incorporated into the SCADA systems. Here the data gathered and the data processing across the multiple stations are connected through computer networking. The latency has been reduced considerably to an extent that system as a whole functioned in near real time. These SCADA systems were economical when compared with first generation, as each station has been assigned with particular tasks. However the protocols used was still proprietary and was not interoperable. But the proprietary protocols had an advantage that beyond the developers, the extent of security or the security flaws are unknown. In other way these SCADA systems were secured through *security through obscurity.*

- *SCADA with standard protocols:* The advancement of communication technology and with the introduction of interoperable SCADA protocols, SCADA broke the geographical barriers and spread across more than one LAN network called Process Control Network. The master station may have several servers running parallel to handle various tasks, such as historian, SCADA, NMS, Development, etc. This makes the system very economical and real-time. However the physical-security is a major concern and must be addressed while designing and implementing.

- *Internet of Things:* By appropriately integrating the advancement of cloud computing, SCADA has taken a new shape and adopted the name Internet of Things. The advantages of amalgamating the various technologies are:

  1. Capable of being flexible and affordable with the ability to go private,

  2. Capable of ingest massive amount of machine data,

  3. Capable of connecting different machines and systems such as SCADA, DCS, and historians,

  4. Capable of connecting various machines having net connectivity and process data across all these sources together,

  5. Capable of real time complex and real time processing of data from multiple sources and

  6. Capable of Big data processing and apply supervised and unsupervised machine learning algorithms to predict outcomes.

Another advantage of incorporating the cloud computing technology is that it significantly reduces the infrastructure costs and increases the ease of maintenance. Further the SCADA operations become near real time and the use of open protocols with TLS security improves the security boundary considerably.

Certain ICT professionals envisage IoT as an appropriate amalgamation of Machine to Machine (M2M) communication, Wireless Sensor Networks (WSN), Radio Frequency Identification (RFID), and SCADA as shown in Figure 3.1.

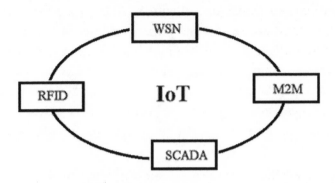

Figure 3.1: Fourth generation SCADA or IoT.

In fact, the fourth generation SCADA or IoT transforms the human centric internet into objects or things centric. It is expected that about 70 billion things may be hooked into internet in the near future while people hooked into the internet may be only 7 billion. However at present, IoT is not a tangible reality but it is a prospective vision of a number of technologies. But once materialized, it can drastically change the way of functioning of our society. Realizing the potential and the opportunity of business, IoT has become a buzzword in many countries. Further it is anticipated that the whole world will be soon under the influence of IoT wave.

Types of Industrial Control Systems

ICSs are classified based on their uses and the separation between the controller and the supervisory components and they are:

- *Process control system:* This system does the automation function in a manufacturing unit, process control systems are mostly seen in factories,

- *Safety instrumented system:* These systems are used in the automation process it will check the process and it prevents unsafe operation processes. They have sensors which will send signals to the controller which can prevent any fault operation,

- *Distributed Control System:* DCS can handle multiple automation processes in a factory, it can control all the automation or it can monitor or supervise the factory process,

- **Building Automation System:** Building Automation System (BAS) controls and monitor the whole building process such as air-conditioning, ventilation, energy management, and fire protection. So one can control the whole building from a control room with the help of BAS,

- **Energy Management System:** An energy management system can control and monitor the transmission and generation of electricity. It can be considered as a type of SCADA which can control the power generation and transmission, and

- **Supervisory Control and Data Acquisition:** SCADA is a type of industrial control system which can observe the automation process across geographical areas which will be miles away. SCADA system can control and monitor remote field controllers, and the result will be given to operators by a human-machine interface. SCADA system can control one or more distributed or process control systems at distant locations.

Control Components of ICS

Control server: This provides the control software for DCS or PLC which is designed to communicate with lower-level control devices.

SCADA server or master control unit: SCADA server acts as the master In the SCADA system, remote terminal units and PLC devises which are located at remote field sites act as slaves.

Remote Terminal Unit: these are designed to support SCADA remote stations, it is a special-purpose data acquisition and control unit. RTU's are used to support remote situations where wire-based communications are unavailable.

Programmable Logic Controller: PLC is a small industrial computer that is designed to perform the logic functions executed by electrical hardware. PLC has the ability to control complex process and they are used in SCADA systems and DCS. PLC's can be used as a field device because they are more economical and flexible.

Intelligent Electronic Device: IED is a smart sensor that has the intelligence to acquire data, communicate to other devices, and it performs local processing and control. Automatic control is possible with the help of IED.

Human-Machine Interface: It can be considered as the combination of the software and hardware which allows operators to check the state of a process if it is under control or not. HMI can be used to modify control settings to change the control objective and it can be used to manually override automatic control operations in case of emergencies. Operators can configure set points or control algorithms with the help of HMI. It can display process, status information, historical information and other information to operators.

Data historian: It is a centralized database for logging all process information within an ICS information that is stored in a database that can be accessed to support various analyses.

Communications gateways: Two dissimilar devices can be communicated by this, it transforms data from a sending system to match the protocol and transmission medium of a destination host.

Field devices: Field devices are sensors transducers and actuators and machinery which directly interface with a controller through a digital or analog input/output module.

I/O server: It is a control component that does the collecting, buffering, and providing access to process information from control sub-components such as PLC, RTU. It can be used to interface with the third party control components such as an HMI and a control server.

Network Components of ICS

Network components of Industrial Control System are briefly described below.

Fieldbus network: this device can link sensors and other devices to a PLC or other controller. With the help of this, the need for point to point wiring between the controller and the device is eliminated *Control network:* It connects the supervisory control level to lower-level control.

Routers: It is a device that can transfer messages between two networks. LAN and WAN are examples of routers, it can be used as a long-distance network medium.

Firewalls: Devices on a network are protected by a firewall, it can protect the network by monitoring and controlling.

Remote Access Points: They are distinct devices which control system remotely.

MODEMS: Modems are used for long-distance serial communications, digital data can be converted by modem and it can transmit data over a telephone line to allow devices to communicate. Remote communication is possible through the help of MODEMS.

Different Operational Zones in ICS

Industrial control systems are very complex, they can be used to control the complex and precision processes in real-time with the help of many components. In order to control the operation process, ICSs are divided mainly into three operational zones they are,

Enterprise zone: This zone comprises of business network and enterprise systems. It has many endpoint devices and is upgraded continuously. The business network is commonly operated on the IP protocols and can be connected to external networks including the internet. These networks are usually kept separate from the operational networks of other zones.

Control zones: This zone has a network-based IP protocol just like the enterprise zone including a control room environment. The devices in this zone are not often updated.

Field zone: It has many field devices and networks in charge of control and automation. The field zone devices and networks are comprised of high reliability and safety.

DCS Communication Architecture

There are three physical communication architectures which are generally popular and deployed in SCADA systems. In certain cases they are deployed in a combined mode. They are,

1. Point to point,
2. Point to multistations, and
3. Relay Stations.

➢ Point-To-Point Between Two Stations

This is the simplest configuration where data is exchanged between two stations. One station can be setup as the master and one as the slave as shown in Figure 3.2. It is possible for both the stations to communicate in full duplex mode (transmitting and receiving on two separate frequencies) or simplex with only one frequency.

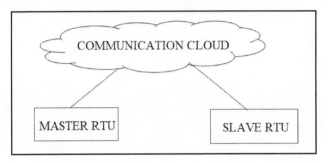

Figure 3.2: Point to Point Master-Slave Communication

➢ Multipoint or Multiple Stations

In this configuration, there is generally one master and multiple slaves which is shown in Figure 3.3. Generally data points are efficiently passed between the master and each of the slaves. If two slaves need to transfer data between each other they would do so through the master who would act as arbitrator or moderator. Alternatively, it is possible for all the stations to act in a peer-to-peer communications manner with each other. This is a more complex arrangement requiring sophisticated protocols to handle collisions between two different stations wanting to transmit at the same time.

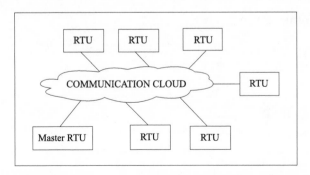

Figure 3.3: Master RTU communicating with multiple station RTUs

Another possibility is the store and forward relay operation. This can be a component of other approaches discussed above where, one station retransmits messages onto another station out of the range of the first station which is shown in Figure 3.4.

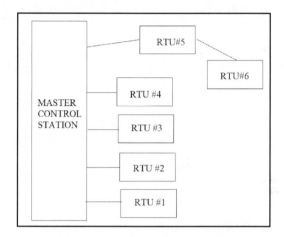

Figure 3.4: Store and forward station

➢ Talk Through Repeaters

This is the generally preferred way of increasing the range of radio systems. This retransmits a radio signal received simultaneously on another frequency. It is normally situated on a geographically high point.

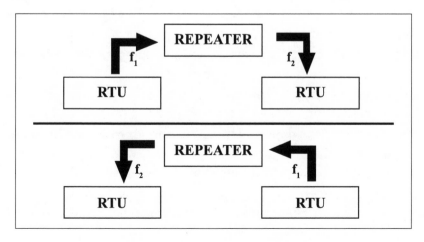

Figure 3.5: Talk through repeaters

The repeater receives on one frequency and retransmits on another frequency simultaneously. This means that all the stations repeating the signal must receive and transmit on the opposite frequencies. It is important that all stations communicate through the talk through repeater. It must be a common link for all stations and thus have a radio mast, high enough to access all RTU sites. It is a strategic link in the communication system; failure would wreak havoc with the entire system. The antenna must receive on one frequency and transmit on a different frequency which is shown in Figure 3.5. This means that the system must be specifically designed for this application with special filters attached to the antennas. There is still a slight time delay in the transmission of data with a repeater. The protocol must be designed with this in mind with sufficient lead-time for the repeater's receiver and transmitter to commence operation.

Communication Philosophies

There are two main communication philosophies in practice. These are polled (or master slave) and Carrier Sense Multiple Access/Collision Detection (CSMA/CD). The one of the notable methods accepted for reducing the amount of data that needs to be transferred from one point to another is to use exception reporting.

➤ Polled or Master Slave

This is one of the simplest master – slave point to point or point to multipoint configuration where the master polls, the slave in predetermined regular intervals and gather the data which is shown in Figure 3.5. Here the master is in total control of the monitoring, decision making and control of the process. The slaves never initiate the data exchange rather, wait for the master's request and respond. Essentially it is a half-duplex communication. In case the slave fails to respond timely, then the master retries typically two or three times. If the slave still fails to respond, the master then moves to the next slave in the sequence with a remark that the particular slave is inactive or faulty and requires attention for rectification. The advantages of this approach are,

- Software development is fairly easy and can be made reliable due to the simplicity of the philosophy,
- Link failure between the master and a slave node is detected fairly quickly,
- No collisions can occur on the network, hence the data throughput is predictable and constant, and
- For heavily loaded systems, each node has constant and bulk data transfer requirements giving a predictable and efficient system.

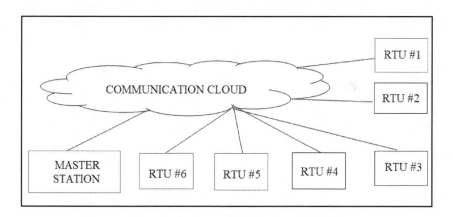

Figure 3.6: Illustration of master-slave polling with RTUs

However it has the certain disadvantages which are described below.

- Variations in the data transfer requirements of each slave cannot be handled,
- Interrupt type requests from a slave cannot be entertained as the master may be either attending or processing some other slave request or data,
- Systems, which are lightly loaded with minimum data changes from a slave, are quite inefficient and unnecessarily slow, and
- Communication between the slaves can be achieved only through the master which adds complexity.

Two applications of the polled or master slave, approach are given in the following two implementations. This is possibly the most commonly used technique and is illustrated in the Figure 3.6.

RTU 1
RTU 2
RTU 5
RTU 6
RTU 3
RTU 4

Table 3.2: Polling table with the master station

The master station details of priority and sequence. Based on this information it prepares a polling cycle as shown in Table 3.2.

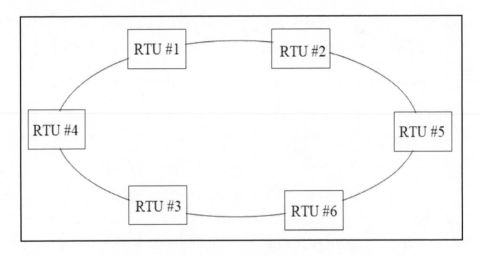

Figure 3.7: Polling cycle as per the polling table

In the scheme of polling, in certain situations, the polling may be modified as,

- if there is no response from a given RTU during a poll, a timeout timer has to be set and three retries (in total) initiated before flagging this station as inactive, and

- if an RTU is to be treated as a priority station it will be polled at a greater rate than a normal priority station. It is important not to put too many RTUs on the priority list, otherwise the differentiation between high and normal priority becomes meaningless.

➢ **CSMA/CD System (Peer-To-Peer)**

RTU to RTU Communication

In certain situations, especially in DCS an RTU in the SCADA system may need to communicate with another RTU. One of the solutions is, while responding to the master station to the poll, a message carrying a request with the destination address of the RTU can be added. The master station will then examine the destination address field of the message received from the RTU and retransmit onto the appropriate remote station. The only attempt to avoid collisions is to, listen to the medium before transmitting. If a collision occurs, the RTU wait for a random time period, and retransmit the data avoiding the collision. In this style of operation, it is possible for two nodes to try and transmit at the same time, with a resultant collision. In order to minimize the chance of a collision, the source node first listens for a carrier signal before commencing transmission. Unfortunately this does not always work where certain stations which cannot hear each other to try and transmit back to the station simultaneously.

➢ **Exception Reporting (Event Reporting)**

On many occasions, the status and the RTU may be the same but the polling mechanism gathers the data from the RTU. This unnecessary transfer of data can be minimized or virtually eliminated with a technique called *exception reporting*. This approach is popular with the CSMA/CD philosophy but it could also offer a solution for the polled approach where there is a considerable amount of data to transfer from each slave.

In exception reporting, the remote station reporting devices such as RTUs monitor itself to identify a change of state or data. If there is a change of state, the remote station writes a block of data to the master station when the master station polls the remote. Typical reasons for using polled report by exception include,

- The polling or scanning is performed with a low data rate due the communication channel constraints,

- There is substantial data being monitored at the remote stations, and

- The number of remote devices connected to master station is reasonably high.

Each analog or digital point that reports back to the central master station has a set of exception reporting parameters associated with it. The type of exception reporting depends on the particular environment but could be,

- High and low alarm limits of analog value,
- Percent of change in the full span of the analog signal, and
- Minimum and maximum reporting time intervals.

The main advantages of this approach are quite clearly to minimize unnecessary (repetitive) traffic from the communications system.

➤ Polling Plus CSMA/CD With Exception Reporting

A practical method to combine all the approaches discussed earlier is to use the concept of a slot time and exception reporting. Here each slave station is assigned a specific time slot comprising the following sub-slot assuming that there is no requirement for communication between the slaves.

- A slave transmitting to a master and
- A master transmitting to a slave.

A slot time is calculated as the sum of the maximums of modem up time, plus radio transmit time, plus time for protocol message, plus muting time of transmitter. The master commences operations by polling each slave in turn. Each slave will be in synchronize with the polling and respond to the master with exception reporting if there is a status change, else respond with passive acknowledgement. As a result, the master move on to poll the next slave by overriding the remaining sub-slots. Otherwise it will complete the data exchange and then move to hear from the next slave. The master thus completes the poll cycle.

The previous and present chapter elaborated the building blocks of SCADA systems starting from the RTU, IEDs, communication systems, master stations and the HMI. Utilities have a variety of options available to mix and match the elements to building a cost-effective, efficient, and operator-friendly SCADA system as per their requirements.

Automation of the power systems started as early as the beginning of the twentieth century, and substations and control centers operate at various stages of automation all over the world. There are legacy systems with RTUs, hardwired communication from the field to the RTU, and traditional software functionalities in the control room, and it is not often financially viable to dismantle everything and purchase a completely new automation system.

Hybrid systems are a viable option, where any automation expansion project can be implemented with new devices, like IEDs, data concentrators, and merging units. The new system will coexist with the legacy RTU-based systems and the data integration and if necessary protocol conversion issues will have to be handled while commissioning the project.

If a utility decides to purchase a completely modern system, the latest building block of the SCADA system, viz, IEDs, merging units, and fiber optic communication facility with brand new HMI with situational awareness and analysis tools, can be implemented.

System Reliability and Availability

Real-time system operation demands high level of availability and reliability to ensure error free operations. The real-time process control systems directly control the process, and any system catastrophe or erroneous operation may lead to process damage and may affect the safety of operations. Thus these applications necessitate a high level of system reliability without compromise. Numerically system reliability is defined as the probability that the system will not fail under specified conditions.

Standards and guidelines are available for the development of safe and secure critical systems. Among these standards, the most pertinent is for power system automation and is the NERC CIP standard. These development standards may be used while designing a power system SCADA. In keeping with these guidelines, an analysis must be performed as the early stage of system design in order to assign a system integrity level which allows the utility to define the accepted failure rate of system under consideration. Before discussing the fail safe system, it is better to have a clue of the two classifications of failures namely Common Cause Failures and Common Mode Failure.

Common Cause Failure (CCF): A Common cause failure occurs when two or more items fall within a specified time such that the success of the system mission would be uncertain. Item failures result from a single cause and mechanism.

Common Mode Failure(CMF): A Common-Mode Failure is the result of an event(s) which because of dependencies, causes a coincidence of failure states of components in two or more separate channels of a redundancy system, leading to the defined systems failing to perform its intended function.

➤ Fail Safe System (FSS)

A fail safe system describes a feature or a device which in the event of failure, responds in a way that will cause no harm or minimum harm to other devices or danger to personnel. Fail safe systems are used wherever the highest degree of safety needs to be guaranteed for humans, machines and the environment. A system being fail safe means, not that failure is impossible or improbable, but rather that the system design prevents or mitigates unsafe consequences of the system failure. That is, if and when a fail-safe system fails in any case, accidents and damage as a result of fault must be evaded at all costs. Thus when controlling, dangerous or critical machinery, it is necessary to device and implement a fail-safe strategy to ensure that the machine operates safely even when, the elements of the control hardware or software fail.

The types of failure are many hence a thorough analysis of the failure mode and effects are used for identifying the failure situations and design safety procedures. Some systems can never be made fail safe, as continuous availability is needed. Redundancy, fault tolerance, or recovery procedures are employed in these situations. This also makes the system, less sensitive for the reliability prediction errors or quality induced uncertainty for the separate items. On the other hand, failure detection, correction and avoidance of CCF become increasingly important to ensure system level reliability.

- In industrial automation, usually alarm circuits are normally closed. This ensures that in case of a wire break the alarm will be triggered. If the circuit were normally open, a wire failure would go undetected, while blocking actual alarm signals.

- In control systems, critically important signals can be carried by a complementary pair of wires. Only states where the two signals are opposite (one is high, the other low) are valid. If both are high or both are low, the control system knows that something is wrong with the sensor or connecting wiring. Simple failure modes such as dead sensor cut or unplugged wires, are thereby detected. An example would be a control system reading both the normally open (NO) and normally closed (NC) poles of a SPDT selector switch against common, and checking them for coherency before reacting to the input.

➤ Fault Tolerant System (FTS)

Certain utility or plant operations, once started have to continue as uninterrupted and nonstop operations, even in the case of a hardware or equipment failure. In other way, these are fault tolerant systems which has the ability of preventing a catastrophic let-down, that could result from a single point of failure. A fault-tolerant system is designed from the ground up for reliability by building multiples of all critical components, such as CPUs, memories, disks and power supplies into the same computer. In the event one component fails, another should take over without skipping a single point of operation. A feasible strategy for a fault tolerant system is by anticipating exceptional conditions and design a system to cope with them. The basic aim is that the system should be able to self-stabilize after the fault and converge towards an error free state. The above strategy may not be successful in some cases. In such applications, fault tolerance is implemented by providing redundancy.

➤ Graceful Degradation Systems

Fault tolerance is often used synonymously with graceful degradation, although the latter is more aligned with the more holistic discipline of fault management, which aims to detect, isolate and resolve problems pre-emptively. A fault-tolerant system swaps in backup component to maintain high levels of system availability and performance. But Graceful degradation allows a system to continue operations, with a reduced state of performance.

Design Considerations of Fault Tolerant System

While designing a Fault Tolerant System, one may consider the business continuity requirements, disaster recovery plan, disaster recovery products presently available in the market, and of course the budget and available manpower for engaging. Nevertheless Fault-tolerant systems are designed to compensate for multiple failures. The failure point has to be specifically identified, and a backup component or an immediate procedure should be taken its place with no loss of service. The failure point can be computer processor unit, I/O subsystem, memory cards, motherboard, power supply, network components in the cloud, communication servers of the service provider, etc. Hence each and every stage should be thoroughly analysed and necessary provisions may be envisaged and implemented.

In a software implementation, the Operating System (OS) provides an interface that allows a programmer to checkpoint critical data at predetermined points within a transaction. In a hardware implementation, the programmer need not to be aware of the fault-tolerant capabilities of the machine.

At a hardware level, fault tolerance is achieved by duplexing each hardware component. Disks are mirrored. Multiple processors are lock-stepped together and their outputs are compared for correctness. When an anomaly occurs, the faulty component is determined automatically, and is taken out of service, but the machine continues to function as usual.

➤ High Availability

Fault tolerance is closely associated with maintaining business continuity via highly available computer systems and networks. Fault-tolerant environments are defined as those that restore service instantaneously following a service outage, whereas a high-availability environment strives for setting up of independent servers coupled loosely together to guarantee system-wide sharing of critical data and resources. The loosely coupled clusters monitor each other's health and provide fault recovery, to ensure applications remain available. Conversely, a fault-tolerant cluster consists of multiple physical systems that share a single copy of a computer's OS. Software commands issued by one system are also executed on the other system. Systems with integrated fault tolerance incur a higher cost due to the inclusion of additional hardware.

➤ Critical Functions

If any operation of plant or process is critical, i.e. if the downtime costs are high or cause any human fatality or any expensive hardware destruction, redundancy must be incorporated into the system to eliminate system failures, due to equipment failure. Such functionalities are categorized as mission critical functions. In fact it is the privilege of the critical function to have software and hardware redundancy to be fault tolerant in a SCADA system. In power system SCADA with remote access RTU sites, both system redundancy and channel redundancy must be ensured for critical functions. In such cases RTU with CPU redundancy and communication port redundancy are highly recommended. At the master station end, the routers, firewalls, and servers must be configured to have redundancy for a fault tolerant system. Mission-critical installations often have separate power sources in case of a power failure, and installations in areas prone to natural disasters or the threat of fire, keep the servers in different geographic locations. However, whatever type of disaster recovery is planned for, it is possible to greatly reduce lost data and downtime by planning the proper system design, and by choosing a SCADA system with built-in redundancy. While ensuring system redundancy requirement for critical functions to be fault tolerant, it is highly recommended to consider the following points.

- Dual networks for full LAN redundancy,
- Redundancy can be applied to specific hardware,
- Supports primary and secondary equipment configurations,

- Intelligent redundancy allows secondary equipment to contribute to processing load,
- Automatic changeover and recovery,
- Mirrored disk I/O devices,
- Mirrored alarm servers, and
- File server redundancy.

A typical redundant and fail safe DCS master control station configuration with HA is shown in Figure 3.8. The sub components such as DMZ, SCADA Control System LAN, Dispatch Training Simulator, and Fail Safe connectivity to Smart Grid MCC using HA are shown separately in Figure 3.8, Figure 3.9, Figure 3.10 respectively. Here a De Militarized Zone (DMZ) is designed carefully and kept exclusively between two Firewalls of different make. The session from the servers of DMZ to the servers of SCADA zone is strictly made forbidden by appropriately defining the Firewall ruleset.

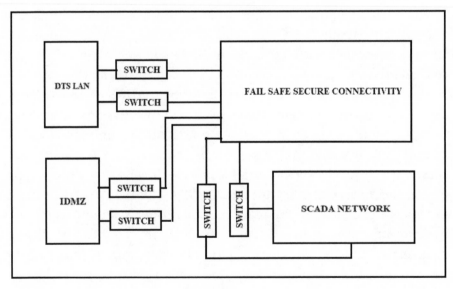

Figure 3.8: Block diagram of a typical DCS MCC with Fail Safe HA connectivity

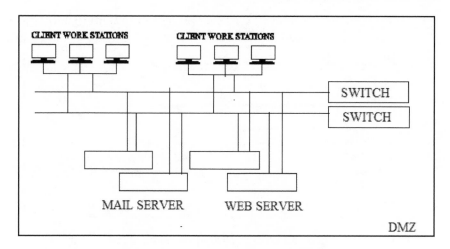

Figure 3.9: De Militarized Zone (DMZ)

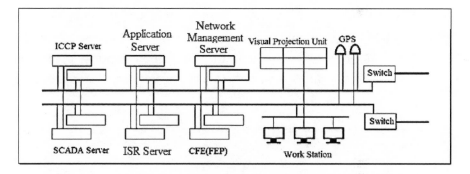

Figure 3.10: SCADA Control System LAN

Dispatcher Training Simulator (DTS) is a subsystem within Distribution Management System (DMS) that operates separately from the real–time system and provides a realistic environment for hands–on dispatcher training under simulated normal, emergency, and restorative operating conditions. The training is based on interactive communication between instructor and trainee. The DMS training simulator serves two main purposes.

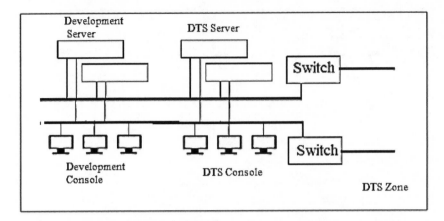

Figure 3.11: Dispatch Training Simulator

- Allowing personnel to become familiar with the DMS system and its user interface without impacting actual substation and feeder operations.

- Allowing personnel to become familiar with the dynamic behavior of the electric distribution system in response to manual and automatic actions by control and protection systems during normal and emergency conditions.

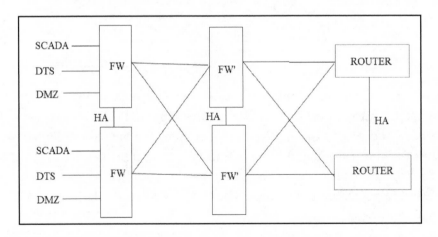

Figure 3.12: Fail Safe connectivity to DCS MCC using HA

The Figure 3.12 describes a Fail Safe connectivity to DCS MCC using HA which is mostly preferred in the Power System SCADA and DCS which control the critical operations.

➤ System Redundancy

Redundancy is the hallmark of fault tolerant systems. It is defined as additional or alternative systems, sub-systems, assets, or processes that maintain a degree of overall functionality in case of loss or failure of another system, sub-system, asset, or process. Normally power system SCADA redundancy, starts from the data capturing units such as RTU or PLC. If the SCADA is a distributed system, then every system component up to the MODEM have to be redundant. Further if the communication to the master control station is by means of unguided media, then system should have antenna redundancy as well. Obviously this adds cost considerably and the implementing agencies/vendors normally find pretexts for compromise which is the general lapse observed in implementing power system SCADA. But this makes the SCADA system unreliable.

Definitely true fault tolerant SCADA systems with redundant hardware are the most costly as the additional components add to the overall system cost. However, fault tolerant systems provide the same processing capacity after a failure as before, and ensures safety.

➤ Channel Redundancy

Most of the power system SCADA is distributed in nature and geographically separated. Hence remote site to site communications are required. This mainly depends on third party communication service providers.

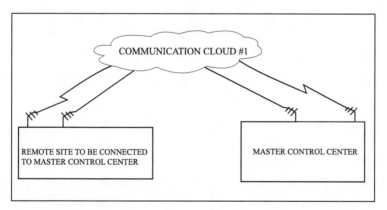

Figure 3.12a: Channel redundancy achieved with a resilient and reliable cloud

While selecting the third party communication providers, channel redundancy has to be ensured to have true system redundancy. Mainly this is achieved in two ways which is explained below

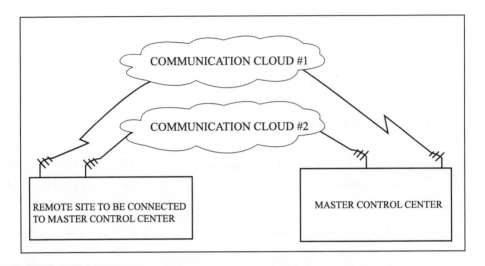

Figure 3.13b: Channel redundancy achieved with two different communication clouds

If the third party communication provider is highly reliable and having a true self-healing communication cloud as per the requirement of the utility, then connectivity to the two geographically different nodes is an acceptable solution on economic reasons. However in the strictest sense, true channel redundancy for critical functions ideally demands two different communication providers with active-active or active-standby mode. These are shown in Figure 3.12a and 3.12 b.

➢ **Design and Configuration Considerations of MCC**

The following aspects are utmost important while designing the Master Control Center of the power system SCADA.

- Sufficient hardware and software redundancy have to be ensured, to achieve the overall system redundancy with High Availability having No Single Point of Failure (NSPF) as the SCADA functions for the power system are critical. This includes communication channel as well,

- The firewall must be properly configured with the appropriate ruleset, after due deliberation with the security policy of the utility. Design with a two layer Firewall configuration, with different make IDS loaded are not a better option but a must, while moving for a DMZ, and

- The CFE or the FEP of the SCADA control center must have high end capabilities with suitable IDS loaded and have cryptographic capabilities. If third party communication media are used, especially using the VPN for data transfer, utmost care must be given for proper VPN termination.

Summary

Chapter begins with explaining Operational Technology (OT) and its difference with Information Technology (IT). Then this chapter describes the Industrial Control Systems, its various types, functioning, control and network components. It then move on to explaining the communication architecture of basic SCADA. Then moves on to describing the common communication philosophies adopted in DCS. As the reliability and availability of DCS functions are the most important, they are briefly introduced, but cater the necessary understanding to industrial security professionals. It then explains the concepts of Fault Tolerant Systems, Fail Safe redundant systems, High Availability, etc.

Critical Infrastructure Components

4.1 INTRODUCTION

Critical Infrastructure is defined as the system that compose the assets, systems, and networks, whether physical or virtual, and/or the computer programs, computer data, content data and/or traffic data so vital to a country that the incapacitation or destruction or interference with such systems and assets would have a debilitating impact on security, national or economic security, national public health and safety, or any combination thereof. SCADA (Supervisory Control and Data Acquisition) is the main underlying technology of Critical Infrastructure and it has been extensively used for monitoring and controlling geographically distributed processes in a variety of industrial processes. The first SCADA systems have been employed only for data acquisition by means of panels of meters, lights and strip chart recorders. Until recently many of the SCADA related products are proprietary, and the knowledge of the components has been acquired by the personnel while operating the system. Now the SCADA component manufactures started to follow standards which support interoperability. These help SCADA professionals to understand and design the SCADA systems in a systematic and structured manner.

All SCADA or Distributed Control System (DCS) starts with the field equipment depending on the process/plant to be monitored and controlled. The appropriate sensors pick up the process parameters and convert into proportional electrical voltage or current signal. These electrical signals are then conditioned and converted as per the requirement into digital form by means of an ADC. This electrical signal in digital format is then communicated to the SCADA server through different devices and protocols depending upon the SCADA architecture and the communication technologies employed. In the succeeding sessions an attempt has been made to elaborate on the essential components of the SCADA starting with Data Acquisition Systems (DAS). Then moves on to elaborate various components such as Remote Terminal Unit (RTU), Programmable Logic Controller (PLC), Bay Control Unit (BCU), Merging Units (MU), Data Concentrators (DC), Master Control Station and SCADA Servers, HMI, etc. along with the network devices generally deployed in the CI-SCADA environment.

4.2 DATA ACQUISITION SYSTEMS (DAS)

A DAS is a system which gathers the input data in digital form accurately, quickly and economically as required. This consists of sensors with suitable signal conditioning, data conversion, data processing, multiplexing, data handling, associated transmission, and storage and display systems.

Objectives and Advantages

The basic objectives of the Data Acquisition System are briefly described below.

1. Acquiring the required data reliably at required intervals.

2. The acquired data has to be appropriately processed and inform the status of the process/plant to the operator from time to time for controlling and decision making.

3. In general, DAS are designed to conceive a complete picture of the process/plant under monitoring intend to keep the plant/process operation safe and optimal.

4. With an effective HMI system or SCADA software, identify problem areas and minimize unit unavailability and maximize productivity at minimum cost.

5. DAS must be able to prepare sequence of events (SOE), summaries and store data for diagnosis, forecasting, etc.

6. Generally DAS are designed to compute unit performance indices using real-time data.

7. DAS must be flexible and capable of being expanded to accommodate future requirements.

8. DAS architecture design must be fail-safe, fault tolerant and reliable and down time must be less than 0.1%.

The major advantages of using DAS are increased reliability, lower operation and maintenance cost, faster restoration of the industrial process, reduction in human intervention and errors, accelerated decision making, with better accuracy, etc.

Single Channel Data Acquisition System

A Block Diagram of Single Channel Data Acquisition System is shown in Figure 4.1. The various components of the system are briefly explained below. It consists of Sensors, Signal Conditioner, Sample and Hold circuit, Analog Digital Converter and a storage device/printer/PC. Followed by an Analog to Digital Converter (ADC), performing repetitive conversions at a free running, internally determined rate. The outputs are in digital code words including over range indication, polarity information and a status output to indicate when the output digits are valid.

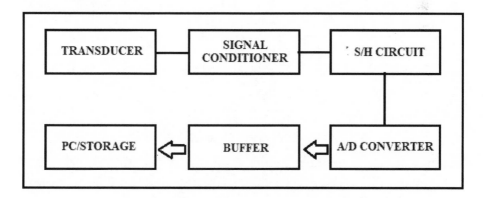

Figure 4.1: Single Channel Data Acquisition System

The digital outputs are further fed to a storage or printout device, or to a digital computer device for analysis. The popular Digital Panel

Meter (DPM) is a well-known example of this. However, there are two major drawbacks in using it as a DAS. It is slow and the BCD has to be changed into binary coding, if the output is to be processed by digital equipment. While it is free running, the data from the A/D converter is transferred to the interface register at a rate determined by the DPM itself, rather than commands beginning from the external interface.

Multi-Channel Data Acquisition System

By suitably incorporating a Multiplexer, a multi-channel DAS can be designed. By suitably selecting the address of the MUX, the input channels can be polled depending upon the priority. A block diagram of a multi-channel DAS is shown in Figure 4.2. Multi-channel DAS is elaborated in subsequent chapters.

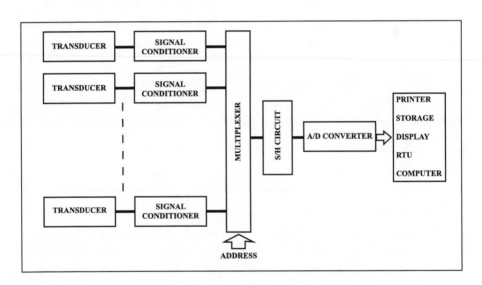

Figure 4.2: Multi-Channel DAS

When simultaneous measurements of the physical quantities are to be taken, the S/H circuit generally placed before MUX as shown in Figure 4.3. All the required parameters which are to be captured simultaneously are sampled and hold at the same instance and then digitized one after the other with software polling.

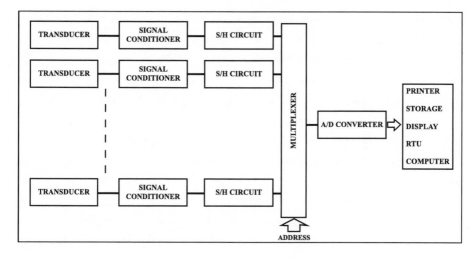

Figure 4.3: Multi-Channel DAS for simultaneous measurement

Sensors

Sensors or Transducers are devices that detects and measure a physical quantity such as pressure, force, temperature, acceleration, etc. and provide a corresponding output in the form of an electrical signal like voltage, current, resistance or frequency. Transducer characteristics define many of the signal conditioning requirements of the measurement system.

Signal Conditioning

In general the quality of the signals obtained from the sensors has to be enhanced appropriately to bring it to an acceptable level to the Analog to Digital Converters (ADC). This includes signal scaling, amplification, attenuation, linearization, filtering, anti-aliasing, excitation etc. Further signal conditioners have an additional responsibility to protect from unintentional or accidental high voltage inputs or surges, etc. Direct digital conversion carried out near the signal source is very advantageous in cases where data needs to be transmitted through a noisy environment. Even with a high level signal of 10 V, an 8 bit converter having a 1/256 resolution can produce 1 bit ambiguity when affected by noise of the order of 40 mV. Presently transducers being developed which is combined with ADC capable of converting to encrypt digital data.

Excitation: Not all sensors are active. In such cases, where the sensing devices are passive, it requires a voltage or current excitation and is supplied by the signal conditioners.

Amplification and Attenuation: If the signal acquired is large, then a simple attenuator, is used to scale down the input gains, in order to make it acceptable to the input signal range of the ADC. However most of the sensors generate the signals of low amplitude of voltage, current, or resistance, etc. In this case an amplifier circuit of suitable gain is employed to bring them to the acceptable level. If the sensor output is in the form of change in resistance, then a bridge circuit is most ideal to detect the change in resistance. A bridge amplifier is most suitable for amplifying the bridge outputs and improving the sensitivity of detection.

Isolation: When involving with high voltage it has to be ensured that the signals are physically isolated between the sensor output and the rest of the system. It is achieved by breaking the conductor paths by magnetic coupling, optical coupling, or by capacitive coupling. Optical coupling uses an LED at the transmitting side and a photo diode at the receiving side. Capacitive coupling uses a capacitor to isolate input and output signals. Magnetic coupling uses a transformer to isolate the input and output. These techniques are advantageous in handling signals from high voltage sources and transmission towers. In biomedical applications such isolation is unavoidable.

Linearization: Sensors which gives non-linearization response can be corrected by proper signal conditioning techniques. Linearization of the data, can be performed by analog techniques using either linear-approximation, or smooth series approximation using a low cost IC amplifier. Alternately linear approximation can be performed digitally after data acquisition and conversion by the use of ROMs by storing a suitable linearization table or programme initially.

Filtering and Anti-Aliasing: As most of the sensor output level is very low, they are very prone to Electro Magnetic Interference. Appropriate filters are used to eliminate the noise from the signals. Table 1.1 summarizes the basic characteristics and signal conditioning requirements of typical transducers.

1.	Thermocouple	Amplification, Linearization and Reference temperature for cold junction compensation.
2.	Strain Gauge	Required excitation voltage or current, Bridge formation, amplification, and linearization.
3.	LVDT	Excitation and linearization.
4.	RTD	Current excitation and linearization
5.	Thermistor	Current or voltage exciter and linearization

Table 4.1: Sensors with signal conditioning requirements

Sample and Hold Circuit

To achieve a reliable and accurate analog to digital conversion, ADCs require a fixed time during which the input signal remains constant called aperture time. This is a requirement of the conversion algorithm used by the A/D converter. If the input changes during this time, the ADC output will be inaccurate. This situation can be managed by suitably incorporating a sample-and-hold device. It samples the output signal from the multiplexer or gain amplifier very quickly and holds it constant for the ADCs aperture time. Usually sample and hold circuit is placed between multiplexer and ADC.

A TO D Converters (ADC)

An analog-to-digital converter, or ADC, is a device or peripheral that converts analog signals into digital signals. In the real world, signals mostly exist in analog form. An ADC with a S/H circuit can be used to sample such signals and the signals can be converted to the digital values. There are four types of A/D converters generally used, and they are

1. Integrating or dual slope ADC,

2. Successive approximation ADC,

3. Parallel Comparator (Flash) type ADC, and

4. Counting type ADC.

ADC specifications

Certain important specifications of A to D converters are briefly explained below.

Accuracy: It includes quantisation error, system noise, linearity, etc. Absolute accuracy refers to the maximum analog error.

Common Mode Rejection Ratio (CMMR): This is the ratio of the resulting output signal to a changing input common-mode signal. It is the degree of the rejection of a common mode signal across the differential output stage.

Conversion time: The conversion time is the time required for an ADC to complete the single conversion. This time does not include the acquisition time and MUX time. The conversion time for a given ADC is preferably less than the throughput time.

Crosstalk: In the multi-channel DAS, coupling between the adjacent channels, and sharing the transmission path, results in crosstalk. This interference appears as a noise in the digital output and quite unwanted.

Input Range: The specified range of the peak to peak, input signal of an A/D converter.

Latency: Latency is the time required for an ideal step input to converge, within an error margin to a final digital output value. The error-band is expressed as a predefined percentage of the total output voltage step. The latency of a conversion is that period between the time where the signal acquisition begins to the time to the next conversion starts.

Linearity errors: With most ADCs gain, offset and zero errors are not critical as they may be calibrated out. Linearity errors, differential non-linearity (DNL) and integral non-linearity INL) are more important because they cannot be removed.

Differential non-linearity (DNL): It is the difference between the actual code width from the ideal width of 1 LSB. If DNL errors are large, the output code widths may represent excessively large and small input voltage ranges. If the magnitude of a DNL is greater than 1 LSB, then at least one code width will vanish, yielding a missing code.

Integral Non-Linearity (INL): INL describes the non-linearity of ADC. It is considered as an important parameter because it is a measure of an ADC non-linearity error. However, as in any Analog or Mixed-Signal Design project, some specifications are important, some are not. It all depends on the project requirements regarding accuracy and precision.

Understanding INL enables the circuit designer to avoid surprises in his or her project. INL is defined as the maximum deviation of the ADC transfer function from the best-fit line.

Resolution: Resolution can be used to describe the general performance of an ADC.It is the smallest change that can be distinguished by an ADC converter. For example, for a 12-bit ADC converter resolution would be 1/4096 = 0.0244%.. It's an important ADC specification because it determines the smallest analog input signal an ADC can resolve.

Monotonicity: This requires a continuously increasing output for a continuously increasing input over the full range of the converter. This term implies that an increase (decrease) in the analog voltage input will always produce no change or an increase in the digital code.

Quantizing uncertainty: Because the ADC can only resolve an input voltage to a finite resolution of 1 LSB, the actual real-world voltage may be up to ½ LSB below the voltage corresponding to the output code or up to ½ LSB above it. An ADC's quantizing uncertainty is therefore always ±½ LSB.

Relative accuracy: This refers to the input to output error as a fraction of full scale with gain and offset error adjusted to zero.

4.3 SCADA COMPONENTS IN CRITICAL INFRASTRUCTURE

The modern Power System SCADA uses Remote Terminal Unit (RTU), Intelligent Electronic Devices (IEDs), IED Architecture and Components, Instrument Transformers with Digital Interfaces Programmable Logic Controller (PLC), Data Concentrators and Merging Units and Bay Control Unit (BCU) depending upon the need necessity, adaptability and economic factors. The Master Control Center (MCC) is made up of SCADA System Software, Master Station Hardware, Servers, Global Positioning Systems (GPS) and Human Machine interface (HMI). The following sections elaborates these components.

Remote Terminal Unit (RTU)

Remote Terminal Unit (RTU) is a microprocessor based device connected to appropriate sensors, transmitters and process equipment for the purpose of remote telemetry and control of plant or process. RTUs find applications in oil and gas remote instrumentation monitoring, networks of remote pump stations, environmental monitoring systems, air traffic equipment, power utilities, etc. RTUs with the aid of appropriate sensors, monitors production processes at remote site and transmits all data to a central station where it is gathered and monitored. An RTU can be interfaced using serial ports such as RS232, RS485, etc. or Ethernet to communicate with the central stations. They also support various protocol standards such as Modbus, IEC 60870, DNP3 making it possible to interface with 3rd party software.

RTU Architecture

The RTU architecture comprises of a CPU, volatile memory and non-volatile memory for processing and storing programs and data. It communicates with other devices via either serial ports or an on-board modem with I/O interfaces. It has a power supply module with a backup battery, surge protection against spikes, real-time clock and a watchdog timer to ensure that it restarts when operating in the sleep mode. Figure 4.4 shows the block diagram of an RTU configuration. A typical RTU hardware module includes a control processor and associated memory, analog inputs, analog outputs, counter inputs, digital inputs, digital outputs, communication interfaces and power supply. Centralized RTU design where all I/O modules are housed in RTU panels and communicating with master station through communication port.

Distributed RTU design in which distributed I/O modules or processor with I/O modules are housed in respective RTU panel. All these distributed I/O modules or I/O modules with processor shall be connected to a central processor for further communication with master station. The customer shall asses the requirement of RTU panels for such design and supply panels accordingly.

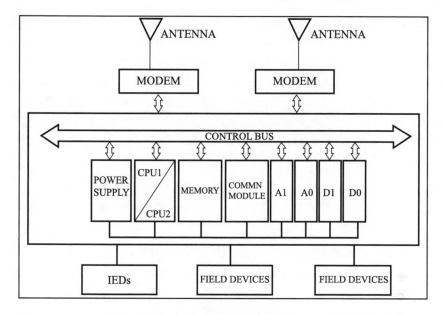

Figure 4.4: RTU Architecture

RTU Components

Central Processing Unit (CPU): Most of the available RTU designs utilize a 16 bit or 32 bits microprocessor with a total memory capacity of 256kbytes expandable to 4 Mbytes. It also has two or three communication ports or multiple Ethernet links. This system is controlled by a firmware and a real-time clock with full calendar used for accurate time stamping of events. A watchdog timer provides a check that the RTU program is executing regularly. The RTU program regularly resets the watchdog timer and if this is not done within a certain time-out period the watchdog timer flags an error. Depending on the requirements of safety, reliability, high availability, and functionality, dual CPU with dual power supplies are often preferred. Thus the system is capable of automatic monitoring without fail with primary and hot standby CPUs. Failures are detected automatically and trigger a switch over from the primary CPU to hot standby CPU.

Analog Input Modules (AI): An analog input signal is generally a voltage or current that varies over a defined value range, in direct proportion to a physical process measurement. 4-10 milliamp signals are most commonly used to represent physical measurements like pressure, flow and temperature. Analog inputs of different types including 0-1 mA, 0–10 V., ±1.5 V, ±5.0 V etc. Are also common and acceptable to RTU. Five main components of the analog input(AI) module are described below.

1. *Multiplexer:* This samples several analog inputs in turn and switches each to the output in sequence. The output goes to the analog digital converter.

2. *Signal Conditioner:* This amplifies and transforms the low-level voltages to match the input range of the board's A/D converter.

3. *Sample and hold circuit:* An analog device that samples the voltage of a continuously varying analog signal and holds its value at a constant level for a specified minimum period of time.

4. *A/D converter:* A system that converts an analog signal into a digital format or a digital code corresponding to the input voltages.

5. Bus interface and board timing system.

Typical analog input modules have the following features.

1. 8, 16, or 32 analog inputs.

2. Resolution of 8 to 12 bits.

3. Range of 4-10 mA.

4. Input resistance typically 140 kΩ to 1 MΩ.

5. Conversion rates typically 10 microseconds to 30 milliseconds.

RTU can also receive analog data via a communication system from a master or Intelligent Electronic Device (IED) which sends data values to it.

Analog Output Module (AO): Though it is not commonly used, analog outputs (AO) modules are included in control devices to deal with varying quantities, such as graphic recording instruments or strip charts. The function of an Analog Output module is to convert a digital value supplied by the CPU to an analog value, by means of a Digital To Analog Converter (DAC). This analog representation can be used for variable control of actuators. The basic features of the Analog output modules are as follows.

1. 8, 16 or 32 analog outputs.

2. Resolution of 8 or 12 bits.

3. Conversion rate from 10 micro seconds to 30 milliseconds.

4. Outputs ranging from 4-10 mA or 0 to 10 volts.

Digital or status inputs (DI): These are used to indicate status and alarm signals. Most RTUs incorporate an input section or input status cards to acquire two state real world information. This is usually accomplished by using an isolated voltage or current source to sense the position of a remote contact (open or closed) at the RTU site. This contact position may represent many different devices, including electrical breakers, liquid valve positions, alarm conditions, and mechanical positions of devices.

Digital Output Modules (DO): RTUs may drive high current capacity relays to switch power on and off to devices in the field. The DO modules are used to drive an output voltage at each of the appropriate output channels with three approaches possible.

1. Triac Switching,

2. Read Relay Switching, and

3. TTL voltage outputs

Power Supply Module: RTUs need a continuous power supply to function, but there are situations where RTUs are located at quite a distance from an electric power supply. In these cases, RTUs are equipped with alternate power source and battery backup facilities in case of power losses. Solar panels are commonly used to power low-powered RTUs, due to the general availability of sunlight. Thermo electric generators can also be used to supply power to the RTUs where gas is easily available like in pipelines. Normally RTU is expected to operate from 110/140 V AC ± 10% 50 Hz or 11/14/48 V DC± 10% typically. Batteries that should be provided are lead acid or nickel cadmium.

Typical backup requirements are for 10-hour standby operation and a recharging time of 11 hours for a fully discharged battery at 15°C. The power supply, battery and associated charger are normally contained in the RTU housing. The monitoring parameters of the battery system of RTU which should be transmitted back to the central site/master station are analog battery reading and alarm for battery voltage outside normal range

Communication interfaces: Modern RTU are designed to be flexible enough to handle multiple communication media such as

1. RS 232/RS442/RS 485 etc.

2. Ethernet.

3. Dial up telephone lines/dedicated landlines.

4. Microwave, and Satellite.

5. X.15 packet protocols, and

6. Radio via trunked/VHF/UHF.

An RTU may be interfaced to Multiple Control Stations and Intelligent Electronic Device (IEDs) with different communication media such as RS232, RS485, etc. An RTU may support standard protocols (Modbus, IEC 60870-5-101/103/104, DNP3, IEC 60870-6-ICCP, IEC 61850 etc.) to interface any third party software.

Data transfer may be initiated from either end using various techniques to insure synchronization with minimal data traffic. There are two methods in general viz. polling and report by exception. In polling method, the master may poll its subordinate unit (Master polls RTU or RTU polls IED) for changes of data on a periodic basis. The report by exception method is used where a subordinate unit initiates an update of data upon a predetermined change in analog or digital data. Periodic complete data transmission must be used periodically, with either method, to insure full synchronization and eliminate stale data. Most communication protocols support both methods, programmable by the installer. Analog value changes will only be reported, usually on changes outside a set limit from the last transmitted value. Digital Status values observe a similar technique and only transmit groups (bytes) when one included point (bit) changes.

Multiple RTUs or multiple IEDs may share a communications line, in a multi-drop scheme, as units are addressed uniquely and only respond to their own polls and commands. IED communications transfer data between the RTU and an IED. This can eliminate the need for many hardware status inputs, analog inputs, and relay outputs in the RTU. Communications are accomplished by copper or fiber optics lines. Multiple units may share communication lines.

Communications to a Master Control Center are generally envisaged and suitably incorporated in larger systems. The communication media used to transfer data may be copper, optical fiber or wireless media communication system. Multiple units usually share communication channels.

Securing Remote Terminal Units

As RTU be the one of the critical component of the DCS and ICS, physical-cyber security of the RTU is most important especially when deployed in critical infrastructure SCADA such as Power System SCADA(PSS), Oil and Gas Industry, etc. Today the Electric utilities are most concerned of statutory security requirements of North American Electric Reliability Corporation Critical Infrastructure Protection (NERC CIP). The flexibility and range of RTU technologies necessitates a proper incorporation of its security and safety procedures.

Physical security of an RTU can be ensured by keeping restricted and authenticated access. Door opening of RTU enclosure can be properly monitored by a status signal, or by placing a surveillance camera which communicates the MCC in real-time RTU to alert system operators regarding the physical security breach of a remote RTU. One of the main standards that define procedures for implementing electronically secure Industrial Control Systems (ICS) is ISA/IEC-62443. This guidance applies to end-users, system integrators, security practitioners, and control systems manufacturers who design, implement, and manage the ICS. While deal with Power System SCADA (PSS), most of the utilities are following the NERC CIP standards as they are exclusively developed for Bulk Electric System (BES).

NERC CIP defines a Critical Asset, as the facility, or system which, if destroyed or degraded, would affect the smooth and proper operation of the Bulk Electric System (BES). In other way, they are the programmable electronic devices and communication networks which comprise hardware, software, and the data. The Critical Cyber Assets (CCA) is defined as Cyber Assets, essential to the reliable operation of Critical Assets. Bulk Electric System(BES) are defined as, the electrical generation resources, transmission lines, sub stations, interconnections with neighbouring systems, and associated equipment, generally operated at voltages of 100 kV or higher. Obviously the RTUs installed at substations which deals with voltages more than 100kV or higher is a Critical Cyber Assets and need NERC CIP compliance and protection to ensure safety and security.

In order to frame the security policies and procedures, it is critical for utilities to understand the necessary RTU functionality and how it can be incorporated to achieve goals. Majority of the RTUs which are Critical Cyber Asset may not be kept in a completely protected area, and may be accessible to people who are not explicitly authorized to access them. This necessitates the key requirement of physical security of RTUs. Most RTU equipment includes, digital input points as a standard feature, and adding a door alarm is a simple way to meet NERC CIP requirements. Including the door alarm input as a sequence of events (SOE) point provides a means of meeting another aspect of the NERC CIP procedures for logging data and maintaining historical records.

Cyber security cannot be mentioned without encryption. Encrypted data transmission and reception makes RTUs more secure. It is obviously harder for an unauthorized user to manipulate the data sent and received. Encrypted data, however, has a disadvantage. Most notably, it will impact the scan rate of the device. Further encrypting and decrypting every message received and transmitted by the RTU amounts to a considerable increase in the processing time, which in turn affects the latency. This demands high computing power and processing capability of RTU CPU. Many RTUs being used in the field are already pushed to the upper limits without consideration for encryption. Another disadvantage is that the data is encrypted and the user will need special tools to view it, as it is often important to examine the data exchanged between devices to ensure they operate properly.

An important feature of RTU is its ability to provide logs of important events. Many of the alarms need to be logged for time of occurrence and the relevant information. Maintenance engineers who are making connections and configuration changes to the unit can be properly evaluated with this chain of events. Sequence of Event (SOE) logs, user logs and system logs can all be used to document events from the safe and secure operations of RTU.

The formation of procedures and plans, which need to be written with current and future capabilities in mind, is most important part of the SCADA security standards such as NERC CIP, IEC 62443, etc. Due to the wide technology range it will not be practical to replace or upgrade every device as quickly or easily. Securing an ICS or DCS is not a job for the faint hearts; rather it is a job that must be done with courage, intelligence, and imagination. A work which requires many hours of hard, thoughtful work for developing a security policy in tune with the utilities general safety and security policy. Today, it is considered that providing cyber security to critical infrastructure is no way inferior to the job of defending a nation by the army generals.

Intelligent Electronic Devices (IEDs)

IEDs are the main components of substation integration and automation. IEDs which integrate metering, protection, and control functions reduce the number of equipment installations, reduce panel and control room space and in turn reduces the cost of the capital expenditure. It also eliminates redundant equipment and databases. Present day IEDs are capable of directly communicating with the SCADA systems in the required standard and interoperable protocols. A single IED is capable of monitoring and providing a number of parameters and status signals such as barker status, switch positions, etc. They are capable of event recording and provide SoE. In fact IEDs revolutionize the substation by Substation.

IEDs facilitate the exchange of operational and non-operational data. Operational data are instantaneous values of power system analog and status points such as volts, amps, MW, MVAR, circuit breaker status, switch position, etc. They are also called SCADA data. Non-operational data consists of files and waveforms such as even summaries, oscillographic event reports, SoE records, SCADA-like points (status and analog points) which have a logical state or a numerical value. These data are not needed in SCADA to monitor and control the power system. The main functions of IEDs are Protection, Control, Monitoring, Metering, and Communication.

IED Architecture and Components

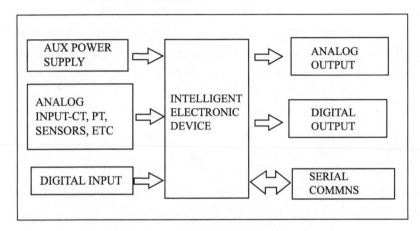

Figure 4.5: Block diagram of an IED

Figure 4.5 depicts the organizational block diagram of a typical Intelligent Electronic Device. The modern IED architecture ensures that the device is multipurpose, modular in nature, flexible and adaptable, and has robust communication capabilities which include multiple selectable protocols, multi-drop facilities with multiple ports, and rapid response for real-time data. Current IEDs coming with tremendous computing power which is capable to carry out a variety of functions, various applications like protection and metering. IEDs have Sequence of Event (SOE) recording capability that can be very useful for post-event analysis, for fault waveform recording, and for power quality measurements. The advantage of this is, it eliminates the requirement of additional digital fault recorders and power quality monitors. IEDs can also accept and send out Analog and Digital signals with selectable settings, thus making the IEDs versatile. The details of the IED building blocks are briefly explained below.

Auxiliary power supply: Unlike older protection relays which may not need an auxiliary supply, IEDs always require an auxiliary power supply. Most IEDs accept an extended range of power supply, usually ranging from 14 -150 V DC or 110 -140 V AC.

Analog inputs: Protection relays are always provided with current transformer (CT) and potential transformer (PT) inputs. In addition, IEDs may be provided with sensor inputs. Hence it is important to specify the rated secondary current and frequency before ordering.

Digital inputs: Some IEDs require potential-free contacts for digital inputs(DI), while others recognize the positive power supply voltage (source) or negative power supply voltage (sink) as a logical '1'. Digital inputs may be commands or status information.

Analog outputs: Some IEDs are provided with transducer outputs. Mostly these outputs are programmable. These outputs can be active or passive. The passive type requires external power supply.

Digital outputs: Digital outputs can be potential free normally open (NO), normally closed (NC) or solid state contacts. It is important to check the switching capability of the output contacts, as the differences can be significant. Digital outputs may be commands or status information.

IEDs have the real time and rapid data exchange capabilities with multi ports. Many IEDs which are available in the market are capable of handling Analog Inputs, Discrete Outputs, Analog Outputs and Discrete Inputs. SoE recording, fault recording, metering and protection are the common features with all IEDs.

The IED integrates many single-function electromechanically relays, control switches, extensive wiring, and much more into a single unit. In addition the IED handles additional features like self and external circuit monitoring, real-time synchronization of the event monitoring, local and substation data access, programmable logic controller functionality, and an entire range of software tools for commissioning, testing, event reporting, fault analysis, etc.

Instrument Transformers with Digital Interfaces

A range of digital instrument transformer solutions enabling full IEC 61850 implementation and contributing to transmission architectures for the Smart Grid networks of present and future have been developed by various manufactures. The innovative design with smart sensor digital instrument transformers is very accurate, intelligent, safe, and cost-effective and very importantly core-less.

These modern product range serves both AC (up to 1200kV) and DC (up to 800kV) transmission systems as well as high current DC applications and provide increased safety, intelligence, flexibility, availability and global savings through a variety of advanced characteristics such as those described below.

1.   Simplified and reduced cabling,

2.   Compact solution and lightweight,

3.   Smaller substation footprint,

4.   Near zero maintenance, and

5.   Reduced inventories.

A new range of Optical Sensor Intelligence (OSI) based Instrument Transformers, are developed which are capable of serving both AC and DC transmission systems. These Cost-effective OSI range brings key technological features and benefits such as wider dynamic range from 1 A to 4800 A. It is very sophisticated and Smart Grid ready, delivering direct digital output for metering applications. It also has measurement improvements resulting from the fact that there is no saturation of the network and a high bandwidth. These products offer greater flexibility due to the ratio being modifiable at any time via a computer connection. There are also considerable economical features compared to conventional instrument transformers. These products are more compact and lighter, uses less wiring, as all signals are transmitted through a fiber optic cable, requires less maintenance, is easy to install with greater flexibility and can be easily upgraded. Further these are more environmentally friendly and more secure with the risk of explosion minimized, reduced leakage, SF6 free, and no issue of end-life-disposal. Typically an optical sensor represents only 10% of the weight of an oil filled transformer, reducing transportation costs and the quantities of materials used. State-of-art Fiber Optical Current Sensor (FOCS) solutions are presented together with Rogowski coil and Electronic Voltage Transformer (EVT) in innovative solutions that deliver significant operational performance, environmental, safety and substation engineering benefits supporting future Smart Grid substation investments.

Programmable Logic Controller (PLC)

A Programmable Logic Controller (PLC) is a computer based solid state device that controls industrial equipment and processes. It was initially designed to perform the logic functions executed by relays, drum switches and mechanical timer/counters. Advanced PLC with Analog control capability are also available today, but RTU based SCADA systems are preferred by power utilities as the RTU can also function as Data Concentrating Unit(DCU) and offers more security especially when unguided remote communication is used. The advantage of a PLC over the RTUs which are available in the market can be used in a general purpose role and can easily be set up for a variety of different functions. The actual construction of a PLC can vary widely and are popular for the following reasons.

1. PLC solution is more economical when compared to general purpose RTU solution.

2. The logic of the PLC can easily be modified to cope with new situations and requirements.

3. Design and installations are relatively easier as many hardware requirements can be suitably substituted with software.

4. If properly installed, PLCs are a far more reliable solution than a conventional hardwired relay solution or RTU based solution.

5. PLCs has more sophisticated control than RTU, mainly due to the software capability.

6. PLCs are very compact and occupy less space when compared to alternative solutions.

7. Trouble shooting is simple and easy to diagnose and fix hardware/ firmware/software problems.

Ladder Logic: Ladder diagrams or ladder logic are a type of electrical notation and symbology frequently used to illustrate how electromechanical switches and relays are interconnected. It is a rule-based programming language rather than a procedure language, which creates and represents a program through ladder diagrams. It is mainly used in developing programs or software for PLCs.

Ladder logic is widely used in industrial settings for programming PLCs where sequential control of manufacturing processes and operations is required. The programming language is quite useful for programming simple yet critical systems or for reworking old hard-wired systems into newer programmable ones. This programming language is also used considerably in advanced automation systems such as electronics and automobile manufacturing companies.

The idea behind ladder logic is that even employees without programming backgrounds can quickly program since it makes use of conventional and familiar engineering symbols for programming. But this advantage is quickly negated since manufacturers of PLCs often also provide ladder logic programming systems with their products, which sometimes do not use the same symbols and conventions as those made for other models of PLCs from other manufacturers. These proprietary symbols and conventions is usually meant only for specific make and models. Hence the programs cannot be ported easily to other PLC models or must be completely rewritten.

Data Concentrators and Merging Units

Another two important building blocks that are very useful in modular design of DCS are Data Concentrators and Merging Units. A brief description is given below.

Data Concentration Units (DCU)

In certain situations the DCS design, especially in PSS, is an intimidating task because of the extremely large number of input and output data.

The variety of large number of field devices and IEDs with different protocols makes the DCS design very complex. Considering the fact that most substations are automated and intended to operate unmanned, these data has to be transmitted to MCC for control and analysis. The RTU in a substation can serve as a data concentrator by gathering or concentrating the data from the field devices. It utilizes a data concentrating device that has lots of I/O ports on it. When connected to all the IEDs and field devices which can send their details as data in a star topology, this devices are polled to gather the data and transmits it to a remote master and/or client server stations. I/O ports on modern data concentrators available with Ethernet ports such as fibre ports and RJ45 ports suitable for CAT5 cable. These ports can enable a TCP/IP communication and establish a LAN or WAN connectivity. Data concentrators offer several additional capabilities. One of them is to serve as a gateway device. That is, any connection to a WAN system is made at only one point in the substation network and is using this device alone. Modern gateway devices, suitable in DCS environment have the following capabilities.

- It has the capability to set up a firewall, with SCADA specific IDS loaded to keep the intruders away,

- It has the capability to provide a secure connection for secure data transmission. Many RTUs/DCUs have the NERC CIP compliance. Remote connection with DCU can be established via the internet using VPN, leased telephone lines, OFC, or unguided medias.

- Modern RTUs support a number of protocols. They also have protocol conversion capabilities. This helps the field devices which do not support modern SCADA protocols such as DNP3 or IEC 61850, can also be connected and communicated with the RTU without replacing the legacy IEDs, and

- Many RTUs have the capability of providing a web based HMI. In certain cases, an HMI has to be kept at remote locations with limited capability or use it as a Local Data Monitoring System (LDMS). In such situations, accommodating devices like a display monitor, keyboard, and mouse, etc. must be connected to the RTU or LDMS in a secure manner.

If the substation is small, then all station IEDs and field devices can be connected directly to the data concentrator. No Ethernet switches are required and additional I/O ports on this device can be installed if necessary.

Merging Unit (MU)

In the simplest sense, Merging Units (MU) is a device that enables the Substation Automation with IEC 61850 protocol process bus by converting analogue signals from conventional CTs and PTs into IEC sampled values. Today MU is one of the most critical elements required for the development of modern digital substations. The MU provides the suitable interface for the implementation of the process bus concept in modern substation automation systems. The IEC61850 standard specifies the communication architecture for communication systems and networks for substations. The basic function of the MU in automation systems is to convert the analogue values of current and voltages measured at the process level to digital format and transmit same to the bay level of the substation where the microprocessor relays are located. In modern substations, its function is to collect multichannel digital signals output by electronic current and electronic voltage transformers synchronously and transmit these signals with the protocol of IEC 61850 to protective, measurement and control devices.

In substations, these multichannel digital signals output by electronic current and electronic voltage transformers are collected synchronously and transmit these signals with the protocol of IEC 61850 to protective, measurement and control devices. The use of merging units for elimination of several multiple wire connections running from the switchyard to the microprocessor relays located in the control room. The conventional MU model collects current and voltage signals from various current and voltage transformers in the switchyard, converts them into digital form and sends the digital equivalents to the microprocessor relays via a single fibre optic cable known as the process bus. Today modern MUs are available with additional features of in-built overcurrent protection and bay control functions. These new models are intended to provide local over-current protection and bay control for all equipment in the bay being monitored by a particular MU.

Existing substations with an RTU can be integrated with IEDs depending on the availability of interoperable features. If the RTU is not supporting the standard protocols, the gateways for protocol conversion have to be appropriately integrated. The implementation of modern IEDs provides a rich new source of data that can benefit the entire utility organization.

Bay Control Unit (BCU)

A Bay Control Unit (BCU), is a very adaptable panel mounted unit which provides wide range of monitoring, control and automation capabilities at the individual bay or circuit level. The main advantage of the BCU is the capability of remote monitoring. The status of the substation equipment and supporting devices are obtained through contact multiplying relay or from auxiliary contacts. Thus both the OPEN and CLOSED positions or a fault or intermediate circuit-breaker or auxiliary contact position can be detected or monitored. BCU control the power equipments in agreement with control commands issued to control equipment and monitoring the bay power apparatus

Monitoring

Remote monitoring of the system is the main advantage of using BCU. The status of primary equipment or auxiliary devices are obtained from auxiliary contacts. Therefore it is possible to detect and indicate the OPEN and CLOSED position or a status of fault circuit-breaker or auxiliary contact position.

Control

BCU also support all control functions that are required for operating substations. The main application is reliable control of switching and other processes. The automation engineer can set specific functions for the automation of switchgear or substation equipments. Functions are activated via function keys, binary input or via communication interface. Switching authority is determined according to parameters, communication or by *LOCAL/REMOTE* switch. If it is set to *LOCAL*, only local switching operations are possible and all remote operations are disabled.

Command Processing

This includes all the functionality of command processing especially the processing of single and double commands with or without feedback. Sophisticated monitoring of the control hardware and software, checking of the external process, control actions using functions such as runtime monitoring and automatic command termination after output are possible. Every switching operation and change of breaker position is kept in the status indication memory.

Master Control Centres (MCC)

Figure 4.6 shows a large master control centre with a dual redundant LAN, with all the components, designed with full redundant hardware and software features to achieve High Availability (HA). The system redundancy and communication channel redundancy must be ensured from remote location to the servers of the master station. The master station must be fault tolerant and fail safe in every respect, so that any natural calamity affecting one station will not cause a problem with the functioning of other stations and the system can be monitored and controlled effectively. Uninterrupted power supplies (UPS) monitoring systems are also very important and must be ensured as most of the process/plants are non-stoppable and cannot be interrupted. The various SCADA components in the MCC are elaborated below.

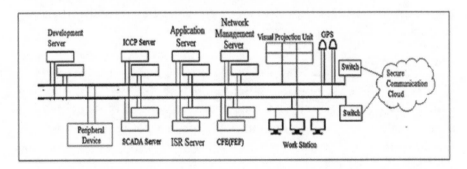

Figure 4.6: Block Diagram of a Typical Master Control Centre

System SCADA Software

These are the data acquisition and control, database design and development, reporting and accounting, and the HMI software. It performs all the basic functionalities which are required in common to all SCADA application. As far as power system SCADA is concerned, all SCADA functions are considered as critical functions.

Today, substation automation is achieved with any one of the modern SCADA devices such as Remote Terminal Unit (RTU), Programmable Logic Controller (PLC), Data Concentrators (DCU), Merging Units (MU), Bay Control Unit (BCU), etc. depending on the situational requirements and economy. However most commonly the substation automation software has the following functional features.

- Advanced protection functions having conventional and IED based,
- Substation automation functions,
- Advanced bus failover and automatic load restoration,
- Feeder sectionalising and islanding,
- Adaptive relaying, and
- Equipment Condition Monitoring (ECM).

Master Station Hardware

The main hardware in a master station are the computer, server systems, display units, printers, plotters, routers, and security and protecting devices such as firewalls in addition to uninterrupted power supply ensuring the power quality. Many servers are used for executing the different tasks to be performed. Hence selection of servers is most important and selection must be based on the requirements of the master station.

Servers in the Master Station

As mentioned, different dedicated redundant, high availability servers are deployed in the SCADA master control station to execute specific tasks. The servers are connected through a high speed dual redundant LAN. The client server architecture ensures that the data is accessed by another server whenever it is required and properly authenticated. The dedicated server systems should have special capabilities and features depending upon the requirements of the application for which it is deployed. Some of these features are CPUs with high computing and fast processing power, high-performance RAMs, redundant and uninterrupted, quality assured power supplies, high end routers and switches for network connections, and high performance Firewalls.

The computer server systems available in a SCADA master station are as follows:

1. SCADA server,

2. Application server,

3. Information Storage and Retrieval (ISR) Server,

4. Development server,

5. Network Management Server (NMS),

6. Video Projection System (VPS),

7. Communication Front End Server (CFE),

8. Inter Control Centre Communications Protocol (ICCP) server, and

9. Dispatcher Training Simulator (DTS) server.

The main functions of each server are described below.

SCADA Server

The SCADA server is assigned with the data acquisition of all inputs and presents it to other servers for displaying, further processing and decision making. It also accomplishes the control command execution as per the directions issued from the SCADA control station. In small SCADA systems the SCADA server directly gathers the data from the field devices and issue control commands directly to the devices. But when the SCADA system is large SCADA server communicates through the CFE server which is described below.

Application Server

Depending upon the nature of process/plant to be controlled, the SCADA application varies. It can be EMS, GMS or DMS as far as power system is concerned. The application software modules are hosted by the application server required for the specific SCADA system.

PSS Distribution Management may have voltage reduction, load management, power factor control, two-way distribution communications, short-term load forecasting, fault identification, fault isolation, service restoration, interface to intelligent electronic devices {IEDs}, three-phase unbalanced operator power flow, interface to/integration with automated mapping/facilities management (AM/FM), interface to customer information system (CIS), trouble call/outage management, and so on. The transmission SCADA may have the Energy Management Systems (EMS) package, which includes network configuration/topology processor, state estimation, contingency analysis, three-phase balanced operator power flow, optimal power flow, etc. For the Generation Management PSS, the application software may include Automatic Generation Control (AGC), economic load dispatch, unit commitment, short-term load forecasting, etc. In case of controlling the refinery plant, necessary process monitoring and control software is loaded in the SCADA server. Same is the case with Water supply and management system.

Information Storage and Retrieval (ISR) Server

An information storage and retrieval is historian server which has the following functionalities.

1. supports the reporting accounting activities,

2. Archiving of data for the system,

3. Real-time data snapshot, and

4. Historical information recording, retrieval, and report generation.

Development Server

All preliminary engineering and commissioning activities of the Power System SCADA (PSS) is done with the development server. Further the changes or developments thereafter have to be handled to keep the system real-time. The various programs such as application software development, display development, and database generation are developed also by the development server.

Network Management Server (NMS)

NMS may be used to monitor both software and hardware components in a network. It is an application or set of applications that helps the network administrator to manage network's independent components inside a larger network. It usually records data from a network's remote points to carry out central reporting to a system administrator. Modern control centres have many digital devices connected via the local network of the master station. In fact a network management system manages the following functions in a SCADA control centre.

1. Network device discovery,

2. Network device monitoring,

3. Network performance analysis,

4. Network device management, and

5. Intelligent notifications or customizable alerts.

Dispatch Training Simulator (DTS) Server

DTS is also an important server in Power System SCADA. A Dispatcher Training Simulator (DTS), also known as an operator training simulator (OTS), is a computer-based training system for operators/dispatchers of electrical power grids, is generally available at a large master station. It is used to train the dispatchers who manage the system. The DTS generally provides the power system model, hydro system model, control centre model, and instructor functions. It performs this role by simulating the behaviour of the electrical network forming the power system under various operating conditions, and its response to actions by the dispatchers. Trainees may therefore develop their skills from exposure not only to routine operations but also to adverse operational situations without compromising the security of supply on a real transmission system. Modern DTS combines or simulates the elements such as Energy Management System (EMS), Distribution Management Systems, SCADA system, load-flow study, and facilities for modelling and optimizing the economic dispatch of generating units.

Communication Front End (CFE)

Communication front end (CFE) interfaces the host computer to a network or peripheral devices. CFE is used to unburden the host computer input and output communications such as managing the peripheral devices, transmitting and receiving message packet assembly and disassembly, and error detection and error collection. This CFE, often referred to as the FEP (front-end processor) must be a high end machine with high computing capabilities so that the communication with a large number of the peripheral devices could be carried in real-time. FEP communicates with the host computer using a high-speed parallel interface. Obviously these computers are costly. FEP/CFE is synonymous with the communication controller. In power system SCADA, CFE has the role of communicating with all RTUs, other field devices which mostly connected through FRTUs, RVDU (Remote Video Display Units), etc.

ICCP Server

ICCP server is an important one in Power system SCADA. This inter-control centre protocol server supports bulk data transmission between the master stations depending on the hierarchy. Typically, the ICCP server at a Regional Load Dispatch Centre (RLDC) exchange data between RLDC and National Load Dispatch Centre (NLDC) as well as with the State Load Dispatch Centre (SLDC) and sub-LDC if required but maintaining the hierarchy.

Video Projection System (VPS)

In large master control stations, especially in power industries where SCADA is employed, the distribution or transmission network is displayed using a video projection system. Master stations must be equipped with high-tech display systems that can display the area of control in a diverse manner as per the requirement of the operators. This display can be GIS information, a Single Line Diagram (SLD) of the network of the region of interest and a separate video projection system handles this function. Supporting software helps in tracing the distribution and transmission network.

Global Positioning Systems (GPS)-Relevance to SCADA

A space based radio navigation system which can provide time information and relocation to a GPS receiver which is placed on or near the Earth surface which has four or more unhindered Line of Sight (LoS) to four or more GPS satellites. There are 14 to 31 geostationary satellites in the mid orbit of the earth which are owned by United States and operated by US Air Force.

Presently time synchronization for all Industrial SCADA components especially in PSS and Smart Grid including the master control station are achieved with the GPS clocks. The GPS system does not require the user to transmit any data, rather it continuously transmit signals to the earth which contain information about the time of transmission and the satellite locations at the time of transmission. On receiving these signals, GPS receivers compute the distance to the satellite based certain equations, the location of the receiver and the time. GPS time is theoretically accurate to about 14 nanoseconds. However, most receivers lose accuracy in the interpretation of the signals and are only accurate to 100 nanoseconds. In PSS and Smart Grid, GPS plays a very vital role, as all the time stamped events, SoE, IED and PMU measurements, etc. critically needs time synchronization.

Human Machine Interface (HMI)

Human Machine Interface (HMI) or user interface (UI) is a combination of software and hardware that allows the interaction between the humans and the system (machine) in a SCADA environment. The main objective of this interaction is effective operation and control of the system being monitored. This aids the operator to make operational decisions and manually override automatic control operations in the event of an emergency. In local and small SCADA control centres, HMI allows a control engineer or operator to configure set points or control algorithms and parameters in the controller. In medium and large SCADA control centres, it also provides process status information, historical information, reports, and other information to operators, administrators, managers, business partners, and other authorized users.

Today the devices and instruments that an operator used in PSS have changed significantly from manual to computer-based devices. The latest expensive hardware, processors with high computing capability, dedicated software, mimic diagrams, and communication protocols with security features especially with end node security have made the system very efficient, compact and human friendly. The location, platform, and interface of HMI may vary a great deal. Further present day HMI could be a dedicated platform in the control centre, a laptop on a wireless LAN, or a browser on any system connected to the Internet.

HMI Building Blocks

In a SCADA system, the HMI components include operator console, operator dialogue, mimic diagram and peripheral devices, etc. are briefly explained below.

Operator Console

The console where the operator monitors and controls the system is of utmost importance and includes the visual display units, alphanumeric keyboard, cursor, communication facilities, ETC. The Visual Display Unit (VDU) includes UI devices like the multiple color monitors (CRT, LCD, LED devices minimum size), with glare-reduction features (antiglare screen coatings) and should provide a display of multiple viewports (windows) on each monitor. The cursor control could be mouse, trackball, or the latest touch-screen facility. A keyboard and cursor pointing device are shared among all monitors at each console and the cursor moves across all screens without switching by user. Generally for power system SCADA each operator has three to four monitors for proper planning and multiple views and the displays should have full graphics capability with zoom facility. Audible alarms are also a prominent feature of the operator console where the operator is informed of the severity of an event in the system. The design of the operator console infrastructure including the table and chair for the operator is important and should follow ergonomics principles to make the operator comfortable during the duty period.

Operator Dialogue

Operator dialogue box is a box that pops up to enable communication between the computer and the operator. Dialogue boxes may ask you questions or give you information. The operator dialogue and commands should be simple and easy to remember. Certain boxes may ask for an action relating to the application which is being used. Function keys of the keyboard can be programmed to incorporate major actions so that the operator can give the commands effortlessly rather than typing long dialogues.

Mimic Diagram

The mimic diagram is an essential part of any control centre or large master station where the operator and the personnel in charge get an overall view of the plant/process under control. This includes LCD/LED large-screen display with full SCADA operability with multiple screens possible. Some control centres have mosaic map board with dynamic or static tile map board and dynamic map board lamps updated by SCADA. Present trend is to use multiple video projection cubes as the dynamic map boards. The major benefit is that when the HMI is updated with system changes, the map board is also automatically updated, since the HMI drives the map board directly.

Peripheral Devices

Generally three printers are required in Master Control Centres. One of them is used to print alarms and SoEs. Another printer usually a colour printer, which is used for capturing screen shots. A black and white laser printer is used to print reports.

HMI Software Functionalities

Selecting HMI software typically starts with an analysis of product specifications and features. The key considerations can include the system architecture, performance requirements, integration and cost of procurement and operations which are described below.

The HMI console should have Role Based Access Control of security to protect unauthorized access to the system. As this HMI is one of the end node of the SCADA system, specific user identification (IDs) and password must be used.

The display of power system to control may be in an effective way. There should be a provision to display all the information about the power system interconnection and the parameters of interest in the HMI, such as voltage, current, frequency, and power flow. This must be in a user friendly manner so that even a new operator could monitor and analyse the events and take corrective and control action, if needed.

HMI software should have the capability of preparing Logs and Reports, and Calculated Values. These reports are required many times to present to various system hierarchies and to different departments of the utility. Today more sophisticated HMI software is structured around mobile, portable platforms. This presents a cost-saving value as the operating systems are distributed on machine-level embedded HMI, solid-state open HMI machines, distributed HMI servers and portable HMI devices.

4.4 NETWORK DEVICES IN CRITICAL INFRASTRUCTURE

HUB

Hub is an inexpensive way to connect devices on a network which works at physical layer and hence connect networking devices physically together. Hubs are fundamentally used in networks that use twisted pair cabling to connect devices. They are designed to transmit the packets to the other appended devices without altering any of the transmitted packets received. They act as pathways to direct electrical signals to travel along. They transmit the information regardless of the fact if data packet is destined for the device connected or not. Hub falls in two categories, and they are Active Hub and Passive Hub.

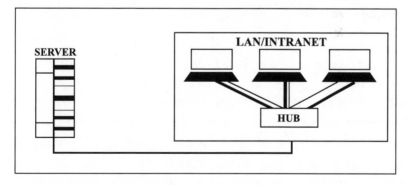

Figure 4.7: Data packets go to all workstations reaching the HUB

Active Hub are smarter than the passive hubs. They not only provide the path for the data signals in fact they regenerate, concentrate and strengthen the signals before sending them to their destinations. Active hubs are also termed as 'repeaters.

Passive Hub are more like point contact for the wires to build in the physical network. They have nothing to do with modifying the signals. Figure 4.7 depicts how data packets go to all workstations reaching the HUB.

Ethernet HUB

It is a device connecting multiple Ethernet devices together and makes them perform the functions as a single unit. They vary in speed in terms of data transfer rate. Ethernet switch do not share the transmission media, do not experience collisions or have to listen for them, can operate in a full-duplex mode, and have bandwidth as high as 200 Mbps, 100 Mbps each way. Either utilizes Carrier Sense Multiple Access with Collision Detect (CSMA/CD) to control Media access. Ethernet hub communicates in half-duplex mode where the chances of data collision are inevitable at most of the times.

An Ethernet switch automatically divides the network into multiple segments, acts as a high-speed, selective bridge between the segments, and supports simultaneous connections of multiple pairs of computers which don't compete with other pairs of computers for network bandwidth. It accomplishes this by maintaining a table of each destination address and its port.

SWITCHES

A switch is more sophisticated than a hub, giving more options for network management, as well as greater potential to expand. They are the connection points of an Ethernet network. Just as in hub, devices in switches are connected to them through twisted pair cabling. But the difference shows up in the manner both the devices; hub and a switch treat the data they receive. Hub works by sending the data to all the ports on the device whereas a switch transfers it only to that port which is connected to the destination device. A switch does so by having an in-built learning of the MAC address of the devices connected to it. Since the transmission of data signals are well defined in a switch hence the network performance is consequently enhanced. Switches operate in full-duplex mode where devices can send and receive data from the switch at the simultaneously unlike in half-duplex mode.

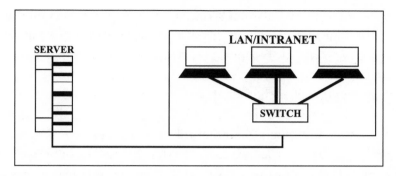

Figure 4.8: Data packets sent to only destination workstations through Switch

The transmission speed in switches is much better than in Ethernet hub. The following methods clarify how data transmission takes place in switches. Figure 4.8 how data packets sent to only destination workstations through SWITCH.

Cut-through transmission: It allows the packets to be forwarded as soon as they are received. The method is prompt and quick but the possibility of error checking gets overlooked in such kind of packet data transmission.

Store and forward: In this switching environment the entire packet are received and 'checked' before being forwarded ahead. The errors are thus eliminated before being propagated further. The downside of this process is that error checking takes relatively longer time consequently making it a bit slower in processing and delivering.

Fragment Free: In a fragment free switching environment, a greater part of the packet is examined so that the switch can determine whether the packet has been caught up in a collision. After the collision status is determined, the packet is forwarded.

Layer 3 and 4 Switches

Layer 2 switches only have the intelligence to forward a frame based on its MAC address and do not have a higher understanding of the network as a whole. A layer 3 switch has the intelligence of a muter. It not only can route packets based on their IP addresses, but also can choose routes based on availability and performance. A layer 3 switch is basically a router with certain added capabilities because it moves the route lookup functionality to the more efficient switching hardware level.

The basic distinction between layer 2, 3, and 4 switches is the header information the device looks at to make forwarding or routing decisions (data link, network, or transport OSI layers). But layer 3 and 4 switches can use tags, which are assigned to each destination network or subnet. When a packet reaches the switch, the switch compares the destination address with its tag information base, which is a list of all the subnets and their corresponding tag numbers. The switch appends the tag to the packet and sends it to the next switch. All the switches in between this first switch and the destination host just review this tag information to determine which route it needs to take, instead of analysing the full header. Once the packet reaches the last switch, this tag is removed and the packet is sent to the destination. This process increases the speed of routing of packets from one location to another. The use of these types of tags, referred to as Multiprotocol Label Switching (MPLS) which will be explained in detail in later sections, not only allows for faster routing, but also addresses service requirements for the different packet types. Some time-sensitive traffic (such as video conferencing) requires a certain level of service (QoS) that guarantees a minimum rate of data delivery to meet the requirements of a user or application When MPLS is used, different priority information is placed into the tags to help ensure that time-sensitive traffic has a higher priority than less sensitive traffic. Many enterprises today use a switched network in which computers are connected to dedicated ports on Ethernet switches, Gigabit Ethernet switches, ATM switches, and more. This evolution of switches, added services, and the capability to incorporate repeater, bridge, and router functionality have made switches an important part of today's networking world.

Because security requires control over who can access specific resources, more intelligent devices can provide a higher level of protection because they can make more detail-oriented decisions regarding who can access resources. When devices can look deeper into the packets, they have access to more information to make access decisions, which provides more granular access control. Switching makes it more difficult for intruders to sniff and monitor network traffic because no broadcast and collision information is continually traveling throughout the network. Switches provide a security service that other devices cannot provide.

Virtual Local Area Networks (VLANs) are a great way to segment a LAN based on users, device types and functions on the network and are an important part of switching networks. It enable the administrators to have more control over their environment by segmenting into logical groups and manageable entities. VLANs are described later in this chapter. Layer 3 switches helps the VLAN routing easier and faster. They make VLANs easier to configure, because a separate router isn't required between each VLAN; all the routing can be done right on the switch. Layer 3 switches also improve VLAN performance, because they eliminate the bottleneck that results from a router forming a single link between VLANs.

Selecting Criteria for Switches

As switches improve the performance and efficiency of a network, they should be used when someone

- Need to make best use of the available bandwidth
- Have multiple file servers
- Require improved performance from file servers, web servers or workstations
- Use high speed multi-media applications
- Are adding a high speed workgroup to a 10Mbit/sec LAN
- Plan to upgrade from 10 to 100Mbit/sec or Gigabit network

BRIDGES

A bridge is a computer networking device used to connect LAN segments which use the same protocol. It works at the data link layer and therefore works with MAC addresses and connects the different networks together and develops communication between them. It connects two local-area networks; two physical LANs into larger logical LAN or two segments of the same LAN that use the same protocol. When a frame arrives at a bridge, the bridge determines whether or not the MAC address is on the local network segment. If the MAC address is not on the local network segment, the bridge forwards the frame to the necessary network segment.

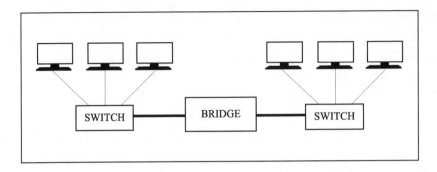

Figure 4.9a: Bridge connects two LAN segments

A bridge is used to divide overburdened networks into smaller segments to ensure better use of bandwidth and traffic control. A bridge amplifies the electrical signal, as does a repeater, but it has more intelligence than a repeater and is used to extend a LAN and enable the administrator to filter frames so he can control which frames go where. The bridge does so by placing itself between the two portions of two physical networks and controlling the flow of the data between them. Bridges nominate to forward the data after inspecting into the MAC address of the devices connected to every segment. The forwarding of the data is dependent on the acknowledgement of the fact that the destination address resides on some other interface. It has the capacity to block the incoming flow of data as well. Today Learning bridges have been introduced that build a list of the MAC addresses on the interface by observing the traffic on the network. This is a leap in the development field of manually recording of MAC addresses. Figure 4.9a demonstrate how a Bridge connects two LAN segments

When using bridges, one has to watch carefully for broadcast storms. Because bridges can forward all traffic, they forward all broadcast packets as well. This can overwhelm the network and result in a broadcast storm, which degrades the network bandwidth and performance.

Types of Bridges

There are mainly three types in which bridges and they are Transparent Bridge, Source Route Bridge, and Translational Bridge. They explained below.

Transparent Bridge:

As the name signifies, it appears to be transparent for the other devices on the network. The other devices are ignorant of its existence. It only blocks or forwards the data as per the MAC address.

Source Route Bridge:

It derives its name from the fact that the path which packet takes through the network is implanted within the packet. It is mainly used in Token ring networks.

Translational Bridge:

A translation bridge is needed if the two LANs being connected are different types and use different standards and protocols. For example, consider a connection between a Token Ring network and an Ethernet network. The frames on each network type are different sizes, the fields contain different protocol information, and the two networks transmit at different speeds. If a regular bridge were put into place, Ethernet frames would go to the Token Ring network, and vice versa, and neither would be able to understand messages that came from the other network segment. A translation bridge does what its name implies: it translates between the two network types.

Another way of categorizing is as local, remote, and translation. A local bridge connects two or more LAN segments within a local area, which is usually a building. A remote bridge can connect two or more LAN segments over a MAN by using telecommunications links. A remote bridge is equipped with telecommunications ports, which enable it to connect two or more LANs separated by a long distance and can be brought together via telephone or other types of transmission lines.

ROUTERS

Routers are network layer devices and are particularly identified as Layer – 3 devices of the OSI Model. When a router receives a packet, it processes the logical addressing information at the Layer 3 source and destination to determine the path the packet should take. Router is used to create larger composite networks by complex traffic routing. It has the ability to connect dissimilar LANs on the same protocol and also has the ability to limit the flow of broadcasts. A router primarily comprises of a hardware device or a system of the computer which has more than one network interface and routing software.

As it has been mentioned when a router receives the data, it determines the destination address by reading the header of the packet. Once the address is determined, it searches in its routing table to get know how to reach the destination and then forwards the packet to the higher hop on the route. The hop could be the final destination or another router.

Routing tables play a very crucial role for the router to makes a decision. Hence a routing table is ought to be updated and complete. The two ways through which a router can receive information are Static routing and dynamic routing.

In static routing the routing information is fed into the routing tables manually. It does not only a time consuming and tedious task but can be prone to errors as well. The manual updating is also required in case of statically configured routers when change in the topology of the network or in the layout takes place. Thus static routing is not feasible for complex and large environments but used when number of routers are limited to a minimum of one or two.

For larger environment dynamic routing proves to be the useful solution. The process involves use of peculiar routing protocols to hold communication. The purpose of these protocols is to enable the other routers to transfer information about to other routers, so that the other routers can build their own routing tables.

BROUTERS

Brouters are the networking devices which combines the functionality of both the bridge and the router. It take up the functionality of the bridge when forwarding data between networks, and serving as a router when routing data to individual systems. Brouter functions as a filter that allows some data into the local network and redirects unknown data to the other network. Brouters are rare and their functionality is embedded into the routers functioned to act as bridge as well.

GATEWAYS

Gateway is a device which is used to connect multiple networks and passes packets from one packet to the other network. Acting as the 'gateway' between different networking systems or computer programs, a gateway is a device which forms a link between them. It allows the computer programs, either on the same computer or on different computers to share information across the network through protocols. A router is also a gateway, since it interprets data from one network protocol to another. Depending on the types of protocols that the networks support, network gateways can operate at any level of the OSI model and act as a protocol converter.

The different network devices and their functionality are tabulated in Table 4.1.

Device	OSI Layer	Functionality
Repeater	Physical	Amplifies the signal and extends networks.
Hub	Physical	Serve as a central connection for the network equipment and handles a data type known as frames.
Bridge	Data Link	Forwards packets and filters based on MAC addresses; forwards broadcast traffic, but not collision traffic.
Router	Network	Separates and connects LANs creating internetworks; routers filter based on IP addresses.
Switch	Data Link	Provides a private virtual link between communicating devices; allows for VLANs; reduces collisions; impedes network sniffing
Gateway	Application	Connects different types of networks; performs protocol and format translations.

Table 4.2: Network Devices and Functionalities

NETWORK INTERFACE CARD (NIC)

The hardware devices through which the computers are allowed to communicate or exchange data over a computer network is the Network Interface Card or NIC. It is both an OSI layer 1 (physical layer) and layer 2 (data link layer) device, as it provides physical access to a networking medium and provides a low-level addressing system through the use of

MAC addresses. It allows users to connect to each other either by using cables or wirelessly.

Most new computers have either Ethernet capabilities integrated into the motherboard chipset, or use an inexpensive dedicated Ethernet chip connected through the PCI or PCI Express bus, eliminating the need for a standalone card. Computer data is translated into electrical signals send to the network via Network Interface Cards. If the card is not integrated into the motherboard, it may be an integrated component in a router, printer interface or USB device. Typically, there is an LED next to the connector informing the user if the network is active or whether or not data is being transferred on it. Depending on the card or motherboard, transfer rates may be 10, 100, or 1000 Megabits per second.

Today's Network Interface Cards are capable to manage some important data-conversion functions and are mostly software configured unlike in olden days when drivers were needed to configure them. Even if the NIC doesn't come up with the software then the latest drivers or the associated software can be downloaded from the internet.

MODEMS

Modem is a device which converts the computer-generated digital signals of a computer into analog signals to enable their travelling via a suitable communication medium. The 'modulator-demodulator' or modem can be used as a dial up for LAN or to connect to an ISP. Modems can be both external, as in the device which connects to the USB or the serial port of a computer, or proprietary devices for handheld gadgets and other devices, as well as internal; in the form of add-in expansion cards for computers and Personal Computer Memory Card International Association (PCMCIA) cards for laptops.

Configuration of a modem differs for both the external and internal modem. For internal modems, IRQ – Interrupt request is used to configure the modem along with I/O, which is a memory address. Typically before the installation of built-in modem, integrated serial interfaces are disabled, simultaneously assigning them the COM2 resources. For external connection of a modem, the modem assigns and uses the resources itself. This is especially useful for the USB port and laptop users as the non-complex and simpler nature of the process renders it far much more beneficial for daily usage. Upon installation, the second step to ensure the proper working of a modem is the installation of drivers. The modem working speed and processing is dependent on two factors:

- Speed of UART–Universal Asynchronous Receiver or Transmitter chip which installed in the computer to which the modem connection is made.

- Speed of the modem itself.

TRANSPARENCY of the MODEM is the most critical parameter while selecting for power system SCADA and smart grids from the perspective of security. Transparency of a device ensures that the device achieves the specific task for which it is designed, and must not perform any other task other than predestined especially if the payload is encrypted. Non-transparent MODEM has many drawbacks as severe vulnerability points can be introduced for War dialers, War divers, etc. If a war dialing hacker plant fake historical data and send it to the alarm system, it will affect the way engineers do troubleshooting; they will do something wrong and, in a worst case scenario, cause a horrific incident. Further non-transparent MODEM may not be real time and having a memory element and chances of espionage is very high. Hence MODEMs when selected for smart grid or power system SCADA must be transparent without any compromise.

Today the presence of a modem on a user system is often one of the greatest woes of a security administrator. Modems allow users to create uncontrolled access points into utility's network. In the worst case, if improperly configured, they can create extremely serious security vulnerabilities that allow an outsider to bypass all perimeter protection mechanisms and directly access the network resources. At best, they create an alternate egress channel that insiders can use to funnel data outside the organization. But these vulnerabilities can only be exploited if the modem is connected to an operational communication channel. One should seriously consider an outright ban on modems in organization's security policy unless utility truly need them for business reasons. In those cases, security officials should know the physical and logical locations of all modems on the network, ensure that they are correctly configured, and make certain that appropriate protective measures are in place to prevent their illegitimate use.

Wireless Access Point (WAP)

A wireless access point (WAP or AP) is a device that allows wireless communication devices to connect to a wireless network using Wi-Fi, Bluetooth or related standards. The WAP usually connects to a wired network, and can relay data between the wireless devices (such as computers or printers) and wired devices on the network.

A typical corporate use involves attaching several WAPs to a wired network and then providing wireless access to the office Local Area Network. Within the range of the WAPs, the wireless end user has a full network connection with the benefit of mobility. In this instance, the WAP functions as a gateway for clients to access the wired network.

A Hot Spot is a common public application of WAPs, where wireless clients can connect to the Internet without regard for the particular networks to which they have attached for the moment. The concept has become common in large cities, where a combination of coffeehouses, libraries, as well as privately owned open access points, allow clients to stay more or less continuously connected to the Internet, while moving around. A collection of connected Hot Spots can be referred to as a lily-pad network.

Home networks generally have only one WAP to connect all the computers in a home. Most are wireless routers, meaning converged devices that include a WAP, router, and often an Ethernet switch in the same device. Many also converge a broadband modem. In places where most homes have their own WAP within range of the neighbors' WAP, it's possible for technically savvy people to turn off their encryption and set up a wireless community network, creating an intra-city communication network without the need of wired networks.

VLAN

The technology within switches has introduced the capability to use VLANs. VLANs enable administrators to separate and group computers logically based on resource requirements, security, or business needs instead of the standard physical location of the systems.

When repeaters, bridges, and routers are used, systems and resources are grouped in a manner dictated by their physical location. Figure 4.10 shows how computers that are physically located next to each other can be grouped logically into different VLANs. Administrators can form these groups based on the users' and company's needs instead of the physical location of systems and resources.

An administrator may want to place the computers of all users in the marketing department in the same VLAN network, for example, so all users receive the same broadcast messages and can access the same types of resources. This arrangement could get tricky if a few of the users are located in another building or on another floor, but VLANs provide the administrator with this type of flexibility. VLANs also enable an administrator to apply particular security policies to respective logical groups. This way, if tighter security is required for the engineering department, the administrator can develop a policy, add all engineering systems to a specific VLAN, and apply the security policy only to the engineering VLAN.A VLAN exists on top of the physical network, as shown in Figure 4.10a. If workstation PI wants to communicate with workstation El, the message has to be routed—even though the workstations are physically next to each other—because they are on different logical networks.

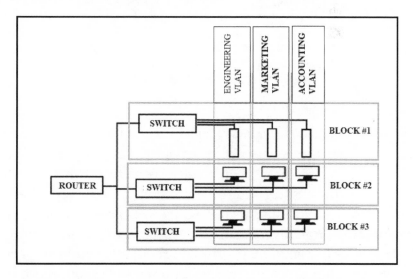

Figure 4.10: VLANs enable administrators to manage logical networks

IEEE 802.1Q is the IEEE standard that defines how VLANs are to be constructed and how tagging should take place to allow for interoperability. While VLANs are used to segment traffic, attackers can still gain access to traffic that is supposed to be walled off in another VLAN segment. VLAN hopping attacks allow attackers to gain access to traffic in various VLAN segments. An attacker can have a system act as though it is a switch. The system understands the tagging values being used in the network and the trunking protocols and can insert itself between other VLAN devices and gain access to the traffic going back and forth. Attackers can also insert tagging values to manipulate the control of traffic at the data link layer.

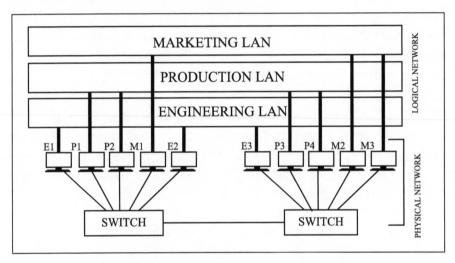

Figure 4.10a: VLANs showing the existence in a higher level than the physical network

VLAN and SCADA Security

VLANS are good for traffic management but not good for security. It work by having Ethernet switches insert a tag (basically a 4-byte field) in to the header of each Ethernet message. Other switches on the network can read this tag and make decisions on whether a message should be forwarded. In fact this allows the switches to provide limited traffic filtering, primarily for managing broadcast traffic. And managing broadcast traffic is important. VLANs are great traffic management tools. But switches with VLANs are not firewalls. They operate at layer

2 (the Ethernet layer) and don't understand the state of the messages flowing through them. This makes the spoofing of VLAN tags trivial – there is no check to detect if a tag has been adjusted by a hacker. Thus the hacking community has lots of tools designed to bypass switch-based security. It is always recommended to *use VLANs as a mechanism for enforcing security policy. They are great for segmenting networks, reducing broadcasts and collisions and so forth, but not as a security tool.*

Usually the interest in VLANs is because of IT teams wanting to use IT network technology to solve a plant floor security issue. VLANs are good tools, but deploying them only for security is categorically not a solution.

MEDIA CONVERTERS

Media converters are simple networking devices that make it possible to connect two dissimilar media types such as twisted pair with fiber optic cabling. They were introduced to the industry nearly two decades ago, and are important in interconnecting fiber optic cabling-based systems with existing copper-based, structured cabling systems. Media converters support many different data communication protocols including Ethernet, T1/E1, T3/E3, as well as multiple cabling types such as coaxial, twisted pair, multimode and single-mode fiber optics. When expanding the reach of a Local Area Network to span multiple locations, media converters are useful in connecting multiple LANs to form one large *campus area network* that spans over a limited geographic area. As local networks are primarily copper-based, media converters can extend the reach of the LAN over single-mode fiber up to 130 kilometers with 1550 nm optics.

DATA DIODES

A data diode is a computer security device that restricts the communication along a network connection between two computers so that data can only be transmitted in one direction. This enables a more sensitive or highly classified computer network to receive data directly from a less secure source while prohibiting the transmission of data in the opposite direction.

Data diodes provide a physical mechanism for enforcing strict unidirectional communication between two networks. They are often implemented by removing transmitting component from one side and receiving component from another side of a bidirectional communication system. Data diodes can only send information from one network (the *low* network) to another network (the *high* network.) The high network often contains data with higher classification level than the low network.

A major limitation of the data diode is that it does not work with the standard TCP/IP protocols. It needs proprietary unidirectional protocols that do not require acknowledgments. On both sides of a data diode, gateways translate unidirectional protocols to standard bidirectional protocols to connect the diode to the rest of the network. However, more high-end products also accept TCP or UDP packets as input. Data diodes can be used to enhance security if placed carefully in combination with other defensive mechanisms.

FIREWALLS

Today a firewall is an indispensable component of a secure M2M communication which is designed to block unauthorized access while permitting authorized communication. It comprises a device or set of devices configured to permit, deny, encrypt, decrypt, or proxy all computer traffic between different security domains based upon a set of rules called ruleset. Firewalls can be implemented in both hardware and software, or a combination of both. Firewalls are frequently used to prevent unauthorized Internet users from accessing private networks connected to the Internet. All messages entering or leaving the computer network pass through the firewall, which examines each message and blocks those that do not meet the specified security criteria. Without proper configuration, a firewall can often become insignificant. Standard security practices dictate a *default-deny* firewall ruleset, in which the only network connections which are allowed are the ones that have been explicitly allowed.

A variety of firewalls are available in the market, depending upon the requirements and security goals to be achieved. Firewalls have gone through an evolution of their own and have grown in complexity and functionality. The generally deployed firewalls today are,

1. Packet Filtering Firewalls
2. Stateful Firewalls

3. Proxy Firewalls

4. Dynamic Packet Filtering Firewalls,

5. Kernel Proxy Firewalls, and

6. Deep Packet Inspection Firewalls

The following sections give brief descriptions of these firewalls.

Packet Filtering Firewalls

Packet filtering was the first generation of firewalls and it is the most elementary type of all of the firewall technologies. It is a firewall technology that makes access decisions by examining the network-level protocol header values. The device that is carrying out packet filtering processes is configured with Access Control Lists (ACL), which dictate the type of traffic that is allowed into and out of specific networks. The filters review the protocol header information at the network and transport levels and carrying out PERMIT or DENY actions on individual packets. This means the filters can make access decisions based upon the following basic criteria,

- Source and destination IP addresses
- Source and destination port numbers
- Protocol types
- Inbound and outbound traffic direction

Packet filtering is built into a majority of the firewall products and routers. Packet filtering is also known as stateless inspection because the device does not understand the context that the packets are working within. This means that the device does not have the capability to understand the *full picture* of the communication that is taking place between two systems, but can only focus on individual packet characteristics.

Some of the disadvantages of packet filtering firewalls are as follows.

- They cannot prevent attacks that employ application-specific vulnerabilities or functions.
- The logging functionality present in packet filtering firewalls is limited.

- Most packet filtering firewalls do not support advanced user authentication schemes.

- Many packet filtering firewalls cannot detect spoofed addresses.

- They may not be able to detect packet fragmentation attacks.

The advantages to using packet filtering firewalls are that they are scalable, they are not application dependent, and they have high performance because they do not carry out extensive processing on the packets. They are commonly used as the preliminary defense to strip out all the network traffic that is obviously malicious or unintended for a specific network.

Stateful Firewalls

The following are some of the important characteristics of a stateful-inspection firewall.

- Maintains a state table that tracks each and every communication session,

- Provides a high degree of security,

- Is scalable and transparent to users,

- Provides data for tracking connectionless protocols like UDP&ICMP, and

- Stores and updates the state and context of the data within the packets.

When packet filtering is used, a packet arrives at the firewall, and it runs through its ACLs to determine whether this packet should be allowed or denied. If the packet is allowed, it is passed on to the destination host, or to another network device, and the packet filtering device forgets about the packet.

When a connection begins between two systems, the firewall investigates all layers of the packet such as headers, payload, and trailers. All of the necessary information about the specific connection such as source and destination IP addresses, source and destination ports, protocol type, header flags, sequence numbers, timestamps, etc. are stored in the state table. Once the initial packets undergo this in-depth inspection the firewall then reviews the network and transport header portions for the rest of the session. The values of each header for each packet are compared to what is in the current state table, and the table is updated to reflect the progression of the communication process. Scaling down the inspection of the full packet to just the headers for each packet is done to increase performance. TCP is considered a connection-oriented protocol, and the various steps and states this protocol operates within are very well defined. A connection progresses through a series of states during its lifetime.

If the acknowledgment and/or sequence numbers are out of order, this could imply that a replay attack is underway and the firewall will protect the internal systems from this activity. Stateful inspection firewalls unfortunately have been the victims of many types of DoS attacks. Several types of attacks are aimed at flooding the state table with bogus information. The state table is a resource, similar to a system's hard drive space, memory, and CPU. When the state table is stuffed full of bogus information, the device may either freeze or reboot. In addition, if this firewall must be rebooted for some reason, it will lose its information on all recent connections; thus, it may deny legitimate packets.

Proxy Firewalls

A proxy firewall stands between a trusted and untrusted network and makes the connection, each way, on behalf of the source. What is important is that a proxy firewall breaks the communication channel; there is no direct connection between the two communicating devices. Where a packet filtering device just monitors traffic as it is traversing a network connection, a proxy ends the communication session and restarts it on behalf of the sending system. Figure 4.11 illustrates the steps of a proxy-based firewall. The firewall is not just applying ACL rules to the traffic, but stops the user connection at the internal interface of the firewall itself and then starts a new session on behalf of this user on the external interface. When the external web server replies to the request, this reply goes to the external interface of the proxy firewall and ends. The proxy firewall examines the reply information and if it is deemed safe, the firewall starts a new session from itself to the internal system. This is just like our analogy of what the delivery man does between the customer and the president.

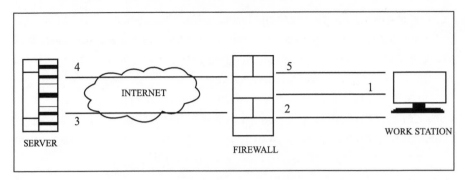

Figure 4.11 Functional steps of a Proxy Firewall

1. User with Web browser configured to use firewall proxy server requests web page internet web site.

2. Proxy Firewall accepts the connection request.

3. Firewall proxy request web page on behalf of end user.

4. Web server responds to HTTP request from proxy server, unaware the request is coming from a user behind a proxy. Once page is cached, proxy sends the user the requested web page.

5. After caching, the requested page is sent to the other.

A circuit-level proxy creates a connection (circuit) between the two communicating systems. It works at the session layer of the OSI model and monitors traffic from a network based view. This type of proxy cannot *look into* the contents of a packet; thus, it does not carry out deep-packet inspection. It can only make access decisions based upon protocol header and session information that is available to it. While this means that it cannot provide as much protection as an application-level proxy, because it does not have to understand application layer protocols, it is considered application independent. So it cannot provide the detail-oriented protection that a proxy that works at a higher level can, but this allows it to provide a broader range of protection where application layer proxies may not be appropriate or available.

Dynamic Packet Filtering

When an internal system needs to communicate to an entity outside its trusted network, it must choose a source port so the receiving system knows how to respond properly. Ports up to 1023 are called *well-known ports* and are reserved for server-side services. The sending system must choose a dynamic port higher than 1023 when it sets up a connection with another entity. The dynamic packet-filtering firewall then creates an ACL that allows the external entity to communicate with the internal system via this high port. If this were not an available option for the customers dynamic packet-filtering firewall, customer would have to allow punch holes in customers firewalls for all ports above 1023, because the client side chooses these ports dynamically and the firewall would never know exactly on which port to allow or disallow traffic.

Kernel Proxy Firewalls

A *kernel proxy firewall* is considered a fifth-generation firewall. It differs from all the previously discussed firewall technologies because it creates dynamic, customized network stacks when a packet needs to be evaluated. When a packet arrives at a kernel proxy firewall, a new virtual network stack is created, which is made up of only the protocol proxies necessary to examine this specific packet properly. If it is an FTP packet, then the FTP proxy is loaded in the stack. The packet is scrutinized at every layer of the stack. This means the data link header will be evaluated along with the network header, transport header, session layer information, and the application layer data. If anything is deemed unsafe at any of these layers, the packet is discarded. Kernel proxy firewalls are faster than application layer proxy firewalls because all of the inspection and processing takes place in the kernel and does not need to be passed up to a higher software layer in the operating system. It is still a proxy-based system, so the connection between the internal and external entity is broken by the proxy acting as a middleman, and it can perform NAT by changing the source address, as do the preceding proxy-based firewalls.

Deep Packet Inspection Firewall

Deep Packet Inspection (DPI) is an advanced method of examining and managing network traffic. It is a form of packet filtering that locates, identifies, classifies, reroutes or blocks packets with specific data or code payloads that conventional packet filtering, which examines only packet headers, cannot detect. DPI usually examines the data part (and possibly also the header) of a packet as it passes an inspection point, searching for protocol non-compliance, viruses, spam, intrusions, or defined criteria to decide whether the packet may pass. DPI enables advanced network management, user service, and security functions as well as internet data mining, eavesdropping, and internet censorship. It is used in a wide range of applications, at the enterprise level, in telecommunications service providers, and in governments. DPI combines the functionality of an Intrusion Detection System (IDS) and an Intrusion Prevention System (IPS) with a traditional stateful firewall. This combination makes it possible to detect certain attacks that neither the IDS/IPS nor the stateful firewall can catch on their own.

Firewall Type	OSI Layer	Characteristics
Packet filtering	Network layer	Verifies the destination and source addresses level, port numbers, services requested, etc. at the routers using ACLs to monitor the network traffic services requested, etc. at the routers using ACLs to monitor the network traffic.
Application-level	Application layer	Verifies deep into packets and makes granular access control decisions. It requires one proxy per protocol. They filter packets not only according to the service for which they are intended (as specified by the destination port), but also by certain other characteristics such as HTTP request string. While application-level gateways provide considerable data security, they can dramatically impact network performance.

Circuit-level proxy	Session layer	Verifies only at the header packet information. It protects a wider range of protocols and services than an application-level proxy, but does not provide the detailed level of control available to an application-level proxy. However monitor the TCP handshaking going on between the local and remote hosts to determine whether the session being initiated is legitimate – whether the remote system is considered trusted.
Stateful	Network layer	It not only examines each packet, but also keep track of whether or not that packet is part of an established TCP session. This offers more security than either packet filtering or circuit monitoring alone, but exacts a greater toll on network performance.
Kernel proxy	Application layer	Faster because processing is done in the kernel. One network stack is created for each packet

Table 4.3: Comparison of Different Types of Firewalls

Summary

This chapter gives an introduction to SCADA with an emphasis on Data Acquisition Systems (DAS) and its components. The objectives and advantages as well as the evolution of SCADA are briefly discussed but with clarity. A brief discussion of the various components of DAS such as Sensors, Signal conditioners, Sample and Hold circuits, Analog to Digital Converters, etc. are also given in this chapter. A brief discussion regarding the selection criteria of the DAS is then given before moving to give a comprehensive description of Remote Terminal Units (RTU), Programmable Logic Controller (PLC) and the different modern components of Power System SCADA such as Intelligent Electronic Devices, Data Concentrator Units, Merging Units, Human Machine Interface, etc. The brief introduction of Data

Concentrators and Merging Units are presented in such a manner that how digital substations can be designed. This chapter then gives an introduction of architecture of SCADA Master Stations and its hardware and software components. It concludes with a brief description of Geographical Positioning System (GPS), Situational Awareness and Alarm Processing.

Chapter Five

Communication in Critical Infrastructure

5.1 INTRODUCTION

The key enabler for the ICS and DCS used in CI is the availability of secure and preferably bi-directional data communications and the proper amalgamation of distributed intelligence and communication technologies. Thus, the design and implementation of a modern, reliable communications infrastructure is a fundamental and important requirement. The medium by which data is transmitted is known as a communication channel or communication media. The transfer of data takes place in the form of analog signals/digital data and the transfer of data is measured in the form of bandwidth, the higher the bandwidth the more the data that will be transferred. Communication media are broadly classified into two categories, namely, guided media (wired) and unguided media (wireless). Both media are used for short distance (LANs, MANs) and long distance (WANs) communication. This chapter elaborates various guided and unguided media used in communication, its merits and demerits, and practical considerations to be taken care while selecting the media for different applications. The chapter also explain the various communication technologies currently available for the deployment in ICS used in CI. Before that, it is better to be familiar with certain terminologies which are briefly explained below.

5.2 TYPES OF TRANSMISSION

There are various transmission classifications depending upon the different technologies employed and they are mainly based on

1. Analog and digital,
2. Synchronous and Asynchronous,
3. Broadcast, Multicast and Unicast,

4. Simplex, Half Duplex, and Full Duplex and

5. Baseband and Broadband.

As the communication is the key enabler of the modern SCADA, a basic understanding of these terms become most essential for an automation engineer. Hence brief explanation of these terminologies are given below.

Analog and Digital

There are two types of communication technologies in practice viz analog and digital. Analog communications occur with a continuous signal that varies in frequency, amplitude, phase, voltage, and so on. The variances in the continuous signal produce a wave shape as opposed to the square shape of a digital signal. Digital communications occur through the use of a discontinuous electrical signal and a state change or on-off pulses. In other way the information is encoded digitally as discrete signals and transmitted electronically to the recipients. Digital signals are more reliable than analog signals over long distances or when interference is present. This is because of a digital signal's definitive information storage method employing direct current voltage where voltage on represents a value of 1 and voltage off represents a value of 0. These on-off pulses create a stream of binary data. Analog signals become altered and corrupted because of attenuation over long distances and interference. Since an analog signal can have an infinite number of variations used for signal encoding as opposed to digital's two states, unwanted alterations to the signal make extraction of the data more difficult as the degradation increases. A brief comparison between these two technologies are summarized below.

1. *Bandwidth:* This factor creates the key difference between Analog and digital communication. Analog signal requires less bandwidth for the transmission while digital signal requires more bandwidth for the transmission.

2. *Power Requirement:* Power requirement in case of digital communication is less when compared to analog communication. Since the bandwidth requirement in digital systems is more thus,

they consume less power. And Analog communication system requires less bandwidth thus more power.

3. *Fidelity:* Fidelity is a factor which creates a crucial difference between Analog and digital communication. Fidelity is the ability of the receiver which receives the output exactly in coherence with that of transmitted input. Digital communication offers more fidelity as compared to Analog Communication.

4. *Noise Distortion and Error Rate:* Analog systems are affected by Noise while digital systems are immune from Noise and Distortion. Error rate is another significant difference which separates Analog and Digital Communication. In Analog instruments, there is an error due to parallax or other kinds of observational method.

5. *Synchronization:* Digital communication system offers to synchronize which is not effective in analog communication. Thus, synchronization also creates a key difference between Analog and Digital Communication.

6. *Cost:* Digital communication equipments are costly and digital signal require more bandwidth for transmission.

7. *Hardware Flexibility and Portability:* The hardware of analog communication system is not as flexible as digital communication. Analog systems are less portable as components are heavy while digital systems are more portable as they are compact equipments.

Synchronous and Asynchronous

Communications are either synchronous or asynchronous. Some communications are synchronized with some sort of clock or timing activity and referred to synchronous communications. It rely on a timing or clocking mechanism based on either an independent clock or a time stamp embedded in the data stream. Synchronous communications are typically able to support very high rates of data transfer. On the other hand, asynchronous communications rely on a stop and start delimiter bit to manage the transmission of data. Because of the use of delimiter bits and the stop and start nature of its transmission, asynchronous communication is best suited for smaller amounts of data. Public

Switched Telephone Network (PSTN) modems are good examples of asynchronous communication devices.

Broadcast, Multicast and Unicast

Broadcast, multicast, and unicast technologies determine how many destinations a single transmission can reach.

Unicast technology supports only a single communication to a specific recipient. In this case there is just one sender, and one receiver. Unicast transmission, in which a packet is sent from a single source to a specified destination, is still the predominant form of transmission on LANs and within the Internet. All LANs and IP networks support the unicast transfer mode, and most users are familiar with the standard unicast applications (e.g. http, smtp, ftp and telnet) which employ the TCP transport protocol.

Broadcast technology supports communications to all possible recipients. In this case there is just one sender, but the information is sent to all connected receivers. Broadcast transmission is supported on most LANs (e.g. Ethernet), and may be used to send the same message to all computers on the LAN (e.g. the Address Resolution Protocol (ARP) uses this to send an address resolution query to all computers on a LAN. Network layer protocols (such as IPv4) also support a form of broadcast that allows the same packet to be sent to every system in a logical network (in IPv4 this consists of the IP network ID and an all 1's host number). One example of an application which may use multicast is a video server sending out networked TV channels. Simultaneous delivery of high quality video to a large number of delivery platforms will exhaust the capability of even a high bandwidth network with a powerful video clip server. This poses a major scalability issue for applications which required sustained high bandwidth. One way to significantly ease scaling to larger groups of clients is to employ multicast networking.

Multicast networking technology supports simultaneous communications to multiple specific recipients. In this case there is may be one or more senders, and the information is distributed to a set of receivers. IP multicast provides dynamic many-to-many connectivity between a set of senders (at least 1) and a group of receivers. The format of IP multicast packets is identical to that of unicast packets and is distinguished only by the use of a special class of destination address, which denotes a specific multicast group. Since TCP supports only the unicast mode, multicast applications must use the UDP transport protocol.

Unlike broadcast transmission (used in LAN), multicast clients receive a stream of packets only if they have previously elect to do so. Membership of a group is dynamic and controlled by the receivers. The routers in a multicast network learn which sub-networks have active clients for each multicast group and attempt to minimise the transmission of packets across parts of the network for which there are no active clients.

The multicast mode is useful if a group of clients require a common set of data at the same time, or when the clients are able to receive and store (cache) common data until needed. Where there is a common need for the same data required by a group of clients, multicast transmission may provide significant bandwidth savings (up to $1/N$ of the bandwidth compared to N separate unicast clients).

The majority of installed LANs are able to support the multicast transmission mode. Shared LANs inherently support multicast, since all packets reach all network interface cards connected to the LAN. The earliest LAN network interface cards had no specific support for multicast and introduced a big performance penalty by forcing the adaptor to receive all packets (promiscuous mode) and perform software filtering to remove all unwanted packets. Most modern network interface cards implement a set of multicast filters, relieving the host of the burden of performing excessive software filtering.

Simplex, Half Duplex and Full Duplex Communication Channels

In a communication system, there will be a transmitter and a receiver. In between the transmitter and the receiver, there is a transmission medium of the data/information, usually referred as the communication channel. Although the required information for transmission originates from a single source, there may be more than one destination or receivers. This depends upon how many receiving stations are linked to the channel and how much energy the transmitted signal possesses. If the channel length is more and the transmission power is less, the receiver situated at a long distance cannot receive the data properly. In a digital communications channel, the information can be represented by a stream of bits called bytes. A collection of bytes can be grouped to form a frame or other higher-level message unit. These types of multiple levels of encapsulation facilitate the handling of messages in a complex data communications network. If any communications channel is considered, it has a direction associated with it.

Simplex Channel: It is conventional that the message source is the transmitter, and the destination is the receiver. A channel whose direction of transmission is unchanging is called as a simplex channel. In other words, a type of data transmission, where message transmission is taken place only in one direction, typical example is the radio station which is a simplex channel because it always transmits the signal to its listeners and never allows them to transmit back. Another example is the television. The advantage of simplex mode of transmission is, since the data can be transmitted only in one direction, the entire band width can be used.

Half Duplex Channel: A half-duplex channel can be considered as a single physical channel in which the direction may be reversed. Messages can flow in two directions in a half-duplex type, but never at the same time. In other words it can be said that at a single time, the transmission of data are done in only one direction. For example, in a telephone call, one party speaks while the other listens. After a pause, the other party speaks and the first party listens. Speaking simultaneously will result in a garbled sound that cannot be understood. The main difficulty of half-duplex mode of transmission is since two channels are used, the band width of the channel should be decreased.

Full Duplex Channel: A full-duplex channel can be used for bi-directional communication. In fact message can be transmitted simultaneously in both directions. It comprises of two simplex channels, a forward channel and a backward (reverse) channel, linking at the same points. The transmission rate of the reverse channel will be very slow if it is used only for flow control of the forward channel. The main problem of the full duplex mode of transmission is, since two channels are required, the band width should be decreased.

Baseband and Broadband

The number of channels that can be pushed into a single wire simultaneously over a cable segment depends on whether the customer use baseband technology or broadband technology. Baseband technology can support only a single communication channel. Analog transmission means that data is being moved as waves, and digital transmission means that data is being moved as discrete electric pulses. Baseband uses a direct current applied to the cable. A current that is at a higher level represents the binary signal of 1, and a current that is at a lower level represents the binary signal of 0. Baseband is a form of digital signal. Ethernet is a baseband technology.

Broadband technology divides the communication channel into individual and independent subchannels so that different types of data can be transmitted simultaneously. Broadband uses frequency modulation to support numerous channels, each supporting a distinct communication session. Broadband is suitable for high throughput rates, especially when several channels are multiplexed. Broadband is a form of analog signal. As an example, a coaxial cable TV (CATV) system is a broadband technology that delivers multiple television channels over the same cable. This system can also provide home users with Internet access, but these data are transmitted at a different frequency spectrum than the TV channels. A Digital Subscriber Line (DSL) uses one single phone line and constructs a set of high-frequency channels for Internet data transmissions. A cable modem uses the available frequency spectrum that is provided by a cable TV carrier to move Internet traffic to and from a household. Mobile broadband devices implement individual channels over a cellular connection, and WiFi broadband technology moves data to and from an access point over a specified frequency set. Characteristics of baseband and broadband are summarized in Table 5.1.

Baseband	Broadband
Digital signals are used	Analog signals are used
Frequency division multiplexing is not possible	Transmission of data is unidirectional
Baseband is bi-directional transmission	Signal travelling distance is long
Short distance signal travelling	Frequency division multiplexing is possible
Entire bandwidth of the cable is consumed by a single signal in a baseband transmission.	The signals are sent on multiple frequencies but are sent simultaneously

Table 5.1: Characteristics of baseband and broadband

5.3 GUIDED MEDIA

Guided media are more commonly known as wired media or bounded media, or those media in which electrical or optical signals are transmitted through a cables or wires. In fact it needs a physical material medium to propagate and the electrical signals are confined within the cable or wire which transmits them. Typical forms of guided media include copper co-axial cables, fiber-optic cables and twisted-pair copper cables, which can be shielded or unshielded. Transmission of digital data through either guided or unguided communication involves the coding of the data at the sender's end, the modulation of the carrier signal, the demodulation of the signal on the receiving end and the decoding of the binary signal.

5.4 UNGUIDED MEDIA

Unguided media are more commonly known as wireless media or unbounded media, in which data is transferred into electromagnetic waves and sent through free space without guiding any specific direction. Hence the name unguided media. All unguided media transmission are classified as wireless transmission which is quickly expanding the field of technologies for networking. The various kinds of unguided media are microwave, cellular radio, radio broadcast and satellite. As wireless technologies continue to proliferate, the organization's security efforts must go beyond locking down its local network. Security should be an end-to-end solution that addresses all forms, methods, and techniques of communication.

Different types of unguided communication are classified based on the frequency spectrum used for communication, the distance between the end stations and the type of encoding used for the communication. Broadband wireless signals occupy frequency bands that may be shared with microwave, satellite, radar, and ham radio use. Unguided communication allows electromagnetic signals to travel between antennas, some of which are on satellites. Antennas can provide point-to-point communication or can send their signals in all directions.

Microwaves Communication

In this kind the data is transferred via air. The waves travel in a straight line. The data is received and transferred via microwave stations. The speed at which data is transferred is 190 Mbps. The two main microwave wireless transmission technologies are satellite (ground to orbiter to ground) and terrestrial (ground to ground). They are widely used by telephone and cable companies.

Terrestrial Communication

This type of communication is limited to line-of-sight (LOS) transmission. This means that microwaves are transmitted in a straight line and that no obstructions can exist, such as buildings or mountains, between microwave stations as shown in Figure 5.1. To avoid possible obstructions, microwave antennas often are positioned on the tops of buildings, towers, or mountains. It finds applications in long-distance telecommunication service. It requires fewer amplifiers or repeaters than coaxial cable but it is line-of-sight transmission.

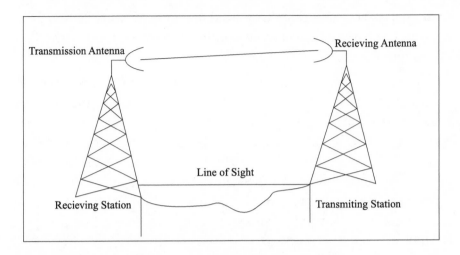

Figure 5.1: Terrestrial communication

Satellite Communication

The satellites are located at a distance of 22300 miles above the earth as shown in Figure 5.2. The signals are received from earth stations. Devices like GPS and PDAs also receive signals from these earth based stations. The process of transferring and receiving data takes place within few seconds. The data is transferred at a speed of 1 Gbps. They are used for purposes like weather forecast, military communication, radio transmission, satellite TV, data transmission, etc.

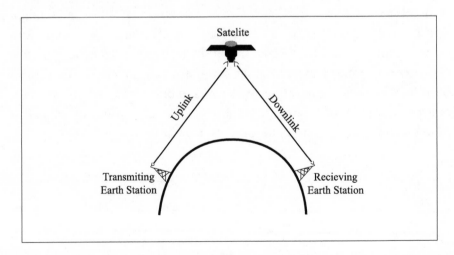

Figure 5.2: Satellite communication

Today the cost of satellite launching has brought down significantly with advanced and reusable launching modules. This made extensive use of satellite communication to provide wireless connectivity between different locations. But for two different locations to communicate via satellite links, they must be bought within the satellite's line-of-sight and area covered by the satellite called footprint. The information or data is appropriately modulated by the ground station and is transmitted to the satellite. A transponder on the satellite receives this signal, amplifies it, and relays it to the receiver. The receiver at the ground station must have an antenna, usually a circular dish like structure normally placed on top of buildings. The antenna contains one or more microwave receivers, depending upon how many satellites it is accepting data from. Satellites provide broadband transmission. If a user is receiving radio or TV data, then the transmission is set up as a one-directional network. If a user is using this connection for internet, then the transmission is set up as a bi-directional network. The available bandwidth depends upon the antenna, terminal type and the service rendered by the service provider.

As the satellite are kilometers above the Earth, time-critical applications may experience delay as the signal has to traverse to and from the satellite. Hence these types of satellites are placed into a low Earth orbit, keeping the distance between the ground stations and the satellites is less when compared to other types of satellites. Further, smaller receivers can be used for reception of signals, which makes low-Earth-orbit satellites ideal for cellular communication, radio and TV stations, Internet, etc. use.

Wired or Guided Media Technologies

Wired or guided media technologies used in industrial SCADA and power system SCADA are Copper UTP, Coaxial, Optical Fibber, Power Line Carrier Communication (PLCC) and Broadband over Power line (BPL). A brief description of these technologies are given below.

Copper UTP

Unshielded Twisted Pair (UTP) is a popular type of cable that consists of two unshielded wires twisted around each other which has been explained earlier in this chapter. Low cost make it attractive, and is used extensively for local-area networks (LANs) and telephone connections. UTP cabling does not offer as high bandwidth or good protection from interference when compared to coaxial or fibre optic cables, but easier to work with.

Optical Fiber

Fibber cables offer several advantages over traditional long-distance copper cabling. The bandwidth for an optical fibre which has the same thickness that of a copper cable is much higher. Fibber cables rated at 10 Gaps, 40 Gaps and even 100 Gaps are standard. As light can travel much longer distances in a fibre cable without attenuation, the need for signal boosters are less. Further fibre is less susceptible to interference. Traditional copper network cable requires shielding to protect it from electromagnetic interference. Though shielding helps to prevent interference, it is not always sufficient especially, when many cables are strung together in close proximity to each other. But fibre optic cables which are made up of glass or silica avoid most of these problems.

Fiber to the Home (FTTH)

Fibber to the Home (FTTH) broadband is one of the fine solutions for providing connectivity. FTTH broadband connections which are referred as fibre optic cable connections to individual houses. It can deliver a large number of digital information including voice, video, and data with more efficiently and economically than coaxial cable. FTTH depend on both active and passive optical networks to provide connectivity. FTTH technology is supposed that it is an apt standard which can provide connectivity without much web traffic congestion.

Hybrid Fiber Coax (HFC)

A hybrid fibre coaxial (HFC) network is a guided media technology where optical fibre cable and coaxial cable are used in different portions of a communication network to carry broadband information such as video, data, and voice. Using HFC, service providers install fibre optic cable as the backbone from the cable distribution centre to the serving nodes located close to customers. From these nodes using coaxial cables connections are provided to the customers. The main advantage of using HFC as backbone is that some of the features of fibre optic cable such as high bandwidth, improved noise immunity and interference susceptibility, etc. can be brought close to the customer premises without the replacement of the existing coaxial cable if it exists already.

Power Line Carrier Communication (PLCC)

Power-line carrier communication (PLCC) is a communication method that uses electrical wiring to simultaneously carry both data and electric power. Although many power utilities use this for longer distances to send data, it is very rarely used within the buildings. But recently PLCC is used to achieve load shedding in Advanced Metering Infrastructure (AMI). As it uses the existing power lines, there is no additional investment on cables and structural alterations to the building. It is an economical and a reliable technique to achieve bi-directional communications which is one of the prime requirements in Smart Grid.

Different PLCC technologies are required for different applications, ranging from home automation to internet access which is often called broadband over power lines (BPL). Most PLCC technologies limit themselves to one type of wire but some can cross between the distribution network and customer premises wiring. Typically transformers prevent propagating the signal, which requires multiple technologies to form very large networks. Various data rates and frequencies are used in different situations. But the main drawback is low bandwidth and point-to-point communication. Although long distance communication is possible, it poses significant challenges, especially in developing countries where the disturbances on transmission lines cause issues.

Broadband Over Power Line (BPL)

PLCC can be broadly grouped as narrow band PLCC and broadband PLCC, also known as low frequency and high frequency respectively. There are four basic forms of PLCC and they are:

1. Narrowband internal applications where home wiring is used for home automation and intercoms but with low bit rate,

2. Narrowband outdoor applications which are mainly used by the power distribution utilities for AMR,

3. Broadband in-house mains power wiring can be used for high speed data transmission for home networking, and

4. Broadband over Power Line which uses outdoor mains power wiring and can be used to provide broadband internet.

Broadband PLCC works at higher frequencies. High data rates (up to 100s of Mbps) is used in shorter-range applications. In fact BPL is a system to transmit two-way data over existing AC medium voltage electrical distribution wiring, between transformers, and AC low voltage wiring between transformer and customer outlets. This makes it suitable for indoor as well as outdoor applications. This avoids the expense of a dedicated network of wires for data communication, and the expense of maintaining a dedicated network of antennas, radios and routers in wireless network.

5.5 SCADA COMMUNICATION TECHNOLOGIES

SCADA communication technologies broadly classified into two viz. wired (guided) or wireless (unguided). They are briefly explained below.

Wireless or Unguided Media Technologies

Presently, the unguided or wireless technology has become the most thrilling area in communications and M2M networking. The advancement of wireless communication has revolutionized Industrial SCADA networks as well. Some of the wireless technologies which find applications in DCS and Smart Grid are Frequency Hopping Spread Spectrum (FHSS), 3G Cellular, WiFi, WiMax, ZigBee, ZWave, and VSAT which are briefly described below.

IEEE and Wireless Standards

Standards are developed so that many different vendors can create various products that will work together seamlessly. Standards are usually developed on a consensus basis among the different vendors in a specific industry. The Institute of Electrical and Electronics Engineers (IEEE) develops standards for a wide range of technologies and wireless being one of them.

The 802.11 standard outlines how wireless clients and Access Points communicate, lays out the specifications of their interface, dictates how signal transmission should take place, and describes how authentication, association, and security should be implemented. IEEE created several task groups to work on specific areas within wireless communications. Each group had its own focus and was required to investigate and develop standards for its specific section. The letter suffixes indicate the order in which they were proposed and accepted. As an example, one of the members of the 802.11 family which specifies WiFi is succinctly described below.

802.11b High Rate or WiFi is an extension to 802.11 which applies to wireless LANS and provides 11 Mbps transmission in the 2.4 GHz band. 802.11b uses only Direct Sequence Spread Spectrum (DSSS). 802.11b is ratification to the original 802.11 standard, allowing wireless functionality comparable to Ethernet.

Wireless LAN products are being developed following the stipulations of this 802.11i wireless standard. Customers should review the certification issued by the WiFi Alliance before buying wireless products as it assesses the systems against the 802.11i proposed standard.

4G Cellular

3G also follows the same pattern of G's which has been introduced in the early 1990's by the ITU. The pattern is actually a wireless initiative called the International Mobile Communications (2000IMT-2000). 3G therefore comes just after 2G and 2.9G, the second generation technologies.2G technologies include, the Global System for Mobile (GSM). 2.9G brings standards that are midway between 2G and 3G, including the General Packet Radio Service (GPRS), Enhanced Data rates for GSM Evolution (EDGE), Universal Mobile Telecommunications System (UMTS), etc. A characteristic Comparison of the various Gs are given in Table 5.2.

2G	3G	3.9G (3GPP)	4G
Higher bandwidth than 2G	voice and data are integrated	Higher data rates	IP packet switched network
Always on technology for e-mail	Packet switched technology,	Use of OFDMA technology.	Packet switched technology.

Table 5.2: Characteristic Comparison of the various Gs

This is a low cost solution to enable long-range communication both within the plant and from field to the MCC. It can be rolled out quickly using the existing cellular infrastructure. Most smart meters in future are expected to use this technology to communicate with the Meter Data Management Systems (MDMS). The constraint is, that it can become undependable if natural disaster strikes.

In DCS like Smart Grid, for remote monitoring and control solution, network coverage for a broad range of locations is necessary. In order to achieve coverage, the remote devices deployed are fitted with wireless modems that enabled communication on a range of frequencies and protocols. This allowed selection of either 2G EDGE, 3G HSPDPA, with a flexible architecture to accommodate Long-Term Evolution (LTE) when deployed by carriers.

WiFi

WiFi is a trademarked phrase for the open standards, is a popular wireless networking technology that uses radio waves to provide wireless high-speed Internet and network connections. One can attain bandwidth from 9 to 94mbs. The limited distance of 100 to 290m and poor reception in buildings are the main drawbacks. WiFi networks have no physical wired connection between sender and receiver as it uses radio frequency (RF) technology. RT being a member of the electromagnetic spectrum associated with radio wave propagation (2.9GHz for 802.11b or 11g, 9GHz for 802.11a). The RF current supplied to an antenna creates an electromagnetic field which makes radio waves to propagate through space. The cornerstone of any wireless network is an access point (AP). The primary job of an access point is to broadcast a wireless signal that computers can detect and tune into. In order to connect to an access point and join a wireless network, computers and devices must be equipped with wireless network adapters.

WiFi Alliance: WiFi is supported by many applications and devices including video game consoles, home networks, PDAs, mobile phones, major operating systems, and other types of consumer electronics. Any products that are tested and approved as *WiFi Certified* by the WiFi Alliance are certified as interoperable with each other, even if they are from different manufacturers. For example, a user with a WiFi Certified product can use any brand of access point with any other brand of client hardware that also is also WiFi Certified. Products that pass this certification are required to carry an identifying seal on their packaging that states WiFi Certified and indicates the radio frequency band used.

WiMax

WiMax (Worldwide Interoperability for Microwave Access) adheres to IEEE 802.16d communication standard. One can get up to 79 MBS bandwidth over 10 to 30 miles. This bandwidth is a savior when an environmental disaster strikes a densely populated area and all smart meters start communicating the outages at same time. WiMax can handle this increased traffic and because of this, WiMax can be an ideal backhaul medium for in-premise WiFi and ZigBee devices. Higher cost and poor market adoption are major constraints at the moment and is not a replacement for WiFi or wireless hotspot technologies. However, all-in-all, it can be cheaper to implement WiMax instead of standard wired hardware like with DSL.

WiMax equipment exists in two basic forms viz. base stations, installed by service providers to deploy the technology in a coverage area and the receivers are installed at client premises. WiMax is developed by an industry consortium, overseen by a group called the WiMax Forum, who certifies WiMax equipment to ensure that it meets technology specifications. Its technology is based on the IEEE 802.16 set of wide-area communications standards. Presently deployments of WiMax are in fixed locations, but a mobile version is under development.

WiMax can be installed faster than other internet technologies because it can use shorter towers and less cabling, supporting even non-line-of-sight (NLoS) coverage across an entire city or country. WiMax isn't just for fixed connections either, like at home. One can also subscribe to a WiMax service for his mobile devices since USB dongles, laptops and phones can have the technology built-in. In addition to internet access, WiMax can provide voice and video transferring capabilities as well as telephone access. Since WiMax transmitters can span a distance of several miles with data rates reaching up to 30-40 Megabits Per Second (Mbps), it's easy to see its advantages, especially in areas where wired internet is impossible or too costly to implement.

ZigBee

It is a low cost and low power technology and uses unlicensed spectrum which covers only short distance. ZigBee is gaining popular in the home energy market and multiple ZigBee enabled products are available in the market. ZigBee enables the smart meter to communicate with home appliances which helps to shed the load. ZigBee technology enables the coordination of communication among thousands of tiny sensors, which can be scattered throughout the offices, farms, factories, picking up information about the operations and process. They are designed to consume very little energy because it will be left in place for five to ten years and their batteries need to last. ZigBee devices communicate efficiently, passing data over radio waves from one to the other like a human chain. At the end of the line, the data can be dropped into a computer for analysis or picked up by another wireless technology like Wi-Fi or WiMax.

ZigBee is constituted of mesh technology and this makes it more robust. ZigBee alliance has come up to ensure interoperability among home appliances but the limited distance and inability to penetrate concrete walls are major constraints. Further the low power consumption limits transmission distances to 10–100 meters line-of –sight, depending on power output and environmental characteristics. ZigBee devices can transmit data over long distances by passing data through a mesh network of intermediate devices to reach more distant ones. ZigBee is typically used in low data rate applications that require long battery life and secure networking. ZigBee networks are secured by 128 bit symmetric encryption keys. ZigBee has a defined rate of 290 kbit/s, best suited for intermittent data transmissions from a sensor or input device. ZigBee is an ideal solution for Personnel Area Networks. However, ZigBee is not for situations with high mobility among nodes. Hence, it is not suitable for tactical ad hoc radio networks in the battlefield, where high data rate and high mobility is present and needed.

ZWave

ZWave is a low cost, low power RF signalling and control protocol used for communication among devices preferably in home area networks. It is developed by a private company named Zensys, Inc. a start-up company based in Denmark. It's technology is based on the concepts of ZigBee. However ZWave attempts to build simpler and less expensive devices than ZigBee. Presently, Zensys is acquired by Sigma Designs of Milpitas, Camay manufacturers make ZWave compatible products, mostly for the building automation and HVAC. ZWave operates at 908.42 MHz in the US and 868.42 MHz in Europe using a mesh networking topology. A ZWave network can contain up to 232 nodes, although reports exist of trouble with networks containing over 30-40 nodes. ZWave operates using a number of profiles, but the manufacturer claims they interoperate. One should be careful when selecting products as some products from certain manufacturers are not compatible with other manufacturers' products.

ZWave uses GFSK modulation with Manchester channel encoding. A network controller, at the center monitors and controls the ZWave network. Each product in the home must be included to the ZWave network before it can be controlled via ZWave. Each ZWave network is identified by a Network ID and each device is further identified by a Node ID. The Network ID is the common identification of all nodes belonging to one logical ZWave network. Network ID has a length of four bytes and is assigned to each device by the primary controller when the device is added into the network. Nodes with different Network ID's cannot communicate with each other. The Node ID is the address of the device/node existing within network. The Node ID has a length of one byte. ZWave uses a source-routed mesh network topology and has central controller. Devices can communicate to one another by using intermediate nodes to route around and circumvent household obstacles or radio dead spots that might occur though a message called healing. A ZWave network can consist of up to 232 devices with the option of bridging networks if more devices are required.

ZWave Alliance: The ZWave Alliance was established as a consortium of companies that make connected appliances controlled through apps on smart phones, tablets or computers using ZWave wireless mesh networking technology. The alliance is a formal association focused on both the expansion of ZWave and the continued interoperability of any device that utilizes ZWave.

ZWave Security: Recently, ZWave Alliance announced stronger security standards for devices receiving ZWave Certification. The security standards are known as Security 2 (S2), it provides advanced security for devices to be connected to ZWave gateways and hubs. Encryption standards for transmissions between nodes, and mandates new pairing procedures for each device, with unique PIN on each device are established. The new layer of authentication is intended to prevent hackers from taking control of unsecured or poorly secured devices.

VSAT

This is widely used today for remote monitoring and control of transmission and distribution substations. It is a proven technology for quick implementation but relatively expensive. Major disadvantage is that severe weather will impacts its reliability. VSAT systems provide high speed, broadband satellite communications for Internet or private network communications. VSAT is ideal for remote monitoring and control such as off-shore wind farms, mining industry, vessels at sea, oil and gas camps or any application that requires a broadband Internet connection at a remote location.

Technically, a VSAT is a two-way satellite ground station with a dish antenna that is smaller than 3.8 meters. The majority of VSAT antennas range from 79cm to 1.2m. Data rates, usually, range from 4 Kbit/s up to 16 Mbit/s. VSATs access satellites in geosynchronous orbit or geostationary orbit to relay data from small remote Earth stations to other stations in mesh topology or master Earth station *hubs* in star topology. VSATs can be used to transmit both narrowband data and broadband data. It also uses portable, phased array antennas or mobile communication infrastructures.

5.6 SECURITY IN WIRELESS COMMUNICATIONS

Wireless communication is a rapidly expanding field of technologies for networking, connectivity, communication, and data exchange. There are literally thousands of protocols, standards, and techniques that can be labelled as wireless. These include cell phones, Bluetooth, cordless phones, and wireless networking. As wireless technologies continue to proliferate, the organization's security efforts must go beyond locking down its local network. Security should be an end-to-end solution that addresses all forms, methods, and techniques of communication. While managing network security with filtering devices such as firewalls and proxies is important, one must not overlook the need for endpoint security. Endpoints are the ends of a network communication link. One end is often at a server where a resource resides, and the other end is often a client making a request to use a network resource. Even with secured communication protocols, it is still possible for abuse, misuse, oversight, or malicious action to occur across the network because it originated at an endpoint. All aspects of security from one end to the other, often called *end-to-end security*, must be addressed. Any unsecured point will be discovered eventually and abused. Endpoint security is the security concept that encourages administrators to install firewalls, malware scanners, and an IDS on every host.

Endpoint Threat Detection and Response (ETDR)

Endpoint security is the concept that each individual device must maintain local security whether or not its network or telecommunications channels also provide or offer security./in a modest way it can be referred as the protection of an organisation's network when accessed via remote devices such as laptops or other wireless or mobile devices. Sometimes this is expressed as the end device is responsible for its own security. However, a clearer perspective is that any weakness in a network, whether on the border, on a server, or on a client, presents a risk to all elements within the organization. Traditional security has depended on the network border sentries, such as appliance firewalls, proxies, centralized virus scanners, and even IDS/IPS/IDP solutions, to provide security for all of the interior nodes of a network. This is no longer considered best business practice because threats exist from within as well as without. A network is only as secure as its weakest element. Lack of internal security is even more problematic when remote access services, including dial-up, wireless, and VPN, might allow an external entity (authorized or not) to gain access to the private network without having to go through the border security gauntlet. Endpoint security should therefore be viewed as an aspect of the effort to provide sufficient security on each individual host. Every system should have an appropriate combination of a local host firewall, antimalware scanners, authentication, authorization, auditing, spam filters, and IDS/IPS services.

Endpoint Threat Detection and Response(ETDR) mainly focuses on the endpoint as opposed to the network, threats as opposed to only malware, and officially declares incident and collection of tools primary usage for both detection and incident response.

Transparency

Just as the name implies, transparency is the characteristic of a service, security control, or access mechanism that ensures that it is unseen by users. Transparency is often a desirable feature for security controls. The more transparent a security mechanism is, the less likely a user will be able to circumvent it or even be aware that it exists. With transparency, there is a lack of direct evidence that a feature, service, or restriction exists, and its impact on performance is minimal. In some cases, transparency may need to function more as a configurable feature than as a permanent aspect of operation, such as when an administrator is troubleshooting, evaluating, or tuning a system's configurations. A security boundary can be the division between one secured area and another secured area, or it can be the division between a secured area and an unsecured area. Both must be addressed in a security policy.

Redundancy

In order to make the SCADA most reliable, it is necessary to have redundancy built into the industrial SCADA. Satellite Communications do not only provide a feasible means for distributed SCADA communication but also for redundancy for SCADA as a whole. Given the rate at which the cost for satellite communications is dropping and the available bandwidth is increasing, satellite communications infrastructure can be deployed along with conventional broadband technologies which are used in urban areas. Also, given the fact that satellite communications may not be used most of the time in urban areas, except for times when the main infrastructure goes down, the cost for satellite communications infrastructure for Smart Grid may drop further.

Satellite communications can be used to provide redundancy in SCADA especially when employed in PSS. One of the advantages is that it do not require much terrestrial equipment. The only equipment required to establish communications are the VSATs and modems. The main advantage of employing the satellite communication is that even during the adverse weather conditions or disasters like floods, systems like cable and WiFi fail because of wires or repeaters being knocked down, satellite communications would still continue to function. This is especially important since utilities might need to know the field conditions of the distributed pant/process during such times, to find faults or problems in the industry and fix the solutions.

VSATs can be run on backup batteries, if the main source of its power goes down and still continue to relay information to the utilities. In this respect satellite communications is the only technology that can efficiently deliver the results during times of disasters and rough weather conditions. One of the fears in the past has been satellite communications connectivity during thick cloud cover or during rains and snow.

5.7 VPN AND MPLS IN CII

Power system automation is a typical example of DCS spanning across a large geographical area in which secure communication is very important. Many utilities do not have their own full-fledged communication network such as optical, copper, or PLCC connectivity to link all remote sites within the automation network. In *such* cases MPLS/VPN is an ideal solution if implemented properly.

A Virtual Private Network (VPN) is a secure, private connection through an untrusted network such as the internet normally established between a client device and a server device. It is considered as a private connection in a public network or in an untrusted network because the encryption and tunneling protocols are used to ensure the confidentiality and integrity of the data in transit. It is important to remember that VPN technology requires a tunnel to work and it assumes encryption.

This is very much useful for establishing secured remote accessing/ connectivity in Smart Grid. Here normally, a VPN client might be a Remote Terminal Unit (RTU) and the VPN server might be a server in the critical control network. Typically the client is the one that initiates the connection, and the server accepts and authenticates incoming connection requests from one or more clients. Once a VPN connection is established between a client and a server, the networks upstream of the client and the server are connected together such that network traffic may pass between them.

In the case of the RTU client as aforementioned, the RTU would appear as if it was actually plugged into the network upstream of the VPN server. As such, it would receive a new virtual IP address suitable for local network and could access other devices just as if it was directly connected to the network. When using VPNs, it's critical to remember that the VPN only secures the tunnel and not the client or server. To ensure network security, it's critical that the VPN is seamlessly integrated into a suitable firewall.

During exigent situations, remote VPN access provides secured way of maintaining the operational continuity and support. Remote VPN access permits bulk power organizations to keep personnel away from sites during dangerous weather conditions. This reduction of travel risks during such conditions permits the power utilities to protect some of their skilled manpower, the most critical assets. Remote VPN access allows bulk power organizations to limit the number of personnel at their facilities during periods of heightened physical security threats.

During increased security risks, bulk power utilities should limit the number of personnel entering their facilities with greater scrutiny screening. This helps in reduction of operational staffs at risk to a physical attack on the facility.

VPN Architecture

For many years the de facto standard VPN software was Point-To-Point Tunnelling Protocol (PPTP), which was made most popular when Microsoft included it in its Windows products. Since most internet-based communication first started over telecommunication links, the industry needed a way to secure PPP connections. The original goal of PPTP was to provide a way to tunnel PPP connections through an IP network, but most implementations included security features also since protection was becoming an important requirement for network transmissions at that time.

The two methods of VPN architecture today used are site-to-site VPN and remote user access VPN. Both these architecture helps the organization to replace long distance dial-up or leased line with local dial-ups or leased line to Internet Service Provider (ISP).

Security Issues of VPN

The advantage of using secure remote access sometimes makes the network susceptible to security breaches. The possibility of accessing enterprises network with laptops having unsecured External Access Points (EAP) cannot be ruled out. If the laptop device or a device connected to the EAP has a virus or some other malicious software, it can spread it to the enterprises network.

Though a properly installed VPN can prevent some of the performance issues associated with supporting multiple protocols and data transmission mediums, VPNs are only as fast as the slowest internet connection between the two endpoints. In addition, most IP applications were designed for low-latency and high reliability network environments. This means that network performance issues will become more pronounced with the increasing use of real-time and interactive applications. While some applications can be reprogrammed or reconfigured to work with increased latency, getting this workaround to work with some applications can be challenging, if not impossible.

Multi-Protocol Label Switching (MPLS)

Multi-Protocol Label Switching (MPLS) was originally presented as a way of improving the forwarding speed of routers based on short path labels rather than longer network addresses but is now emerging as a crucial standard technology that offers new capabilities for large scale IP networks. Directing the data from one network node to the next based on short path labels rather than long network addresses, avoids complex lookups in a routing table. This technique saves significant time over traditional IP-based routing processes. In fact, MPLS is a protocol for speeding up and shaping network traffic flows. Furthermore, MPLS is designed to handle a wide range of protocols through encapsulation. Thus, the network is not limited to TCP/IP and compatible protocols. This enables the use of many other networking technologies, including T1/E1, ATM, Frame Relay, SONET, and DSL. MPLS got its name because it works with the internet Protocol (IP), Asynchronous Transfer Mode (ATM) and Frame Relay network protocols. Any of these protocols can be used to create a Label Switched Paths (LSPs). It was created initially to save router's idling time by avoiding stop and look up routing tables. A common misconception is that MPLS is only used on private networks, but the protocol is used for all service provider networks including internet backbones. Today, Generalized Multi Protocol Label Switching (GMPLS) extends MPLS to manage Time Division Multiplexing (TDM), Lambda Switching and other classes of switching technologies beyond packet switching.

MPLS allows most packets to be forwarded at Layer 2 (the switching level) rather than having to be passed up to Layer 3 (the routing level). Each packet gets labelled on entry into the service provider's network by the ingress router. The label determines the pre-determined path LSP which the packet has to follow. LSPs, allow service providers to decide the best way for certain types of traffic to flow within a private or public network ahead of time. All the subsequent routing switches perform packet forwarding based only on those labels. These labels never look the IP header until they are badly required. Finally, the egress router removes the labels and forwards the original IP packet towards its final destination.

Service providers can use MPLS to improve Quality of Service (QoS) by defining LSPs that can meet specific Service Level Agreements (SLAs) on traffic latency, jitter, packet loss and downtime. For example, a network might have three service levels and they are,

1. level for voice,

2. level for time sensitive traffic, and

3. level for best effort traffic.

MPLS also supports traffic separation and the creation of virtual private networks (VPNs), Virtual Private LAN Services (VPLS) and Virtual Leased Lines (VLLs).

Choosing MPLS VPN Services

While choosing MPLS VPN service for an utility, one must be clearly aware of the requirements, network design and options of service providers. It is better to keep the following points in mind while selecting the MPLS VPN.

1. Carefully evaluate the needs and optimized requirements,

2. Gather the service providers offers in the near geographic area,

3. Compare between the requirements and options of service providers, which matches the best to the requirements of the utility, and

4. Recommendations from an experienced consultant is always better particularly, when the utility is selecting the MPLS services for the first time.

In many cases, finding the best MPLS VPN service need to combine multiple services. For example, many enterprises use Layer 3 MPLS VPNs for smaller sites, pseudo wires for point-to-point links between data centers and Virtual Private LAN Service (VPLS) for sites that need high availability to control convergence speed and routing protocol behaviour. If the customer is planning for an MPLS VPN connectivity, it would be better to consider the following points, while finalizing the vendor evaluation.

1. *Internet access:* Most vendors allow customer to connect their MPLS VPN directly to the internet through a shared network firewall. However, some of them restrict the outbound traffic, while others allow establishing an IPSec tunnel to the network firewall and then hopping into customer's network. Still others allow inbound access through an encapsulated GRE tunnel that dumps off in front of another firewall in control, and

2. *The full mesh:* While MPLS technology typically facilitates a full mesh of connectivity among all of the customer's sites, this requires a single MPLS network. Some service providers have split their MPLS networks into geographic regions, and customer has to pay more to get connectivity from one region to another. Without this, traffic from one location to another may be forced through a third site acting as a hub. This can unnecessarily complicate the routing and make it inefficient.

Keep the point in mind that MPLS VPNs are not encrypted, rather they logically separate the customer data from other customer's data. The data shares the same physical path with other customers of the service provider, just like Frame Relay or any other WAN. Some vendors may offer additional services that allow the customer to encrypt their traffic. In fact, the customer may want to explore the possibility of using their existing IPSec VPN equipment to create permanent tunnels between sites over a new high speed MPLS backbone to get the best of both worlds.

Advantages and Disadvantages of MPLS VPNS

The main advantages of MPLS VPN are briefly described below.

Many MPLS VPNs offer more cost effective price points with more flexibility than other WAN technologies. The label switching technology offers Class of Service (CoS) and Quality of Service (QoS) capabilities. As an encapsulation and VPN mechanism, MPLS brings many benefits to the IP networks which are described below.

1. *Faster packet processing with MPLS when compared to IP:* MPLS was designed to provide faster packet processing when compared to IP based lookup. As MPLS works with label switching operation

instead of IP destination based lookup, it provides faster processing and provides performance benefit.

2. *Border Gateway Protocol (BGP) Free Core with MPLS:* If BGP is running on a network, without MPLS, it needs to run on every device on the path. MPLS eliminates this need which reduces the requirements of protocols, making the network simpler and easy to maintain.

3. *Hiding service specific information from the core of the network:* When MPLS is used on the network, only the edge devices has to keep the customer specific information such as MAC address, VLAN number, IP address, etc. Core of the network only provides reachability between the edges.

4. *Improve scalability:* Does not have service specific information on the core of the network which provides better scalability. From the point of view of CPU and memory utilization and with the routing protocol updates, link state changes and many other problems become immaterial from the core of the network by using MPLS.

5. *MPLS Layer 2 and Layer 3 VPNs:* Probably the most important reason and main benefit of MPLS is MPLS VPNs. MPLS is most suitable to create point-to-point, point-to-multipoint and multipoint-to-multipoint type of MPLS layer 2 VPN and MPLS layer 3 VPNs. By using BGP, LDP or RSVP protocols, VPNs can be created.

6. *Traffic Engineering:* MPLS with the Resource Reservation Protocol – Traffic Engineering (RSVP-TE) Provides traffic engineering capability which allows better capacity usage and guaranteed SLA for the desired service.

   a. *Fast Reroute:* With RSVP-TE, MPLS provides MPLS Traffic Engineering Fast Reroute Link and Node Protection. RSVP-TE is one of the options but possible with Label Distribution Protocol (LDP), Loop Free Alternate (LFA) and Remote LFA. This can be setup if RSVP-TE is not used in the network. MPLS Traffic Engineering Fast Reroute can protect the important service in any kind of topology. On the other hand,

IP Fast Reroute (IP FRR) mechanisms require highly meshed topology to provide full coverage in the case of failures.

b. MPLS doesn't bring security by default. If security is needed then IPSec should run on top of MPLS. MPLS is used mainly for the Wide Area Network (WAN).

Though MPLS VPN offers many advantages, it has certain disadvantages and the communication engineer or power system engineer should be aware of these drawbacks while opting for MPLS/VPN connectivity. With MPLS VPN, service providers run the core of user's network, which presents several disadvantages which are described below.

- User routing protocol choice might be limited,

- User's end-to-end convergence is controlled primarily by the service provider,

- The reliability of user's L3 MPLS VPN is influenced by the service provider's competence level,

- Deciding to use MPLS VPN services from a particular service provider also creates a very significant lock-in. It's hard to change the provider when it's operating user's network core, and

- An additional layer is added and the router has to understand MPLS.

Summary

This chapter has focused on various communication aspects of the industrial SCADA with an emphasis on DCS and Smart Grid. It begin with discussing various types of transmission technology in very modest way so that it is very apt and most essential for an automation engineer who engaged in the design and implementation of SCADA and Smart Grid. The chapter then discusses the guided and unguided media used today for communication in such a manner that it is very useful for a practicing communication professional, which includes the various cabling issues as well. The various but most relevant communication technologies which find space not only in industrial SCADA but also in other smart automation technologies today are discussed comprehensively. Finally the chapter focused on the security issues of the wireless communication technology.

Risk Assessment in CII

6.1 INTRODUCTION

Strong security requires a proper assessment of vulnerabilities and risk, which in turn requires that security analysts think like an attacker. This chapter provides a high-level overview of common attack methodologies, and how industrial networks present a unique attack surface with common attack vectors to many critical areas. Chapter begins with different risk assessment methods, then move onto ICS risk analysis especially follows in critical infrastructure sectors across the world. This chapter also discusses penetration testing and patch management strategies.

6.2 COMMON ATTACK SURFACES ON CII

Many review reports reveals that the following vectors are the most prevalent presently for cyber-attacks on ICS.

➢ Weak authentication,

➢ Network scanning/probing,

➢ Removable media,

➢ Brute force intrusion,

➢ Abuse of access authority,

➢ Spear phishing, and

➢ Structured Query Language (SQL) injection.

Risk management is mainly the responsibility of the top management in every organisation. It is their duty to initiate and support risk analysis and assessment by defining the scope and purpose of the effort. The actual processes of performing risk analysis are often delegated to security professionals or to an evaluation team. However, all risk assessments, results, decisions, and outcomes must be understood and approved by the top level management as an element in providing prudent due care. All cyber assets and systems have risk and there is no way to eliminate the risk completely. Instead, top management must decide which risks are acceptable and which are not acceptable. A detailed risk assessment is required to identify to comprehend and determine the risks which are acceptable and which are not acceptable.

There are two risk assessment methodologies viz. quantitative and qualitative assessment. In q*uantitative risk analysis, the loss of an asset will be calculated in terms money value. In qualitative risk analysis* the loss of an asset is calculated subjective. Both methods are necessary for a complete risk analysis. Most organisations employ a hybrid of both risk assessment methodologies in order to obtain a sensible assessment of the security concerns.

The words *vulnerability, threat, risk, and exposure* are often interchanged, even though they have different meanings. It is important to understand each word's definition and the relationships between the concepts they represent. Hence the important terminology for risk assessment are briefly described below.

Vulnerability: A vulnerability is a lack of a countermeasure or a weakness in a countermeasure that is in place. It can be a software, hardware, procedural, or human weakness that can be exploited. A vulnerability may be a service running on a server, unpatched applications or operating systems, an unrestricted wireless access point, an open port on a firewall, lax physical security that allows anyone to enter a server room, or unenforced password management on servers and workstations.

Threat: A threat is any potential danger that is associated with the exploitation of a vulnerability. The threat is that someone, or something, will identify a specific vulnerability and use it against the company or individual. The entity that takes advantage of a vulnerability is referred to as a *threat agent*. A threat agent could be an intruder accessing the network through a port on the firewall, a process accessing data in a way that violates the security policy, a tornado wiping out a facility, or an employee making an unintentional mistake that could expose confidential information.

Risk: A risk is the likelihood of a threat agent exploiting a vulnerability and the corresponding business impact. If a firewall has several ports open, there is a higher likelihood that an intruder will use one to access the network in an unauthorized method. If users are not educated on processes and procedures, there is a higher likelihood that an employee will make an unintentional mistake that may destroy data. If an intrusion detection system (IDS) is not implemented on a network, there is a higher likelihood an attack will go unnoticed until it is too late. Risk ties the vulnerability, threat, and likelihood of exploitation to the resulting business impact.

Exposure: An exposure is an instance of being exposed to losses. A vulnerability exposes an organization to possible damages. If password management is lax and password rules are not enforced, the company is exposed to the possibility of having users' passwords captured and used in an unauthorized manner. If a company does not have its wiring inspected and does not put proactive fire prevention steps into place, it exposes itself to potentially devastating fires.

Control: A control, or countermeasure, is put into place to mitigate (reduce) the potential risk. A countermeasure may be a software configuration, a hardware device, or a procedure that eliminates a vulnerability or that reduces the likelihood a threat agent will be able to exploit a vulnerability. Examples of countermeasures include strong password management, firewalls, a security guard, access control mechanisms, encryption, and security-awareness training.

Safeguards: A *safeguard*, or *countermeasure*, is anything that removes or reduces a vulnerability or protects against one or more specific threats. A safeguard can be installing a software patch, making a configuration change, hiring security guards, altering the infrastructure, modifying processes, improving the security policy, training personnel more effectively, electrifying a perimeter fence, and installing lights, and so on. It is any action or product that reduces risk through the elimination or lessening of a threat or a vulnerability anywhere within an organization. Safeguards are the only means by which risk is mitigated or removed. It is important to remember that a safeguard, security control, or countermeasure need not involve the purchase of a new product; reconfiguring existing elements and even removing elements from the infrastructure are also valid safeguards.

Attack: An attack is the exploitation of a vulnerability by a threat agent. In other words, an attack is any intentional attempt to exploit a vulnerability of an organization's security infrastructure to cause damage, loss, or disclosure of assets. An attack can also be viewed as any violation or failure to adhere to an organization's security policy.

Breach: A breach is the occurrence of a security mechanism being bypassed or thwarted by a threat agent. When a breach is combined with an attack, a penetration, or intrusion, can result. A penetration is the condition in which a threat agent has gained access to an organization's infrastructure through the circumvention of security controls and is able to directly imperil assets.

Exposure Factor: The *exposure factor (EF)* represents the percentage of loss that an organization would experience if a specific asset were violated by a realized risk. The EF can also be called the *loss potential.* In most cases, a realized risk does not result in the total loss of an asset. The EF simply indicates the expected overall asset value loss because of a single realized risk. The EF is usually small for assets that are easily replaceable, such as hardware. It can be very large for assets that are irreplaceable or proprietary, such as product designs or a database of customers. The EF is expressed as a percentage.

6.3 TARGETING INDUSTRIAL NETWORKS

While the basic hacking methods such as *Reconnaissance, Scanning, Enumeration, Disruption, Infection and Persistence* apply to industrial networks but need additional considerations at all stages of an attack when targeting a control system. Industrial control systems, because they utilize specialized systems and protocols, present new opportunities to an attacker. In addition, industrial enterprise network hacking methods remain available, OT networks present a greater overall attack surface, which is an advantage to an attacker.

Industrial networks can be difficult to attack if properly air gapped. The establishment of secure zone or zones and a clear definition between enterprise, supervisory, and operation systems provides extra layers that an attacker must penetrate before reaching the most critical and the most vulnerable field equipments. Once the attacker has penetrated the zones, they must discover the continued path into the control system. Finally, in addition to normal user accounts and authentications, there are device Master/Slave relationships that can be discovered and manipulated to gain *authenticated* access to control system assets. In other words, there are specific Reconnaissance, Scanning and Enumeration techniques to Supervisory Control and Data Acquisition (SCADA) and distributed control systems (DCS) environments.

6.4 VULNERABILITY ASSESSMENTS (VA)

A vulnerability assessment is the process of defining, identifying, classifying and prioritizing vulnerabilities in computer systems, applications and network infrastructure. It is one of the very important testing tools of cyber security professional. Vulnerability scans and penetration tests provide a perspective on the flaws in technical control of a system or applications to a cyber-security professional.

Scanning Industrial Networks

A network scan can identify hosts as well as the ports and services those hosts are using. In industrial networks, network scanning works almost the same way. The results of the scan can quickly identify SCADA and DCS communications, allowing the attacker to focus on these items. For instance, a device found using port 502 is known to be using Modbus/TCP and is therefore very likely an HMI system or some supervisory workstation that is communicating with the HMI.

Port	Service
102	ICCP
502	Modbus TCP
530	RPC
593	HTTP RPC

Continued...

2222	Ethernet/IP
4840	OPC UA
4843	OPC UA over TLS/SSL
19,999	DNP-Sec
20,000	DNP3
34,962–34,964	Profnet
34,980	EtherCAT
44,818	Ethernet/IP

Table 6.1: SCADA communication ports

The following are TCP ports are also useful in interpreting port scan results.

Port	Services
21	FTP
22	SSH
23	Telnet
25	SMTP
53	DNS
80	HTTP
110	POP3
123	NTP
443	HTTPS
1433	Microsoft SQL Server
1521	Oracle
1723	PPTP
3389	RDP

Table 6.2: Important TCP ports

In general, there are three types of scanning re performed in an industrial network viz. Network Discovery Scanning, Network Vulnerability Scanning and Web Vulnerability Scanning. Assessing vulnerabilities and documenting them is a compliance requirement of many security standards especially NERC CIP-007.

Network Discovery Scanning

It is a scanning technique used to scan a range of IP addresses, searching for open network ports of a system. Network discovery scanners provide a report showing the systems detected on a network and the list of ports that are exposed through the network and server firewalls that present on the network path between the scanner and the scanned system.

> ➤ **TCP Connect Scanning:** A TCP connect scan is performed by establishing a full TCP connection with each scanned port on a remote host. This specific recipe demonstrates how we can use Nmap to perform a TCP connect scan. Opens a full connection to the remote system on the specified port. This scan type is used when the user running the scan does not have the necessary permissions to run a half-open scan.

> ➤ **TCP ACK Scanning:** Sends a packet with the ACK flag set, indicating that it is part of an open connection.

> ➤ **Xmas Scanning** Xmas scans derive their name from the set of flags that are turned on within a packet. These scans are designed to manipulate the PSH, URG and FIN flags of the TCP header. So in other words, the Xmas scan in order to identify listening ports on a targeted system will send a specific packet.

The most common tool used for network discovery scanning is an open source tool called Nmap.

Network Vulnerability Scanning

Network vulnerability scans go deeper than discovery scans. They don't stop with detecting open ports but continue on to probe a targeted system or network for the presence of known vulnerabilities. These tools contain databases of thousands of known vulnerabilities, along with tests they can perform to identify whether a system is susceptible to each vulnerability in the system's database. When the scanner tests a system for vulnerabilities, it uses the tests in its database to determine whether a system may contain the vulnerability. In some cases, the scanner may not have enough information to conclusively determine that a vulnerability exists and it reports a vulnerability when there really is no problem. This situation is known as a *false positive* report and is sometimes seen as a nuisance to system administrators. Far more dangerous is when the vulnerability scanner misses a vulnerability and fails to alert the administrator to the presence of a dangerous situation. This error is known as a *false negative* report.

Web Vulnerability Scanning

Web applications pose significant risk to enterprise security. By their nature, the servers running many web applications must expose services to Internet users. Firewalls and other security devices typically contain rules allowing web traffic to pass through to web servers unfettered. The applications running on web servers are complex and often have privileged access to underlying databases. Attackers often try to exploit these circumstances using SQL injection and other attacks that target flaws in the security design of web applications.

Known vulnerabilities play an important role in any security testing program because they may discover flaws not visible to network vulnerability scanners. When an administrator runs a web application scan, the tool probes the web application using automated techniques that manipulate inputs and other parameters to identify web vulnerabilities. The tool then provides a report of its findings, often including suggested vulnerability remediation techniques.

Web vulnerability scans are an important component of an organization's security assessment and testing program. It's a good practice to run scans in the following circumstances.

➢ Scan all applications when you begin performing web vulnerability scanning for the first time. This will detect issues with legacy applications.

➢ Scan any new application before moving it into a production environment for the first time.

➢ Scan any modified application before the code changes move into production. Scan all applications on a recurring basis.

Limited resources may require scheduling these scans based on the priority of the application. For example, you may wish to scan web applications that interact with sensitive information more often than those that do not.

One must be cautious when scanning ICS networks, because many industrial network protocols are extremely sensitive to latency and latency variation, a hard scan could actually cause the industrial network to fail. It is easy enough to scan through a firewall, meaning that if real-time protocols are only protected by a firewall, they are highly prone to DOS attacks using very basic hacking techniques.

When scanning an active control system, safe scan methods should always be used. If manual control of the system is possible, personnel capable of performing manual control must be present during the security testing. Ideally, a test system will be available for hard testing in a non-production environment. If possible, build out a test system, or plan to perform hard tests against production systems during scheduled maintenance windows or other periods of downtime. Ideally, a test system will be available for hard testing in a non-production environment.

Modern industrial networks consist of clearly defined security zones but legacy systems have overlapping or poorly defined security zones. Knowing where to perform a scan is as important as knowing how to perform a scan. A rule of thumb is whenever attempting to functionally isolate a group of devices or services, first quantify that group into a defined zone logically. Then perform a penetration test against it. This requires first scanning the network immediately outside of the zone, as well as scanning from within the zone to ensure that there are no outbound vulnerabilities.

In a network that contains nested security zones, some zones may not be immediately vulnerable from every other zone. It may not be possible to exploit an RTU directly from the Internet. But once enterprise network and the SCADA DMZ is breached, there may be new vulnerabilities present to compromise an RTU. Hence in a zone based ICS of a CI, before starting a VA, it will be anyway better to carry out a penetration test from the outermost entry points such as an Internet firewall or a VPN gateway. Then move into the next in zone and perform another penetration test assuming that the first line of defense has been compromised. This helps to detect all addressable vulnerabilities within nested zones and helps to identify ports and services that are in use so that secure communications policies can be implemented wherever possible.

For instance, in a control system zone that utilizes Modbus TCP, port 502 will be open to support this protocol. To protect that traffic, port 502 should be filtered in the next outermost zone (in this example, it is perhaps the SCADA DMZ), if possible. In our example, the SCADA DMZ probably requires Modbus TCP connections as well, and so port 502 should be filtered at the outer boundary of the DMZ instead. In this way, the protocol is *disjointed*, meaning there is no single path from the Internet to the control system over port 502.

6.5 VULNERABILITY MANAGEMENT

Once a vulnerability has been identified, it needs to be eliminated. Depending upon the nature of the vulnerability, it may be addressable via a software patch or a configuration adjustment, or it may need to be removed. If the vulnerability is not addressable via a patch or configuration change, the vulnerable service should be removed. This may be easy or difficult depending upon the criticality of the vulnerable system.

Patch Management

NIST identifies patch management as the *process for identifying, acquiring, installing, and verifying patches for products and systems*, while NERC CIP-007-5 R2.1 states Responsible Entities for High and Medium impact BES Cyber Systems are required to implement a *process for tracking, evaluating, and installing cyber security patches for applicable Cyber Assets*. In fact patch management is an act *or practice of detecting, assessing, acquiring, validating, deploying and tracking updates to software in order to mitigate a security vulnerability.* According to NERC CIP-007-5 R2.2 an organization must, at least once every 35 calendar days, evaluate security patches for applicability that have been released since the last evaluation from the source or sources.

Proper tracking of software updates from availability through applicability, acquisition, validation and deployment allows an organization to maintain full visibility of patch management and enables other management processes such as asset management, configuration management, and vulnerability management to succeed. Missteps during the patch management lifecycle can snowball into noncompliance and lead to vulnerable systems and unexpected downtime.

The most secure and effective method of obtaining and applying a software patch is through the use of a dedicated patch management system. Because this system will be responsible for connecting to the Internet and downloading unverified software, it should be treated with caution and carefully isolated from other systems. According to NIST SP 800-40, creating a Patch and Vulnerability Management Program, the following risks may be introduced when obtaining patches through a commercial patch management system. The software vendor's patch might have been corrupted or infected with malware, either prior to distribution or during the distribution process. The patch management system could become infected, compromising all subsequently obtained patches. The patch management tool could be used by an attacker as centralized attack vector to industrial systems, leveraging the patch distribution capabilities. The patch management system could be used by an attacker to identify participating systems, as well as which patches have/have not been applied to participating systems. Once breached, the patch management software could be used to elevate privileges of participating systems, gain administrative access to participating systems.

Configuration Management

Configuration management is a process for maintaining computer systems, servers, and software in a desired, consistent state. It's a way to make sure that a system performs as it's expected to as changes are made over time. In fact it is to maintain systems in a desired state.

The logic is simple: any change could introduce risk, so once a system has been appropriately patched and configured, that system should not be changed. If a new vulnerability is found, the configuration management process allows a new configuration to be validated, at which point systems are reassessed against the new valid configuration. Configuration management helps users and administrators know where certain services exist and what the current state of applications are. Proper configuration management tools are:

- Classify and manage systems by groups and subgroups.
- Centrally modify base configurations.
- Roll out new settings to all applicable systems.
- Automate system identification, patches, and updates
- Identify outdated, poor performing, and noncompliant configurations.
- Prioritize actions.
- Access and apply prescriptive remediation.

With configuration management, you can accurately replicate an environment with the correct configurations and software because you know what exists in the original environment. Traditionally, this was handled manually or with custom scripting by system administrators. Today softwares are available to configuration management in order to reduce cost, complexity, and errors.

Device Removal and Quarantine

When a vulnerability cannot be remediated via patch or configuration management, the vulnerable system should be removed. If the service is critical, and there is no viable and secure replacement, the only alternative is completely isolate that vulnerability. Quarantining a service based upon enforced policies requires that all access to the vulnerable service is cut off from any non-essential communications, with all essential communications being encrypted for further protection.

6.6 RISK ASSESSMENT

Vulnerability assessments are different from risk assessments as vulnerability assessments just find the vulnerabilities (the holes) while a risk assessment calculates the probability of the vulnerabilities being exploited and the associated business impact. Asset identification, system characterization, mapping the network, vulnerability identification, threat modelling and Mitigation Strategies are the major steps in risk assessment. They are briefly described below.

Asset Identification

Asset identification is particularly intended to decide the potential targets of the attackers in an ICS and identify the weaknesses and the attack vectors to that target which allow the attackers to launch the successful attack. Asset identification involve System Characterization, Vulnerability Identification, and Threat Modelling.

Identification of Critical Information Infrastructure

This is one of the most important and preliminary responsibility in risk assessment process. Identification of cyber assets and critical cyber assets have been described in subsequent chapters.

System Characterization

Many methods are used to gather information about a system such as Physical surveillance, public domain information aggregation, scanning, etc. Physical characterization methods can range from simply observing the facility to entering the facility and carrying out a tour secretly posing as a vendor or maintenance person. This helps a security professional to gather amazing information about the ICS. Tours can provide a huge information, including how well an organization has physically protected, information about the control systems at a site and how well the organization protects them, etc. Electronic asset discovery methods can range from simply collecting and aggregating using freely available tools to fingerprint systems. It is very important to gather information regarding the spear-phishing targets and possibilities when a plant or office is unattended. The device-specific intelligence, and air gaped systems in the organization must be specially identified. Threat actors can easily obtain IP address ranges through domain registry searches. Crafting an Internet query designed to return an error message can also yield information about the system (for example, database errors often indicate that someone is using the database). Free tools, such as Nmap (Network Mapper), can be used to gather about devices, ports, protocols, and services which are open; whether a firewall is in place, what type of firewall is in use and the location of the network where it is kept.

Mapping the Network

Thoroughly verify the industrial network and prepare the present network diagram with all IP addresses, active services, firewall rules, etc. This help the security professional to understand the present data flow and the configurations in detail. Make sure that the network diagram is updated with the changes made.

Vulnerability Identification

Vulnerability assessment has been discussed in detail in section 6.4 of this chapter.

Threat Modelling

Threat modelling starts with combining information of threat sources and threat vectors to create possible threat events to exploit a vulnerabilities existing in the ICS is shown in Figure 6.1.

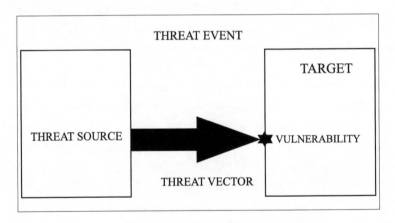

Figure 6.1: Threat Event

A threat source can be an internal threat sources such as employees or contractors or process implementation agencies. It can be also former employees, hackers, enemy nations, terrorists, and malwares. Preparing a list of threat sources is one of the basic functions of the threat modelling. The next stage is identifying the threat vectors used by the threat sources which mostly include the following components.

> ➤ SCADA network,

> ➤ Business LAN,

> ➤ Internet,

> ➤ Spear fishing,

> ➤ DCS and ICS systems and devices,

> ➤ Workstations and applications,

> ➤ Environment and physical security,

> ➤ Mobile systems and devices, and

> ➤ Remote access.

Risk Analysis

During a risk assessment, the threats and vulnerabilities are identified. The possibility of a vulnerability being exploited is multiplied by the value of the assets being assessed, which results in the total risk. Once the controls gap (protection the control cannot provide) is factored in, the result is the residual risk. Implementing countermeasures is a way of mitigating risks. Because no company can remove all threats, there will always be some residual risk. The question is what level of risk the company is willing to accept.

The process by which the goals of risk management are achieved is known as *risk analysis*. It includes examining an environment for risks, evaluating each threat event as to its likelihood of occurring and the cost of the damage it would cause if it did occur, assessing the cost of various countermeasures for each risk, and creating a cost/benefit report for safeguards to present to upper management. In addition to these risk-focused activities, risk management requires evaluation, assessment, and the assignment of value for all assets within the organization. Without proper asset valuations, it is not possible to prioritize and compare risks with possible losses.

Risk Analysis Approaches

To perform a risk analysis, the utility must decides initially what assets must be protected and to what extent they must be protected. It also indicates the amount of money that can go toward protecting specific assets. Next, it must evaluate the functionality of the available safeguards and determine which ones would be most beneficial for the environment. Finally, the company needs to appraise and compare the costs of the safeguards. These steps and the resulting information enable management to make the most intelligent and informed decisions about selecting and purchasing countermeasures.

The two approaches to risk analysis are quantitative and qualitative. A *quantitative risk analysis* is used to assign monetary and numeric values to all elements of the risk analysis process. Each element within the analysis (asset value, threat frequency, severity of vulnerability, impact damage, safeguard costs, safeguard effectiveness, uncertainty, and probability items) is quantified and entered into equations to determine total and residual risks. It is more of a scientific or mathematical approach to risk analysis compared to qualitative.

A *qualitative risk analysis* uses a *soft* approach to the data elements of a risk analysis. It does not quantify that data, which means that it does not assign numeric values to the data so that they can be used in equations. As an example, the results of a quantitative risk analysis could be that the organization is at risk of loosing £100,000 if a buffer overflow was exploited on a web server, £25,000 if a database was compromised, and £10,000 if a file server was compromised. A qualitative risk analysis would not present these findings in monetary values, but would assign ratings to the risks, as in Red, Yellow, and Green.

Quantitative and qualitative approaches have their own pros and cons, and each applies more appropriately to some situations than others. Company management and the risk analysis team, and the tools they decide to use, will determine which approach is best.

Quantitative Risk Analysis

The six major steps or phases in quantitative risk analysis, and they are:

1. Usually the Business Continuity Planning (BCP) team will sit down and draw up a list of organization assets and then assign an asset value (AV) in monetary terms to each asset. Then List out all assets with the asset value.

2. Research each asset, and produce a list of all possible threats of each individual asset. For each listed threat, calculate the exposure factor (EF) and Single Loss Expectancy (SLE). The SLE is a numerical money value that is assigned to a single event that represents the company's potential loss amount if a specific threat were to take place. The equation is laid out as follows:

   a. Asset Value × Exposure Factor (EF) = SLE

3. Perform a threat analysis to calculate the likelihood of each threat being realized within a single year-that is, the annualized rate of occurrence (ARO).

4. Derive the overall loss potential per threat by calculating the annualized loss expectancy (ALE).

5. Research countermeasures for each threat, and then calculate the changes to ARO and ALE based on an applied countermeasure.

6. Perform a cost/benefit analysis of each countermeasure for each threat for each asset. Select the most appropriate response to each threat.

In fact we to carry out a quantitative analysis and use mathematical equations for the data interpretation process. The most commonly used equations used for this purpose are the *single loss expectancy (SLE)* and the *annual loss expectancy (ALE).*

The SLE is the amount that is assigned to a single event that represents the company's potential loss amount if a specific threat were to take place. The equation for SLE is:

Asset Value × Exposure Factor (EF) = SLE

The *exposure factor (EF)* represents the percentage of loss a realized threat could have on a certain asset. For example, if a data warehouse has the asset value of £150,000, it can be estimated that if a fire were to occur, 25 percent of the warehouse would be damaged, in which case the SLE would be:

Asset Value (£150,000) × Exposure Factor (25%) = £37,500

This tells us that the company can potentially lose £37,500 if a fire took place.

As the security budget is on annual basis, the ALE equation becomes

SLE × Annualized Rate of Occurrence (ARO) = ALE

The *annualized rate of occurrence (ARO)* is the value that represents the estimated frequency of a specific threat taking place yearly. The range can be from 0.0 (never) to 1.0 (once a year) to greater than 1 (several times a year) and anywhere in between. For example, if the probability of a fire taking place and damaging our data warehouse is once every ten years, the ARO value is 0.1.

So, if a fire taking place within a company's data warehouse facility can cause £250,000 in damages, and the frequency (or ARO) of a fire taking place has an ARO value of 0.1 (indicating once in ten years), then the ALE value is £25,000 (£250,000 × 0.1 = £25,000).

The ALE value tells the company that if it wants to put in controls to protect the asset (warehouse) from this threat (fire), it can sensibly spend £25,000 or less per year to provide the necessary level of protection. Knowing the real possibility of a threat and how much damage, in monetary terms, the threat can cause is important in determining how much should be spent to try and protect against that threat in the first place. It would not make good business sense for the company to spend more than £3,750 per year to protect itself from this threat.

Asset	Threat	Single Loss Expectancy (SLE in £)	Annualized Rate of Occurrence (ARO)	Annualized Loss Expectancy (ALE in £)
Facility	Fire	250000	0.1	25000
Trade secret	Stolen	50000	0.01	500
File server	Failed	12000	0.1	1200
Data Virus	Virus	7000	0.1	700
Customer credit card info	Stolen	300000	3	900000

Table 6.3: Breakup of SLE and ALE Values

Now that we have all these numbers, what do we do with them? Let's look at the example in Table 2-7, which shows the outcome of a quantitative risk analysis.

With this data, the company can make intelligent decisions on what threats must be addressed first because of the severity of the threat, the likelihood of it happening, and how much could be lost if the threat were realized. The company now also knows how much money it should spend to protect against each threat. This will result in good business decisions, instead of just buying protection here and there without a clear understanding of the big picture. Because the company has a risk of losing up to £6,500 if data is corrupted by virus infiltration, up to this amount of funds can be earmarked toward providing antivirus software and methods to ensure that a virus attack will not happen.

When carrying out a quantitative analysis, some people mistakenly think that the process is purely objective and scientific because data is being presented in numeric values. But a purely quantitative analysis is hard to achieve because there is still some subjectivity when it comes to the data. How do we know that a fire will only take place once every ten years? How do we know that the damage from a fire will be 25 percent of the value of the asset? We don't know these values exactly, but instead of just pulling them out of thin air they should be based upon historical data and industry experience. In quantitative risk analysis, we can do our best to provide all the correct information, and by doing so we will come close to the risk values, but we cannot predict the future and how much the future will cost us or the company.

Uncertainty

In risk analysis, *uncertainty* refers to the degree to which you lack confidence in an estimate. This is expressed as a percentage, from 0 to 100 percent. If you have a 30 percent confidence level in something, then it could be said you have a 70 percent uncertainty level. Capturing the degree of uncertainty when carrying out a risk analysis is important, because it indicates the level of confidence the team and management should have in the resulting figures.

Results of a Quantitative Risk Analysis

The risk analysis team should have clearly defined goals. The following is a short list of what generally is expected from the results of a risk analysis:

> ➢ Monetary values assigned to assets
>
> ➢ Comprehensive list of all possible and significant threats
>
> ➢ Probability of the occurrence rate of each threat
>
> ➢ Loss potential the company can endure per threat in a 12-month time span
>
> ➢ Recommended controls

Although this list looks short, there is usually an incredible amount of detail under each bullet item. This report will be presented to senior management, which will be concerned with possible monetary losses and the necessary costs to mitigate these risks. Although the reports should be as detailed as possible, there should be executive abstracts so senior management can quickly understand the overall findings of the analysis

Residual Risk

The reason a company implements countermeasures is to reduce its overall risk to an acceptable level. As stated earlier, no system or environment is 100 percent secure, which means there is always some risk left over to deal with. This is called *residual risk*.

Only by reassessing the risks on a periodic basis can a statement of safeguard performance be trusted. If the risk has not changed, and the safeguards implemented are functioning in good order, then it can be said that the risk is being properly mitigated. Regular IRM monitoring will support the information security risk ratings. Vulnerability analysis and continued asset identification and valuation are also important tasks of risk management monitoring and performance. The cycle of continued risk analysis is a very important part of determining whether the safeguard controls that have been put in place are appropriate and necessary to safeguard the assets and environment.

Residual risk is different from *total risk,* which is the risk a company faces if it chooses not to implement any type of safeguard. A company may choose to take on total risk if the cost/benefit analysis results indicate this is the best course of action. For example, if there is a small likelihood that a company's web servers can be compromised, and the necessary safeguards to provide a higher level of protection cost more than the potential loss in the first place, the company will choose not to implement the safeguard, choosing to deal with the total risk.

There is an important difference between total risk and residual risk and which type of risk a company is willing to accept. The following are conceptual formulas:

threats × vulnerability × asset value = total risk

(threats × vulnerability × asset value) × controls gap = residual risk

total risk − countermeasures = residual risk

Qualitative Risk Analysis

Another method of risk analysis is *qualitative,* which does not assign numbers and monetary values to components and losses. The process of performing qualitative risk analysis involves judgment, intuition, and experience. Qualitative analysis techniques include judgment, best practices, intuition, and experience. Examples of qualitative techniques to gather data are Delphi, brainstorming, storyboarding, focus groups, surveys, questionnaires, checklists, one-on-one meetings, and interviews. The risk analysis team will determine the best technique for the threats that need to be assessed, as well as the culture of the company and individuals involved with the analysis.

The team that is performing the risk analysis gathers personnel who have experience and education on the threats being evaluated. When this group is presented with a scenario that describes threats and loss potential, each member responds with their intuitive feeling and experience on the likelihood of the threat and the extent of damage that may result. The method of combining quantitative and qualitative analysis into a final assessment of organizational risk is known as hybrid assessment or hybrid analysis quantitative and qualitative analysis into a final assessment of organizational risk is known as hybrid assessment or hybrid analysis.

Risk Calculation in ICS

With threats to sensitive data and ICS growing in both number and sophistication every day, organizations cannot afford a scatters hot approach to security. Instead, they need to focus their limited cyber security budgets and resources on the specific vulnerabilities in their unique security posture. To do this, organizations need to identify, analyse and prioritize the risks to the confidentiality, integrity or availability of their data or information systems, based on both the likelihood of the event and the level of impact it would have on the business.

The risk calculation is based on the severity, criticality, likelihood and the impact. In fact risk is a function of these variables and many formulae has been developed depending upon the significance of the ICS. A general accepted risk calculation formula is *Severity* is a number ranging from zero to ten, given to the vulnerability by a service like National vulnerability Database Scoring System by applying an algorithm like the common Vulnerability Scoring System.

$$Risk = \frac{S + 2*(C+L+I)}{4}$$

where
$$S = severity$$
$$L = likelihood$$
$$C = criticality$$
$$I = impact$$

Criticality is a number between 1 and 5 that reflects the importance of the system under control to the overall ICS functionality.

Likelihood is a number between 1 and 5 reflecting the chance of the vulnerability becoming a successful threat event.

Impact is a number between 1 and 5 that reflects the financial impact on the company, the associated damage to the image of the company, the potential impact on the environment, and the associated risk to employees.

6.7 PENETRATION TESTING

Network is the nerve system of an organization by storage its information and driving its communication. Network penetration test is to identify exploitable vulnerabilities in network, systems, hosts, and network devices such as routers, switches, etc. before hackers are able to discover and exploit them. Penetration testing will reveal the actual opportunities for hackers to be able to compromise systems and networks in such a way that allows for unauthorized access to sensitive data or even-over systems for malicious purposes. The main objectives of the penetration test is to

➢ identify seemingly flaws present in the environment,

➢ understand the level of risk for your organization (risk assessment), and

➢ mitigation and fix the identified network security flaws.

Penetration testing is commonly known as pen test or ethical hacking. A proper pen test can make recommendations for fixing problems within the network that were discovered during the pen test. The main purpose of the pen test is to improve network security and provide protection for the entire network and connected devices against future attacks.

There is a misconception regarding the risk assessment and the penetration testing, and often used interchangeably in reality. Vulnerability assessment refers to the process of evaluating the network systems and the services that provides for potential security problems while pen test involves methods used to perform legal exploits to prove that a security issue actually exists. Pen test usually designed to go beyond a vulnerability assessment by performing a simulation of the same scenario a hacker would use to penetrate a network. Vulnerability assessment usually covered within the pen test. The purpose of the simulation is to identify security issues before hackers can locate them and perform an exploit.

As pen tests simulate methods hackers would use to attack a network, network security professionals should have the appropriate authorization from organizational management before proceeding to conduct the pen test on the network. An improperly conducted pen test can be detrimental to daily process and business operations.

There are various methodologies used in penetration testing. They are mainly black box testing, white box testing and grey box testing. Other network monitoring testing such as intrusion detection, packet sniffing, etc. are also use to determine the status of the network security.

Black box pen test is conducted without the knowledge of any information related the technical aspect of a network. This mainly to conduct a comprehensive network exploration in an effort to determine the best way to organize a simulated attack. White box attack usually carried out after gathering all data and information associated with a network and the architecture and its configuration. Grey box approach of penetration testing is performed according to internal information for a network including technical documents, user privilege credentials, etc. Based on the internal information collected, a highly sophisticated network attack can be launched to determine what can happen when hackers gain access to critical information and infrastructure.

Pen test reveal how security issues were identified and confirmed during the test to determine how the issue should be fixed. It provides a list of all network vulnerabilities that were discovered during the test. Usually pen test reports contains priority wise security risk levels, suggestions for tightening the network security as a whole and recommendations to fix the issues as well. In addition, it may explain how the risks can affect business or process continuity and potential financial losses that can be incurred as a result of a breach.

The organisation shall carry out regularly Vulnerability Assessment of all Cyber Assets owned or under their control. If a Cyber Asset is found vulnerable to any exploits or upon any patch updates or major configuration changes, then further Penetration Testing may be carried out to determine other vulnerabilities that may have not been identified so far.

Summary

In recent years CI is one of the main target of cyber-attackers, enemy nations and a number of cyber incidents have occurred to the power grids. Risk and vulnerability assessment are very important issues in ICS and SCADA systems. Unless security flaws are not properly identified, they cannot be fixed. For this computer professionals and automation engineers have to have an in-depth knowledge of industrial networking to guide and implement right solutions to fix the security holes. This chapter begins with describing Risk Calculation, Risk Assessment Steps such as Asset Identification, System Characterization, Threat Modelling and Mitigation Strategies. Chapter concludes with a short description about Pentest.

Chapter Seven

Mitigation With Defense in Depth Architecture

7.1 INTRODUCTION

Cyber security is, and will continue to be, both costly and crucial. Concerns are rising within both private industry and all levels of government about their ability to keep pace with attackers and infiltrators those who are using sophisticated cyber-attacking methods to compromise CI. One of the ICS architecture which gained much popularity with the incorporation of modern firewall technology is the defense-in-depth architecture. A single security product, technology or solution cannot adequately protect a SCADA by itself. A multiple layer strategy involving two or more different overlapping security mechanisms is desired so that the impact of a failure in any one mechanism is minimized.

A defense-in-depth architecture strategy includes the use of firewalls, the creation of demilitarized zones, intrusion detection capabilities along with effective security policies, training programs and incident response mechanisms. In addition, an effective defense-in-depth strategy requires a thorough understanding of possible attack vectors on a ICS. These include,

1. backdoors and holes in network perimeter,

2. vulnerabilities in common protocols,

3. attacks on field devices,

4. database attacks, and

5. communications hijacking and *Man-In-The-Middle (MITM)* attacks.

The control systems cyber-security using *defense-in-depth strategies* for organizations use control system networks which maintain a multi-tier information architecture which requires,

- maintenance of various field devices, telemetry collection, and/ or industrial level process systems,

- access to facilities via remote data link or modem, and

- public facing services for customer or corporate operations. This strategy includes firewalls, the use of demilitarized zones and intrusion detection capabilities throughout the ICS architecture.

This chapter presents the *defense-in-depth strategies starting from the Purdue Reference Architecture, and explain the five level security needed to secure the ICS viz.* Physical Security, Network Security, Computer Security, Application Security and Device Security.

7.2 THE MYTH OF AIR GAP IN CRITICAL INFRASTRUCTURE

Even in this age of open networking, open SCADA protocols and unguided industrial networks, there is still the misperception that a true air gap exists, protecting critical industrial infrastructure simply because they are not connected to the IT network. In reality, even a real air gap is of little use in defending against cyber-attacks, because cyber-attacks have evolved past physical connectivity. Many assets that were not designed or intended to support wireless network communications include embedded WiFi capabilities at the microprocessor level, which can be exploited by attackers ranging from the skilled cyber terrorist to a disgruntled employee with an understanding of wireless technologies. In addition, there is the high possibility that a threat could be walked into a critical network, stepping across the air gap with the aid of a human carrier. Only strong security awareness and strong technical security controls can truly gap a networked system.

7.3 COMMON SCADA NETWORK SECURITY ATTACKS

1. DOS and DDOS Attack

There are many cases where a website's server gets overloaded with traffic and simply crashes. But more commonly, this is what happens to a website during a DoS or DDoS attack. When a website has too much traffic, it's unable to serve its content to visitors.

A DoS attack is performed by one machine and its internet connection, by flooding a website with packets and making it impossible for genuine users to access the content of flooded website.

A distributed denial-of-service attack, is similar to DoS, but is more forceful. It's harder to overcome a DDoS attack. It's launched from several computers, and the number of computers involved can range from just a couple of them to thousands or even more. Since it's likely that not all of those machines belong to the attacker, they are compromised and added to the attacker's network by malware. These computers can be distributed around the entire globe, and that network of compromised computers is called botnet. Since the attack comes from so many different IP addresses simultaneously, a DDoS attack is much more difficult for the victim to locate and defend against.

2. Phishing

Phishing is a method of gathering personal information using misleading e-mails and websites. A method of a social engineering with the goal of obtaining sensitive data such as passwords, usernames, credit card numbers mainly using deceptive e-mails. The recipient of the email is tricked into opening a malicious link, which leads to the installation of malware on the recipient's computer. It can also obtain personal information by sending an email that appears to be sent from a bank, asking to verify the identity and stealing away the private information.

3. Rootkit

Rootkit is a collection of software tools that enables remote control and administration level access over a computer or computer networks. Once remote access is obtained, the rootkit can perform a number of malicious actions as it come equipped with key loggers, password stealers and antivirus disablers. Rootkits are installed by hiding in legitimate software when the user give permission to that software to make changes to the OS, the rootkit installs itself in the computer and waits for the hacker to activate it. Other ways of rootkit distribution include phishing emails, malicious links, files, and downloading software from suspicious websites.

4. SQL Injection Attack

Many servers store data for websites using SQL. SQL Injection Attack is a common attack vector that uses malicious SQL code for backend database manipulation to access information that was not intended to be displayed. This information may include any number of items, including sensitive company data, user lists or private customer details. With the advancement of technology, network security threats become sophisticated, making threat of SQL injection common and dangerous to privacy issues and data confidentiality.

5. Man-in-the-Middle Attacks

Man-in-the-middle attacks are cyber security attacks that allow the attacker to eavesdrop on communication between two targets. It can listen to a communication which should, in normal settings, be private. As a typical example, a man-in-the-middle attack happens when the attacker wants to intercept a communication between person A and person B. Person A sends their public key to person B, but the attacker intercepts it and sends a forged message to person B, representing themselves as A, but instead it has the attackers public key. B believes that the message comes from person A and encrypts the message with the attackers public key, sends it back to A, but attacker again intercepts this message, opens the message with private key, possibly alters it, and re-encrypts it using the public key that was firstly provided by person A. Again, when the message is transferred back to person A, they believe it comes from person B, and this way, it has an attacker in the middle that eavesdrops the communication between two targets. Some of the various types of MITM attacks are mentioned below.

- DNS spoofing
- HTTPS spoofing
- IP spoofing
- ARP spoofing

- SSL hijacking
- Wi-Fi hacking

6. Computer Virus

A computer virus is a type of computer program that, when executed, replicates itself by modifying other computer programs and inserting its own code. When this replication succeeds, the affected areas are then said to be *infected* with a computer virus for everyday Internet users, computer viruses are one of the most common threats to cyber security. Statistics show that approximately 33% of household computers are affected with some type of malware, more than half of which are viruses.

Computer viruses are pieces of software that are designed to be spread from one computer to another. They're often sent as email attachments or downloaded from specific websites with the intent to infect the computer and other computers on contact list by using systems on the user network. Viruses are known to send spam, disable the security settings, corrupt and steal data from the computer including personal information such as passwords, even going as far as to delete everything on the hard drive.

7. Rogue Security Software

Rogue security software poses a growing threat to computer security. It is malicious software that mislead users to believe there is a computer virus installed on their computer or that their security measures are not up to date. Then they offer to install or update users' security settings. They'll either ask the user to download their program to remove the alleged viruses, or to pay for a tool. Both cases lead to actual malware being installed on the computer.

8. Trojan Horse

Trojan horse or Trojan refers to tricking someone by inviting into a securely protected area to deceive. In computing, it holds a very similar meaning. It is a malicious bit of attacking code or software that tricks users into running it willingly, by hiding behind a legitimate program. The spread of Trojan horse is often by phishing email. When user click on the email and its included attachment, malware got downloaded immediately to the computer. Trojans also spread when click on a false advertisement. Once inside the computer, a Trojan horse can record the user passwords by logging keystrokes, hijacking the webcam, and stealing any sensitive data from the computer.

9. Adware and Spyware

Adware is deceptive software that earns its creators money through fraudulent user clicks. Fortunately, it's one of the most detectable types of malware. Adware may slow down your computer and affect browsing experience. It could also add vulnerabilities to the computer that could be exploited, and at times, it can collect and send the browsing history to third parties without the user consent. It can also trick you into installing a real malware using its ad network.

Spyware works similarly to adware, but is installed on the computer without the user's knowledge. It can contain key loggers that record personal information including email addresses, passwords, even credit card numbers, making it dangerous because of the high risk of identity theft.

10. Computer Worm

Computer worms are pieces of malware programs that replicate quickly and spread from one computer to another. A worm spreads from an infected computer by sending itself to all of the computer's contacts, then immediately to the contacts of the other computers.

A worm spreads from an infected computer by sending itself to all of the computer's contacts, then immediately to the contacts of the other computers. Interestingly, they are not always designed to cause harm; there are worms that are made just to spread. Transmission of worms is also often done by exploiting software vulnerabilities.

7.4 PURDUE REFERENCE ARCHITECTURE FOR ICS

Purdue model is an Enterprise Reference Architecture developed by Theodore J.Willaims and colleagues of Purdue University for ICS and was adopted model by ISA-99 as a concept model for ICS network segmentation. This reference model is a resource for segmenting the modern ICS architecture and also help to understand the Industrial Cyber Security Landscape.

The Purdue model divides the ICS architecture into three zones and they are, Enterprise zone, Industrial Demilitarized zone and Industrial or process zone. Process zone is further divided into four levels and they are,

- Level 3: Site operations – managing production work flow to produce the desired products. Batch management such as manufacturing execution/operations management systems, (MES/MOMS) such as laboratory, maintenance and plant performance management systems, data historians and related middleware, Time frame such as shifts, hours, minutes, and seconds, etc.

- Level 2: Area supervisory control – supervising, monitoring and controlling the physical processes. Real-time controls and software; DCS, human-machine interface (HMI), supervisory and data acquisition (SCADA) software.

- Level 1: Basic control – sensing and manipulating the physical processes. Process sensors, analyzers, actuators and related instrumentation.

- Level 0: The process – defines the actual physical processes.

The enterprise zone has been divided into two levels viz. enterprise network and site business and logistics. These levels manage the business-related activities of the manufacturing operation. ERP is the primary system; establishes the basic plant production schedule, material use, shipping and inventory levels. Time frame can be months, weeks, days or shifts. In fact Purdue model Increases resiliency by segmenting the OT network.

The Enterprise Zone

The enterprise zone is the part of the ICS where business systems such as ERP and SAP typically live. Here, tasks such as scheduling and supply chain management are performed.

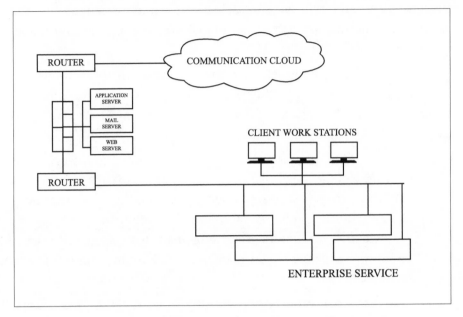

Figure 7.1: Enterprise zone

The can be subdivided into two levels viz.

- Level 5: Enterprise network
- Level 4: Site business and logistics

Level 5 - Enterprise Network

The systems on the enterprise network normally sit at a corporate level and span multiple facilities or plants. They take data from subordinate systems out in the individual plants and use the accumulated data to report on the overall production status, inventory, and demand. Technically not part of the ICS, the enterprise zone relies on connectivity with the ICS networks to feed the data that drives the business decisions.

Level 4 - Site Business Planning and Logistics

Level 4 is home to all the Information Technology (IT) systems that support the production process in a plant of a facility. These systems report production statistics such as uptime and units produced for corporate systems and take orders and business data from the corporate systems to be distributed among the Operation Technology (OT) or ICS systems. Systems typically found in level 4 include database servers, application servers (web, report, MES), file servers, email clients, supervisor desktops, and so on.

Industrial Demilitarized Zone (IDMZ)

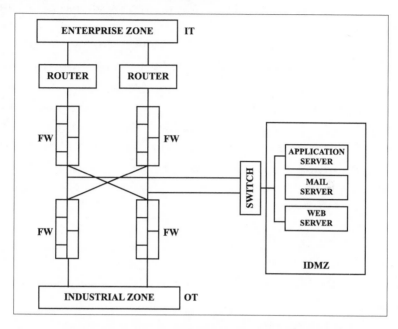

Figure 7.2: Industrial Demilitarized Zone (IDMZ)

Usually the Industrial Demilitarized Zone (IDMZ) lies between the enterprise zone and the Industrial zone as shown in Figure 7.2. Like the traditional (IT) DMZ, the OT-IDMZ allows to securely connect networks with different security requirements. Here different make firewalls at the two different levels are recommended for improves security.

DMZs are in essence a network between networks, and in the industrial security context, an added network layer between the OT, ICS, or SCADA, network and the less-trusted IT or enterprise network. Deploying the DMZ between two firewalls means that all inbound network packets are screened using a firewall or other security appliance before they arrive at the servers the organization hosts in the DMZ. There are many organizations and standard bodies that recommend segmenting the enterprise zone from the industrial zone by utilizing an industrial demilitarized zone (IDMZ). It acts as a zone and conduit system protecting physical processes, separating networks according to their different purposes, requirements and risks.

In the Purdue model, the Industrial DMZ is information sharing layer between the business or IT systems in levels 4 and 5 and the production or OT systems in levels 3 and lower created as per security standards such as the NIST cyber security Framework and NERC CIP. Direct communication between IT and OT systems is prevented and having a proxy service in the IDMZ relay adds an extra layer of separation and scrutiny. Systems in the lower layers are not directly exposed to attacks or compromise. If something were to compromise a system at some point in the IDMZ, the IDMZ is configured such a manner that it will automatically shut down without compromising and the production will be continued. Systems typically kept in the Industrial Demilitarized Zone are WEB servers, Microsoft domain controllers, Mail servers, etc.

The Manufacturing Zone

The manufacturing zone is where the action is; it is the zone where the process lives, by all means, this is the core of the. The manufacturing zone is subdivided into four levels viz.

➢ Level 3: Site operations,

➢ Level 2: Area supervisory control,

➢ Level 1: Basic control and

➢ Level 0: The process.

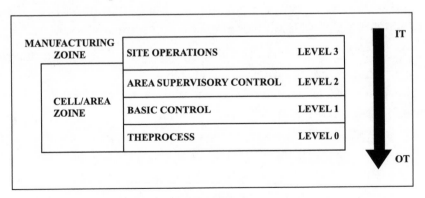

Figure 7.3: Manufacturing Zone

Level 3 - Site Operations

Level 3 is where systems that support plant wide control and monitoring functions reside which is shown in Figure 7.3. At this level, the operator is interacting with the overall production systems. Think of centralized control rooms with HMIs and operator terminals that provide an overview of all the systems that run the processes in a plant or facility. The operator uses these HMI systems to perform tasks such as quality control checks, managing uptime, and monitoring alarms, events, and trends.

Level 3, site operations, is also where the OT systems that report back up to IT systems in level 4 live. Systems in lower levels send production data to data collection and aggregation servers in this level, which can then send the data to higher levels or can be queried by systems in higher levels (push versus pull operations).

Systems typically found in level 3 include database servers, application servers (web and report), file servers, Microsoft domain controllers, HMI servers engineering workstations, and so on.

Level 2 - Area Supervisory Control

Many of the functions and systems in level 2 are the same as for level 3 but targeted more toward a smaller part or area of the overall system. In this level, specific parts of the system are monitored and managed with HMI systems. Think along the lines of a single machine or skid with a touch screen HMI to start or stop the machine or skid and see some basic running values and manipulate machine or skid-specific thresholds and set points.

Systems typically found in level 2 include HMIs (standalone or system clients), supervisory control systems such as a line control PLC, engineering workstations, and so on.

Level 1 - Basic Control

Level 1 is where all the controlling equipment lives. The main purpose of the devices in this level is to open valves, move actuators, start motors, and so on. Typically found in level 1 are PLCs, Variable Frequency Drives (VFDs), dedicated proportional-integral-derivative

(PID) controllers, and so on. Although one could find a PLC in level 2, its function there is of supervisory nature instead of controlling.

Level 0 - Process

Level 0 is where the actual process equipment that we are controlling and monitoring from the higher levels lives. Also known as Equipment under Control (EUC), level 1 is where we can find devices such as motors, pumps, valves, and sensors that measure speed, temperature, or pressure. As level 0 is where the actual process is performed and where the product is made, it is imperative that things run smoothly and uninterrupted. The slightest disruption in a single device can cause mayhem for all operations.

In fact Purdue model is a zone based architecture. At this point of establishing zone based architecture it is better to note the following points.

- Identify the boundaries of each zone so that perimeter defenses can be deployed in the correct location.
- Make any necessary changes to the network so that the network architecture aligns with the defined zone.
- Document the zone for purposes of policy development and enforcement.
- Document the zone for purposes of security device configuration.

7.5 PHYSICAL SECURITY

Physical security is the first line of defense against environmental risks and fickle human behavior. It is the protection of physical property, encompasses both technical and nontechnical components. Most of the information security experts often-overlooked physical security as they do about information and computer security and the associated hackers, ports, viruses, and technology-oriented security countermeasures. But information security without proper physical security could be very dangerous. The physical threats that an organization faces fall into the following categories viz.

- Natural disaster like floods, earthquakes, fires etc.,
- Strikes, riots, terrorist attacks etc.,

- Location and layout of building infrastructure,
- Power supply failure, communication interruptions, water supply interruption etc.,
- Unauthorized access and damage by disgruntled employees, employee errors and accidents, fraud, theft etc.,
- Unsecure network devices used.

In all situations, the primary consideration, above all else, is that nothing should obstruct life safety goals as it has given the highest priority. A wise planning can balance life safety and other security measures.

The physical security of computers and their resources in the decades back was not as challenging as it is today because computers were mostly mainframes that were locked away in server rooms, and only a few people knew what to do with them. Presently, a computer is available with almost every desk in every utility, and access to devices and resources is spread throughout the environment. Organizations have server rooms, and remote access, resources out of the facility. Properly protecting these computer systems, networks, facilities, and employees has become an overwhelming task to many companies.

Theft, fraud, sabotage, and accidents are raising costs for many companies because environments are becoming more complex and dynamic. Security and complexity are at the opposite ends of the spectrum. As environments and technology become more complex, more vulnerabilities are introduced that allow for compromises to take place. Most companies have had memory or processors stolen from workstations, while some have had computers and laptops taken. Even worse, many companies have been victims of more dangerous crimes, such as robbery at gunpoint, a shooting rampage by a disgruntled employee, anthrax, bombs, and terrorist activities.

Many companies may have implemented security guards, closed-circuit TV (CCTV) surveillance, intrusion detection systems (IDSs), and requirements for employees to maintain a higher level of awareness of security risks. These are only some of the items that fall within the physical security boundaries. If any of these does not provide the necessary protection level, it could be the weak link that causes potentially dangerous security breaches.

From a holistic view of physical security, there are so many components and variables such as secure facility construction, risk assessment and analysis, secure data center implementation, fire protection, IDS and CCTV implementation, personnel emergency response and training, legal and regulatory aspects of physical security, etc. Each has its own focus and skill set, but for an organization to have a solid physical security program, all of these areas must be understood and addressed.

Many thefts and deaths could be prevented if all organizations were to implement physical security in an organized, mature, and holistic manner. When security professionals look at *information* security, they think about how someone can enter an environment in an unauthorized manner through a port, wireless access point, or software exploitation. When security professionals look at *physical* security, they are concerned with how people can physically enter an environment and cause an array of damages.

Physical security must be implemented based on a *layered defense model*, which means that physical controls should work together in a tiered architecture. The concept is that if one layer fails, other layers will protect the valuable asset. Layers would be implemented moving from the perimeter toward the asset.

➢ **Mitigation Strategies**

Presently the physical security is implemented based on a layered defence model and it generally falls in to the following categories.

- Building Location And Layout
- Building Infrastructure.
- Utilities Such as Power, Water, Fire Suppression, etc. and
- Network Devices Used.

Layered security includes

- Fencing
- Reinforced Barricades

- Walls
- Gates/Entry Points
- Vehicle Barriers
- On-Site Security Guards
- CCTV Cameras
- Motion Detectors
- Intrusion Detection Systems
- Vibration Detectors
- Secured Cabling

Control room should be highly secured, such as the control room access may be depend on time, employment status, work assignment, level of training etc. The authentication for the access to the control room should be reliable such as biometric devices, cipher locks or access cards. The devices in the control room must be fixed permanently. Adequate lighting should be provided. Regular auditing of access logs must be done. Natural disasters must not affect the proper functioning of the firm. Field devices must be protected from the intruders using proper alarms, cipher locks with proper authentication.

While designing and implementing Physical Security it is better to categorise it as three groups viz.

1. Administrative,
2. Technical, and
3. Physical.

Administrative physical security controls include facility construction and selection, site management, personnel controls, awareness training, and emergency response and procedures.

Technical physical security controls include access controls; intrusion detection; alarms; closed-circuit television (CCTV); monitoring; heating, ventilating, and air conditioning (HVAC); power supplies; and fire detection and suppression.

Physical controls for physical security include fencing, lighting, locks, construction materials, mantraps, dogs, and guards.

7.6 NETWORK SECURITY

The ICT network security is the most important as it connects the field devices, corporate networks, SCADA networks, DR network, etc. A proper zone base segmentation and security based on functionalities using firewalls, gateways, data diodes, etc. are the present techniques employed for ensuring network security.

From a mitigation perspective, simply deploying IT security technologies into an ICS may not be a viable solution. Although modern control systems use the same underlying protocols that are used in IT and business networks, the very nature of control system functionality may make even proven security technologies inappropriate. Some sectors, such as energy, transportation, and chemical, have time sensitive requirements, so the latency and 'throughput' issues associated with security strategies may introduce unacceptable delays and degrade or prevent acceptable system performance. Due to these facts, currently the main mitigation strategy is a security conscious segmentation. A network segment is also known as a network security zone which is a logical grouping of information and automation systems in an ICS network. Usually an Industrial Control Network has been segmented into four security zones with different trust levels as described below.

- Enterprise Zone   -   Low Trust Level
- Industrial Demilitarised Zone   -   Medium Trust Level
- Industrial Zone   -   High Trust Level
- Cell Area Zone   -   High Trust Level

Understanding attack vectors is essential to building effective security mitigation strategies. The degree of understanding of the control system by the security engineers regarding these vectors are most essential to mitigate these vulnerabilities effectively and efficiently. Effective security depends on how well the security engineers and vendors understand the ways that architectures can be compromised. Critical cyber security issues that need to be addressed include those related to,

- Backdoors and holes in network perimeter
- Vulnerabilities in common protocols

- Attacks on Field Devices
- Database Attacks
- Communications hijacking and *Man-in-the-middle* attacks

Demilitarized Zone (Level 3.5). This first line of defence in isolating the OT network from IT network. This is a critical segmentation because IT network are generally targeted before OT network. Manufacturing Zone (Level 3). This segmentation protects each ICS system/remote sites/factories. The purpose of this segmentation is to keep this site operational even if other ICS systems/sites come under attack. Cell Zone (Level 2). To further increase resiliency of each ICS environment, each functional cell or production line within the ICS network is further segmented. This will ensure that if a functional cell is attacked, other adjacent functional cell are still functioning. A SCADA network security engineer must perform the following tasks without any compromise.

- Ensure the firewalls and Intrusion Prevention Systems (IPS) are properly placed in the network with proper configuration as per the organisation's security policy and standards adopted such as NERC CIP, IEC62443 etc.
- Security engineer must be aware of the port scan by the external attackers and their capability of exploiting vulnerabilities.
- Must be aware of internet connections, remote access capabilities, layered defences and placements of hosts on networks.
- Aware of the interaction of the security devices installed in the network such as firewalls, IPSec, antivirus etc. and their routable protocols if supports.
- Must be aware of the vulnerable protocols such as SSL.
- Unprotected ports which are commonly attacked.
- Network monitoring and maintenance.

For nearly three decades, digital network DMZs or *demilitarized zones* have been used as a data protection strategy in IT networks to broker access to information by external untrusted networks. This IT DMZ model and approach is well established, but is not necessarily an effective security measure when applied to OT networks.

In ICS network, DMZs is a network between networks, an added network layer between the OT, ICS, or SCADA, network and the less-trusted IT or enterprise network. If correctly implemented, no TCP or any other connection exchanging messages should ever traverse between IT and OT; through DMZ, it is a place where information originates from, or terminates completely.

For industrial purposes, what should be placed inside the DMZ is all of the applications and servers that have TCP connections out to the IT network. In practice, this can be a whole range of things; so when designing IT/OT network integration architectures, one must generally see customers deploy an intermediate system to aggregate OT data which needs to be shared with the enterprise. The most common aggregator is one of the many process historians, or one of the many variants of OPC server.

The modern industrial DMZ acts as a zone and conduit system protecting physical processes, separating networks according to their different purposes, requirements and risks. The best practice for implementing an IT/OT DMZ is to put two firewalls around the DMZ, one between the OT network and DMZ network, the other between the DMZ and the IT network. This practice supports the assumption that two firewalls reduce the likelihood that single firewall software vulnerability will open an attack pathway straight in to control system networks. In addition, all three networks must be on separate domains with their own authentication systems and no sharing of domain credentials.

Network segmentation has traditionally been accomplished by using multiple routers. Firewalls should be used to create DMZs to protect the control network. Multiple DMZs could also be created for separate functionalities and access privileges, such as peer connections, the data historian, the Inter Control Center Communications Protocol (ICCP) server in SCADA systems, the security servers, replicated servers, and development servers. All connections to the Control System LAN should be routed through the firewall, with no connections circumventing it. Network administrators need to keep an accurate network diagram of their control system LAN and its connections to other protected subnets, IDMZs, the corporate network, and the outside.

Generally it is observed that, most sites deploy only a single firewall with three ports-one connected to IT, one connected to OT and one to the DMZ network – meaning single vulnerabilities are again a concern. More fundamentally, modern attacks don't exploit software vulnerabilities, modern attacks exploit permissions. From an attack perspective, exploiting vulnerabilities involves a lot of work and code writing unless of course someone else has already done the work and released an attack tool to the public. Exploiting permissions, on the other hand, can be as easy as stealing the firewall password or stealing a password on the IT network that the OT network then trusts or allows an attacker to go into a historian or other system in the DMZ right through the firewall.

7.7 COMPUTER/SERVER SECURITY

When consider the computer/server security, one of the important task is the patch management. Keeping regular IT systems and applications with the latest firmware, software, and patch management is a daunting task especially in the industrial zone of the ICS network.

Uptime requirements for the critical ICS computer systems do not allow them to reboot after updates. For those critical systems that are allowed to be altered, a different strategy to protect them is better and generally employed. For systems that can be updated and patch especially in the field operation zone, a readily available, update and convenient patching solution should be provided. Typical examples are windows server updates services and system center configuration manger of Microsoft.

End node protection is another important task in the computer system. This defensive control in the form of end node protection software and can be installed locally with remote administrative capability. Some of the generally available end node protection software are

- Host Based Firewalls,
- Anti Malware software, and
- Application Whitelisting software.

7.8 APPLICATION SECURITY

Application security is the process of making applications more secure by finding, fixing, and enhancing the security of apps. Much of this happens during the development phase, but it includes tools and methods to protect apps once they are deployed. This is becoming more important as hackers increasingly target applications with their attacks. SCADA systems need to have a strategy that supports not only management of knowledge and training but security knowledge that include policy, standards, design and attack patterns, threat models, code samples, reference architecture and security framework. Application security can help organizations protect all kinds of applications used by internal and external stakeholders including customers, business partners and employees. Vulnerabilities in SCADA applications include the following key components.

- Input Validation Vulnerabilities
- Software Tampering
- Authorisation and Authorisation Vulnerabilities
- Configuration Vulnerabilities
- Session Management Vulnerabilities
- Parameter management Vulnerabilities

SCADA software security must be viewed holistically. It is achieved through the combination of effective people, process and technology with none of these three on their own capable of fully replacing the other two entities. This also means that just like software quality in general, software security requires that we focus on security throughout the application's life cycle.

> ➤ **Input Validation Vulnerabilities**

An input validation attack is any malicious action against a computer system that involves manually entering strange information into a normal user input field. Input validation attacks take place when an attacker purposefully enters information into a system or application with the intentions to break the system's functionality. The best form of defense against these attacks is to test for input validation prior to deploying an application. A few common types of input validation attacks include:

- Buffer Overflow: This is a type of attack that sends too much information for a system to process, causing a computer or network to stop responding. A buffer overflow might also cause excess information to take up memory that was not intended for it, sometimes even overwriting memory.

- Canonicalization attacks: A canonicalization attack takes place when someone changes a file directory path that has digital permissions to access parts of a computer in order to allow access to malicious parties that use this unauthorized entry to steal sensitive information or make unapproved changes.

- XSS attacks (cross site scripting): These attacks involve placing a malicious link in an innocuous place, like a forum, which contains most of a valid URL with a dangerous script embedded. An unsuspecting visitor might trust the site they are on and not worry that a comment or entry on the site contains a virus.

- SQL injection attacks: SQL injection attacks involve taking a public URL and adding SQL code to the end to try to gain access to sensitive information. An attacker might enter code into a field commanding a computer to do something like copy all of the contents of a database to the hacker, authenticate malicious information, reveal hidden entries in a database or delete information without consent.

➢ **Software Tampering**

Modifying the application code before or while running the application is known as software tampering. Software tampering can lead to override or bypass the security or protective controls. Modifying the unauthorised application's runtime behaviour to perform unauthorised actions, exploitation via binary patching, code substitution, software licence cracking, trojenisation of applications, etc. are the common attacks associated with software tampering vulnerabilities.

> **Authorization & Authentication:**

Authorization and Authentication deal with appropriate mechanisms to enforce access control on protected resources in the system. Authentication vulnerabilities include failure to properly check the authentication of the user or bypassing the authentication system altogether. Login bypassing, Fixed parameter manipulation, Brute force and dictionary attacks, Coockie replay and Pass-the-hash attacks are generally identified as authentication vulnerabilities.

Authorization is the concept that follows access to resources only to those who are permitted to use them. It comes after the successful authentication. Authorization flaws could result in either horizontal or vertical privilege escalation. The usage of strong protocols to validate the identity of a user or components. Further, issues such as the possibility or potential for authentication attacks such as brute-force or dictionary based guessing attacks. Elevation of privileges, disclosure of confidential data, data tampering are some of the authorization vulnerabilities.

> **Configuration Vulnerabilities**

This will consider all issues surrounding the security of configuration information and deployment. It is very crucial in the security of an application. Usually the systems and applications will run with a default configuration as it has been described in the manual. This helps attackers to guess the passwords, bypass login pages and finding setup vulnerabilities. Hence configuration especially the configuration of Firewalls must be done as per the requirement of the security policy of the organization.

> **User and Session Management Vulnerabilities**

This concerns how a user's account and session is managed within the application. The quality of session identifiers and the mechanism for maintaining sessions are some of the considerations here. Similarly, user management issues such as user provisioning and de-provisioning, password management and policies are also covered as part of this category. By mismanaging a session handling, an attacker can guess or reuse a session key and take over the session and the identity of a legitimate user. Session management and session replay are the common session management vulnerabilities associated with session management.

➢ Parameter Management Vulnerabilities

The manipulation of parameters exchanged between a client and the server inorder to modify application data, such as user credentials and permissions, price and quantity of products, etc. Cookie manipulation, form field manipulation and query string manipulation are common parameter manipulation vulnerabilities.

➢ Security requirements in the Software Development Cycle

Developing security architecture and engineered approach to the problem are generally recommended because current technology is not enough to prevent cyber-attacks. Developing requirements for control systems with security features and use of simulation models based on a framework could improve the definition of requirements and reveal problems early in the software development cycle.

➢ Auditing and Logging

This concerns with how information is logged for debugging and auditing purposes. The security of the logging mechanism itself, the need and presence of an audit trail and information disclosure through log files are all important aspects.

➢ Compliance to standards for software development

Software development for control systems can be improved by following documents such as NIST published guidelines SCADA Security, Configuration, Guidelines, general assessment methods and tools for SCADA vulnerabilities and Holzman's rules

➢ Data Protection in Storage & Transit

This includes handling of sensitive information such as social security numbers, user credentials or credit card information. It is also covers the quality of cryptographic primitives being used, required/ minimum key lengths, entropy and usage of industry standards and best practices.

7.9 DEVICE SECURITY

Devices such as routers, firewalls and even network hosts including servers and workstations must be assessed as part of the security testing process. certain high level security vulnerabilities usually found on many network devices can also create many problems, hence one must ensure that HTTP and Telnet interfaces to the routers, switches and firewalls are properly configured and not with a blank, default or easy to guess passwords. If a malicious insider or other attacker gains access to the network devices, he can own the network and can lockout administrative access, setup backdoor user accounts, reconfigure ports, and even bring down the entire network.

When HTTP, FTP and TELNET are enabled in network devices with the help of free tools and a few minutes of time one can sniff the network and capture login credentials as they are sending clear texts. In case of wireless devices one must watch out for unauthorised Access Points (APs) and wireless clients that are attached to the network, else chances for social engineering and there are chances of connecting in to the malicious network and systems.

Mobile computing is convenient for personal, business and hacking. If secured mobile devices are not properly connected to the enterprise networks which represents thousands of unprotected islands as the phones, tablets and laptops which running numerous operating system platforms with a number of applications and infinite number of risks are associated with mobile computers.

➢ **Physical attack**

- Manipulation of the mechanical and electrical part of an ICS device is always feasible if the attacker gets physical access to the device which is not a matter of IT security. However being able to manipulate the programmed functionality of an ICS device, such an attack can be simultaneously applied to a large number of devices by a single attacker. A manipulated device can also be used by an attacker as a platform to compromise other parts of the system. A device that is compromised by a physical attack might have privileged access to other components and its segments, and there for act as a backend to attack farther devices.

- As a counter measure against physical security problems, ensure that Aps, Antennas and other wireless and network infrastructure equipment are located away in secure closets, ceilings or places which are difficult to access physically. Terminate the APs outside any firewall or any network perimeter security devices wherever possible. Placing unsecured wireless equipment inside the secured network, it can negate any benefits which can be obtained from the perimeter security devices such as the firewall.

➤ **Device hardening**

- One of the areas of the device hardening is disabling unnecessary and unused options and features on ICS devices if the ICS devices do not provide the ability to disable unnecessary and unused options place these behind an industrial firewall and blocking the corresponding service port. Industrial firewalls are available with CISCO, TOFFINO, ROCKWELL, etc.

- Another method for ICS device hardening is restricting physical access to the device. It can be done by both administratively disabling the unused communication ports and physically block those ports from being connected to with block out devices. Keep the ICS devices in an enclosure that can be safely locked is another option. As the availability is more important than integrity and confidentiality, the device hardening of ICS presently have to confirm redundant power supplies, redundant communication port/paths, redundant I/O and redundant computing and controls.

➤ **Device patching**

- Make sure that the ICS devices are installed with latest firmware and software releases on a consistent basis and within a reasonable time and updates with new releases ensure that the software, firmware, patches and manuals are from reputable reliable sources or from OEMs also check that the ICS vendors offers cryptographically signed firmware versions for their devices this feature prevents installing and using tampered firmware.

- New firmware images, OS and patches to ICS should be tested in a testing and or developing environment to make sure that the new revisions works with the existing setup approximately before deploying to the production network this indeed save lots of headache and down time.

It is better to be aware the following points when deals with device security.

Mobile Device security is the range of potential security options or features that may be available for a mobile device. Not all Portable Electronic Devices (PEDs) have good security features. But even if devices have security features, they're of no value unless they're enabled and properly configured. Hence be sure to consider the security options of a new device before you make a purchase decision.

> **Full Device Encryption**

Some mobile devices, including laptops, tablets, as well as mobile phones, may offer device encryption. If most or all the storage media of a device can be encrypted, this is usually a worthwhile feature to enable. However, encryption isn't a guarantee of protection for data, especially if the device is stolen while unlocked or if the system itself has a known backdoor attack vulnerability.

> **Remote Wiping**

It's becoming common for a remote wipe or remote sanitation to be performed if a device is lost or stolen. A remote wipe lets you delete all data and possibly even configuration settings from a device remotely. The wipe process can be triggered over mobile phone service or sometimes over any Internet connection. However, a remote wipe isn't a guarantee of data security. Thieves may be smart enough to prevent connections that would trigger the wipe function while they dump out the data. Additionally, a remote wipe is mostly a deletion operation. The use of undelete or data recovery utilities' can often recover data on a wiped device. To ensure that a remote wipe destroys data beyond recovery, the device should be encrypted. Thus the undeletion operation would only be recovering encrypted data, which the attacker would be unable to decipher.

➢ GPS

Many mobile devices include a GPS chip to support and benefit from localized services, such as navigation, so it's possible to track those devices. The GPS chip itself is usually just a receiver of signals from orbiting GPS satellites. However, applications on the mobile device can record the GPS location of the device and then report it to an online service. You can use GPS tracking to monitor your own movements, track the movements of others (such as minors or delivery personnel), or track down a stolen device. But for GPS tracking to work, the mobile device must have Internet or wireless phone service over which to communicate its location information.

➢ Application Whitelisting

Application whitelisting is a security option that prohibits unauthorized software from being able to execute. Whitelisting is also known as *deny by default* or *implicit deny*. In application security, whitelisting prevents any and all software, including malware, from executing unless it's on the preapproved exception list, the whitelist. This is a significant departure from the typical device-security stance, which is to allow by default and deny by exception (also known as blacklisting). Due to the growth of malware, an application whitelisting approach is one of the few options remaining that shows real promise in protecting devices and data. However, no security solution is perfect, including whitelisting. All known whitelisting solutions can be circumvented with kernel-level vulnerabilities and application configuration issues.

➢ BYOD Concerns

BYOD is a policy that allows employees to bring their own personal mobile devices into work and use those devices to connect to (or through) the company network to business resources and/or the Internet. Although BYOD may improve employee morale and job satisfaction, it increases security risk to the organization. If the BYOD policy is open ended, any device is allowed to connect to the company network. Not all mobile devices have security features, and thus such a policy allows noncompliant devices onto the production network. A BYOD policy that mandates specific devices may reduce this risk, but it may in turn require the company to purchase devices for employees who are unable to purchase their own compliant device. Many other BYOD concerns are discussed in the following sections. Users need to understand the benefits, restrictions, and consequences of using their own devices at work. Reading and signing off on the BYOD policy along with attending an overview or training program may be sufficient to accomplish reasonable awareness.

➢ Supply Chain Attack

Supply chain attacks are designed to exploit trust relationships between an organization and external parties. These relationships could include partnerships, vendor relationships, or the use of third-party software. Cyber threat actors will compromise one organization and then move up the supply chain, taking advantage of these trusted relationships to gain access to other organizations' environments. The supply chain of CI especially power grid is a growing concern as the IT/OT convergence within SCADA systems accelerates. As utilities modernize the embedded SCADA systems within the electricity grid, the cyber and operational technology attack surface increases as do the potential risks and consequences. The electricity sector has long recognized physical risks against the system such as natural events and kinetic attacks. Recent years have seen a shift in focus from physical to cyber security threats. It is high time to focus on operational technology threats. Though not covered in detail in this book, asset procurement and supply chain assurance should be treated with utmost importance to reduce the risk of new equipment, pre-infected with malware, from being procured and deployed.

7.10 MODERN APPROACH TO IT/OT INTEGRATION

In other than air gapped or standalone ICSs, the most crucial area of concern is the IT/OT integration especially in critical infrastructure.

Modern approach describes and recommends that one side of the IT/ OT DMZ be protected with unidirectional gateways to replicate OT systems to the IT network. The defining feature of a unidirectional gateway is that it is hardware-enforced. A combination of hardware and software that physically moves information in one direction only which means no messages whatsoever (including attacks) can enter the protected OT network from external sources, thus fulfilling the mission and purpose of implementing an IT/OT DMZ. The software element of unidirectional gateways replicates industrial servers and applications in two common scenarios with a Modern IT/OT DMZ. Today many countries are strictly enforcing this approach while integrating the IT networks with OT networks especially in critical infrastructure domain like power system, oil & gas, water supply, etc.

- either replicating a historian or OPC server insider the OT network with a unidirectional gateway to the DMZ network whereby the IT network accesses the replicated server inside the DMZ through a firewall as shown in Figure 7.4,

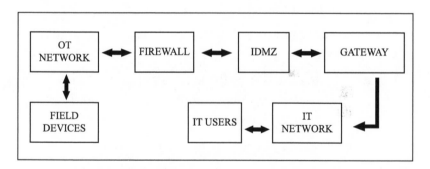

Figure 7.4: Modern IT/OT DMZ Scenario No.1

- or, replicating the historian or OPC server which sits inside the DMZ with a unidirectional gateway to a replica server sitting on the IT network for corporate use as shown in Figure 7.5. In both scenarios, the IT replica of the DMZ OPC or historian server is still the focus for IT/OT data exchange. It is now thoroughly protected in its original operational state.

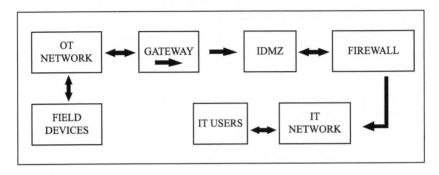

Figure 7.5: Modern IT/OT DMZ Scenario No.2

Enterprise Zone

This is in fact the ERP and administrative zone which deals with the complete information regarding the functionality of enterprise, its planning, operations, etc. All IT data protection strategies are expected to be implemented at this zone. A network security engineer in an ICS has to be aware and ensure that

- the devices, such as firewalls and IPS are properly placed on the network and configured.
- should be aware how the attackers perform port scans and exploit vulnerabilities.
- while designing the IDMZ, the security engineers must be aware of the internet connections, remote access capabilities, layered defences and placement of firewalls in the network.
- should be aware of ports which are unprotected.

If any attacker, compromises any one of the systems in the network, exploiting vulnerabilities due to the lack of proper security implementation, then

- the attacker can launch a Denial of Service (DoS) whichever can take down the internet connection, or entire network.
- with the use of a network analyser can steal confidential information of emails and files send over the network.
- a hacker can set up a backdoor access to the network.

Hence while integrating IT and OT; a prompt testing must be carried out between IDMZ and internal network of the enterprise. Obtain permissions from the predetermined and remotely connected other network for vulnerabilities on other systems that can affect the enterprise network mainly due to open ports, lack of firewalls and improper configured routers.

At this point it is better to note the use of data diodes for achieving unidirectional data flow which is briefly described below.

7.11 INCREASING RESILIENCY BY SEGMENTING THE OT NETWORK

Industrial Control Systems (ICS) and Supervisory Control and Data Acquisition (SCADA) systems are being increasingly targeted by attackers involved in terrorism and cyber warfare. Besides factories, these systems run critical infrastructure like power plants, water treatment systems, and traffic control systems. At stake is not just financial loss and brand reputation, but these attacks can result in national security threats and even death.

Based on our experience when evaluating ICS and SCADA systems, we almost always find security weaknesses that can be easily taken advantage of. These weaknesses allow the ICS components to be manipulated and controlled beyond its intended parameter. The root of the problem can be trace to,

- Patching: Unable to install the latest patch because it is not approved by Original Equipment Manufacturer (OEM)

- No or weak authentication: Any device that can get connected to the system can change value and configuration of PLCs easily or bypass its authentication.

- Backdoors: Use of undocumented and unrestricted access to critical functions

- Buffer overflow: Poorly written software that allows restrictions to be bypassed or functions to be manipulated

- No encryption: Data and information can be deciphered easily for manipulation.

The previous best-practice for ICS systems was to keep them segregated (air-gapped) from IT networks to prevent outside interference. However, we are seeing ICS networks increasingly being connected to the IT network. This convergence event is exposing ICS systems to threats and vulnerabilities that were previously protected through isolation.

Summary

Designing secure computing systems is a complex task, and many security engineers have dedicated their entire careers to understanding the innermost workings of information systems and ensuring that they support the core security functions required to safely operate in the current environment. It can seem as a difficult task to keep track of all the ICS security threats those are out there, and the new ones that just keep emerging. Whether the media is creating a culture of fear out of being online and placing trust in leaving the information out for all to see and manipulate, or whether the threats that wait in the dark corners of the internet are truly serious and can happen to anyone. The best thing one can all do is to be prepared to mitigate with preventive and counter measures. There is no way to be completely sure that a system is impenetrable by cyber threats. The responsibility of the computer professionals and automation engineers is to ensure that the ICS systems are secure as much as possible. This chapter gives the modern aspects of ICS security based on the *Defence-in-Depth architecture* describing all the five levels of security *viz.* Physical Security, Network Security, Computer Security, Application Security and Device Security.

Protocols, Standards and Guidelines

8.1 INTRODUCTION

Standards define compulsory requirements for the homogenous use of hardware, software, technology, and security controls. They provide a course of action by which technology and procedures are uniformly implemented throughout an organization. Standards are tactical documents that define steps or methods to accomplish the goals and overall direction defined by security policies.

Guidelines are the next element of the formalized security policy structure. A guideline offers recommendations on how standards and baselines are implemented and serves as an operational guide for both security professionals and users. Guidelines are flexible so they can be customized for each unique system or condition and can be used in the creation of new procedures. They state which security mechanisms should be deployed instead of prescribing a specific product or control and detailing configuration settings. They outline methodologies, include suggested actions, and are not compulsory.

A procedure is a detailed, step-by-step how-to document that describes the exact actions necessary to implement a specific security mechanism, control, or solution. A procedure could discuss the entire system deployment operation or focus on a single product or aspect, such as deploying a firewall or updating virus definitions. In most cases, procedures are system and software specific. They must be updated as the hardware and software of a system evolve. The purpose of a procedure is to ensure the integrity of business processes. If everything is accomplished by following a detailed procedure, then all activities should be in compliance with policies, standards, and guidelines. Procedures help ensure standardization of security across all systems.

All too often, policies, standards, baselines, guidelines, and procedures are developed only as an afterthought at the urging of a consultant or auditor. If these documents are not used and updated, the administration of a secured environment will be unable to use them as guides. And without the planning, design, structure, and oversight provided by these documents, no environment will remain secure or represent proper diligent due care.

The security policies are the foundation of the overall structure of organized security documentation. Then, standards are based on those policies as well as mandated by regulations and contracts. From these the guidelines are derived. Finally, procedures are based on the three underlying layers of the structure.

Standard and pen protocols which are becoming prevalent today are IEC 61850, IEC 60870-5-101 or 104, and DNP3. These communication protocols are standardized and adopted by almost all major SCADA vendors. Many of these protocols are now considerably modified and contain extensions to operate over TCP/IP as well. However it is a good security engineering practice to avoid connecting SCADA systems to the internet so that the attack surface can be considerably reduced. RTUs and other automatic controller devices were being developed before the advent of industry wide standards for interoperability. This results in multitude of control protocols. This chapter is dedicated to explain various protocols, standards and guidelines which are relevant to CI environment with an emphasis on cyber-security.

8.2 EVOLUTION OF SCADA COMMUNICATION PROTOCOLS

SCADA protocols evolved out of the need to send and receive data and control information locally and over distances in deterministic time. Deterministic in this context refers to the ability to predict the amount of time required for a transaction to take place when all relevant factors are known and understood. To accomplish communication in deterministic time for applications in ICS and DCS systems, manufactures developed their own protocols and communication bus structure. Profibus of Siemens and Modbus of Schneider Electric, are typical examples. Since all the protocols are proprietary, interoperability became a major challenge. This made the control industries and standards organizations to develop open SCADA protocols for control systems which would be nonproprietary and not exclusive to one manufacturer. Further as the internet gained popularity, manufactures started incorporating the protocols and tools which are developed internet such as TCP/IP series of protocols and internet browsers. In addition, manufactures and open standards organizations modified the highly popular and efficient Ethernet LAN technology for implementing data acquisition and control networks.

De jure standards are developed by national and international standardization development organizations such as ANSI, IEEE, NIST, IEC, etc. Many de facto industrial standards are made de jure, after appropriate evaluation. Modbus is one of the typical SCADA communication protocol extensively deployed today. The following sections discuss a few of the popular communication protocols used in DCS scenario. ICCP (IEC 60870-6) is the international standard for one control center to communicate with another control center of Power System SCADA. For communication from master stations to substations DNP3 is used in North America and IEC T-101 serial and T-104 (TCP/IP) are used in Europe. For communication between field equipment, IEC 61850, DNP3 (IEEE1815) and Modbus are developed.

8.3 SCADA COMMUNICATION PROTOCOLS

As explained above, the use of international open protocol standards are now recognized throughout the industry especially in electric utility as a key to successful integration of the various parts of the electric utility enterprise. Benefits of open systems include longer expected system life, investment protection, upgradeability and expandability, and readily available third party components. The following sections elaborate some of the important communication protocols which are presently used by many industries and power utilities.

Distributed Network Protocol 3 (DNP 3)

DNP3 is extensively used in many industries in automation like electricity, oil and gas, and water. It is popular and extensively used in the United States of America, Canada, South America, Australia, and parts of Asia and Africa. It is a set of an open SCADA protocol that is used for serial or IP communication between control devices, initially developed by Westronics in Calgary, Alberta, Canada. DNP3 is mainly used between components in process automation systems especially in SCADA systems employed in electric and water companies, but usage in other industries is not common. It has larger data frames and can carry larger RTU messages, and is very much useful for communications between various types of data logging and control devices such as Remote Terminal Units (RTUs), Data Concentrators and Intelligent Electronic Devices (IEDs). It is specifically designed to achieve reliability and efficiency when used in real-time data transfer. Another feature is that it supports time-stamped data communications between a master station and RTUs or IEDs or Phasor Measurement Units (PMU).

DNP3 faces the similar cyber-security problems as IEC 60870-5-104 [T-104] is explained in subsequent sections. Scrutiny made by security engineers for integrity in DNP3 revealed that it lacks authentication and encryption. The DNP3 function codes and data types are well known, hence it can be easy to manipulate and compromise a DNP3 communication session.

Protocol Architecture of DNP3

DNP3 is based on the Enhanced Performance Architecture (EPA) and uses the frame format FT3 specified by IEC 60870-5. The lower layers of physical and data link defining the communication between devices are similar to IEC 60870-5-101 and the higher levels of data units and functionality are different. DNP3 uses cyclic redundancy check for error detection.

The DNP3 protocol structure uses the basic three layer EPA model with some added functionality. It adds an additional layer named the pseudo-transport layer. The pseudo-transport layer is a combination of network and transport layer of the Open Systems Interconnection (OSI) model and also includes some functions of the data link layer. Network function is concerned with the routing and data flow over the network from sender to receiver. Transport function includes proper delivery of the message from sender to receiver, message sequencing, and corresponding error correction. This function of a transport layer is limited when compared to the OSI layer, and hence the name pseudo-transport layer, as shown in Figure 8.1.

OSI MODEL	DNP 3 (DISTRIBUTED NETWORK PROTOCOL 3)
	USER DEFINED PROCESS APPLICATION FUNCTIONS
Application Layer	Application Layer (ASDUs)
Presentation Layer	
Session Layer	
Transport Layer	PSEUDO TRANSPORT LAYER
Network Layer	
Data Link Layer	Data Link Layer
Physical Layer	Physical Layer

Figure 8.1: DNP3 and OSI model layers

MODBUS

Modbus is the oldest and perhaps the most widely deployed industrial control communications protocol. It was designed in 1979 by Modicon presently owned by Schneider Electric for use in their PLCs. Modbus is a request-response serial communications protocol implemented using a master-slave relationship where communication always occurs in pairs. Which means one device (the slave) must initiate a request and then wait for a response, and the initiating device (the master) is responsible for initiating every interaction is shown in Figure 8.2. Typically, the master is a Human Machine Interface (HMI) or SCADA server and the slave is a sensor, RTU, PLC, or Programmable Automation

Controller (PAC). The content of these requests and responses, and the network layers, across which these messages are sent, are defined by the different layers of the protocol.

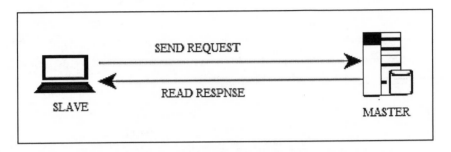

Figure 8.2: A Master-Slave Networking Relationship

Modbus is originally published by Modicon which is presently owned by Schneider Electric for use in their PLCs. Modbus being simple and robust, is a de facto standard communication protocol. It is now commonly available and used for connecting industrial electronic devices in ICS. The main reasons for the use of Modbus in the industrial environment are,

- developed with industrial applications in mind,
- openly published and royalty-free,
- easy to deploy and maintain, and
- moves raw bits or words without placing many restrictions on vendors.

Modbus enables communication among many devices connected to the same network, for example, a system that measures temperature and humidity and communicates the results to a computer. Modbus is often used to connect a supervisory computer with RTUs in SCADA systems. Many of the data types are named from its use in driving relays viz. a single-bit physical output called a coil, and a single-bit physical input called a discrete input or a contact.

The development and update of Modbus protocols has been managed by the Modbus organization, since Schneider Electric transferred rights to that organization. The Modbus organization is an association of users and suppliers of Modbus-compliant devices that seek to drive the adoption and evolution of Modbus.

Variants

The popularity of Modbus has led to the development of several variations to suit particular needs. Modbus RTU, These include Modbus RTU and Modbus ASCII, which support binary and ASCII transmissions over serial buses, respectively. Modbus TCP is a variant of Modbus developed to operate on modern networks using the IP. Modbus Plus is a variant designed to extend the reach of Modbus via interconnected busses. The following are the Modbus variants are given below.

- Modbus ASCII,
- Modbus TCP/IP or Modbus TCP,
- Modbus over UDP,
- Modbus over TCP/IP or Modbus RTU/IP,
- Modbus over UDP or Modbus Plus,
- Pemex Modbus, and
- Enron Modbus.

Among these Modbus RTU, Modbus ASCII, and Modbus TCP/IP or Modbus TCP are the popular versions. In Modbus, data transactions are traditionally stateless, making them highly resistant to disruption from noise. It requires minimal recovery information at either end. Programming operations, on the other hand, expect a connection-oriented approach. This was achieved on the simpler variants by an exclusive login token, and on the Modbus Plus variant by explicit program path capabilities which maintained a duplex association until explicitly broken down. The main reason why the connection-oriented TCP/IP protocol is used is to keep control of an individual transaction by enclosing it in a connection, which can be identified, supervised, and cancelled without requiring specific action on the part of the client and server applications. This gives the mechanism of wide tolerance to network performance changes, and allows security features such as firewalls and proxies to be easily added.

Modbus is typically deployed between PLCs and HMIs, or between a Master PLC and slave devices such as PLCs, HMIs, Drivers, Sensors, I/O devices, etc. Typically up to 247 devices are supported in a single, nonbridged bus. A common deployment uses Modbus on TCP/IP within a SCADA DMZ or Supervisory LAN, where master HMIs provide a central management capability to a number of Master PLCs, each of which may connect serially over a bus topology to a number of PLCs and/or HMIs, responsible for a distinct control loop.

MODBUS Limitations

1. Modbus protocol does not provide any security against unauthorized commands.

2. Modbus was designed and developed initially for the communication with the PLC. Hence the number of data types was limited to those which understood by PLCs at that time.

3. No standard way exists for a node to find the description of a data object, such as determining whether a register value represents a temperature between T1 and T2 degrees.

4. Since Modbus is a master-slave protocol, there is no way for a field device to *report by exception*. As a result the master node must routinely poll each field device and look for changes in the data. This consumes considerable bandwidth and network time in applications.

5. Modbus is restricted to addressing 254 devices on one data link, which limits the number of field devices that may be connected to a master station.

6. Modbus transmissions must be contiguous, which limits the types of remote communications devices to those that can buffer data to avoid gaps in the transmission.

Security Concerns

1. Lack of authentication. Modbus sessions only require the use of a valid Modbus address and valid function code. One can be easily guessed or spammed, whereas the other is easily obtainable information.

2. Lack of encryption. Commands and addresses are transmitted in clear text and can therefore be easily captured and spoofed due to the lack of encryption.

3. Lack of message checksum (Modbus TCP only). A spoofed command is even easier over some implementations of Modbus TCP, as the checksum is generated at the transmission layer, not the application layer.

4. Lack of broadcast suppression (serial Modbus variants only). All serially connected devices will receive all messages, meaning a broadcast of unknown addresses can be used for effective denial of service (DoS) to a chain of serially connected devices.

5. Programmability. By far, the most dangerous quality of Modbus— which is shared with many industrial protocols—is that it is intentionally designed to program controllers, and could be used to inject malicious logic into an RTU or PLC.

Attacks on DNP3 and MODBUS

As the original focus while developing these was not security rather efficiency, Modbus and DNP3 virtually have no security measures incorporated. The lack of authentication in Modbus means that remote terminals accept commands from any machine that appears to be a master. The lack of integrity checking or encryption allows messages to be intercepted, changed and forwarded. In fact it is susceptible to Man in the Middle attack (MITM) which is most perilous in ICS and DCS which control Critical Infrastructure. For DNP3, message from an outstation can easily be spoofed, making it appear to be unavailable to the master. It is also common that passwords may be sent across the network in clear text. Though the DNPSecure has been developed, deployment is difficult as most of the systems using DNP3 are in the Critical Infrastructure, where downtime is very crucial and almost not feasible.

Modbus protocol is highly vulnerable to attacks like response and measurement injection, and command injection. A scrutiny on Modbus protocol with various levels of injection attacks ranging from naïve injection to complex injections targeting specific fields and values based on domain knowledge, reveals the possible consequences, such as sporadic sensor measurements, altered system control schemes and altered actuator states. This can result in partial communication disruption to complete shutdown of the device.

PROFIBUS

Profibus is an open standard, serial, smart field-bus technology widely used in time-critical control and data acquisition systems. It can provide data transmission rates of 31 Kbps, 1Mbps, and 2,5 Mbps in the physical layer. It provides determinism for real-time control applications and supports multimaster communication networks.

Profibus uses the bus topology where a central line, or bus, is wired throughout the system. Devices are attached to this central bus. One bus eliminates the need for a full-length line going from the central controller to each individual device. In the past, each Profibus device had to be connected directly to the central bus. Technological advancements, however, have made it possible for a new *two-wire* system. In this topology, the Profibus central bus can connect to a ProfiNet Ethernet system. In this way, multiple Profibus buses can connect to each other.

Profibus devices which are connected to a central line can communicate information in an efficient manner which can go beyond the automation messages. Profibus devices can also participate in self-diagnosis and connection diagnosis. At the most basic level, Profibus benefits from superior design of its OSI layers and basic topology. There are three variants of Profibus, and they are:

1. Profibus PA
2. Profibus DP
3. Profibus FMS

Communication Architecture of Profibus

Figure 8.3 illustrate the communication architecture of the Profibus versions and shows their relationships in the OSI seven layer model.

OSI MODEL	Profibus PA	Profibus DP	Profibus FMS
Application Layer	Application layer not used	Application layer not used	Application layer field bus message specification
Presentation Layer			
Session Layer			
Transport Layer			
Network Layer			
Data Link Layer	Data link layer IEC interface	Data link layer fieldbus data link	Data link layer fieldbus data link
Physical Layer	Physical layer IEC 61158-2	Physical layer EIA-485, fiber optics, radio waves	Physical layer EIA-485, fiber optics, radio waves

Figure 8.3: Profibus PA, DP, and FMS layered protocols.

Profibus systems can have three types of physical media. The first is a standard twisted-pair wiring system, in this case RS485. Two more advanced systems are also available. Profibus systems can now operate using fiber-optic transmission in cases where that is more appropriate. A safety-enhanced system called Manchester Bus Powered (MBP), is also available in situations where the chemical environment is prone to explosion. The physical layers can also use either the EIA-485 standard or the IEC 61158-2 standard. If desired, all three Profibus versions can use the same bus line if they employ EIA-485 in the physical layer. However, if the application requires intrinsically safe circuitry, IEC 61158-2 operates at 31.25Kbps.

Security Concerns

Profibus lacks authentication inherent to many of its functions, allowing a spoofed node to impersonate a master node, which in turn provides control over all configured slaves. A compromised master node or a spoofed master node could also be used to capture the token, inject false tokens, or otherwise disrupt the protocol functions, causing a DoS. A rogue master node could alter clock synchronization to slave devices, snoop query responses (across all masters), or even inject code into a slave node. Profibus over Ethernet (Profinet) is a real-time Ethernet protocol, and as such it is susceptible to any of the vulnerabilities of Ethernet. When used over the IP, it is also susceptible to any vulnerabilities of IP.

IEC 60870-5-101/103/104

IEC 60870 was introduced by the IEC Technical Committee 57 and widely used in ICS and DCS communication. It is mainly popular in Europe and China and suitable for controlling electric power transmission grids and other geographically widespread ICS. This is an open protocol originally written for serial communication and was released in 1995. The IEC 60870-5-104 standard, released in 2000, present a combination of the application layer of IEC 60870-5-101 and the transport functions provided by TCP/IP. Presently this is widely used in SCADA and DCS communication protocol for monitoring and controlling of remote field locations of DCS especially in electrical grids. The structure of IEC 60870-5 standard is hierarchical and has six parts, each having different sections, and has four companion standards. Main part of the standard defines the fields of application, whereas the companion standards elaborate the information regarding the application field by specific details. These companion standards may be referred to as T-101, T-102, T-103, and T-104, where T stands for Tele-control. The five documents specify the base IEC 60870-5 Tele-control equipment and systems. The six sections of Part 5 of the IEC 60870-5 are described below.

1. IEC 60870-5-1 Transmission Frame Formats.

2. IEC 60870-5-2 Data Link Transmission Services.

3. IEC 60870-5-3 General Structure of Application Data.

4. IEC 60870-5-4 Definition and Coding of Information Elements.

5. IEC 60870-5-5 Basic Application Functions.

6. IEC 60870-5-6 Guidelines for conformance testing for the IEC 60870-5 companion standards.

7. IEC TS 60870-5-7 Security extensions to IEC 60870-5-101 and IEC 60870-5-104 protocols by applying IEC 62351.

IEC 60870-5-101 [T-101]

An Enhanced Performance Architecture (EPA) based protocol released by IEC in the beginning of 90s, which found extensive acceptance in power system SCADA. It is a master slave communication for multi-drop or bus topology. It polls data by cyclic polling technique using the data link layer and use parity check as well as checksum error detection techniques. The data error is decreased by these checks in IEC 60870 protocols. This standard is widely used in power system communications for tele-control, teleprotection, and associated telecommunications. The application function of T-101 includes station initiation, parameter loading, data acquisition, cyclic data transmission, clock synchronization, etc. for a remote substation. This is completely compatible with IEC 60870-5-1 to IEC 60870-5-5 standards and uses standard asynchronous serial tele-control channel interface between master and slave. The standard is suitable for multiple configurations like point-to-point, star, multidropped etc. The specific features of IEC 608705-101 are described below.

1. Both master initiated and master/slave initiated modes of data transfer are available,

2. It functions based on Link address and Application Service Data Unit (ASDU) bit,

3. ASDU addresses are provided for classifying the end station,

4. Data can be classified into different information objects and each information object is provided with a specific address,

5. Capability to assigning priority to the data before transmitting the data,

6. Option of classifying the data into 16 different groups to get the data according to the group, by issuing specific group interrogation commands from the master,

7. Capability for time synchronization, and

8. Various schemes for data transfer are available which is very much useful in IED's to transfer the SoE and disturbance files for fault analysis.

IEC 60870-5-103 [T-103]

This is a master-slave standard protocol based on the EPA architecture and is mainly used to couple the central unit to several protection devices and is primarily used in the energy sector. The standard is especially designed for the communication with protection devices and therefore difficult to adapt it to other applications. It defines a companion standard that enables interoperability between protection equipment and devices of a control system in a substation. It handles protection functions as status indications of circuit breakers, types of fault, trip signals, auto-reclosure, relay pickup, etc. The device complying with this standard can send the information using two methods for data transfer, either using the explicitly specified ASDU or using generic services for transmission of all the possible information. The standard supports some specific protection functions and provides the vendor a facility to incorporate its own protective functions on private data ranges. IEC 60870-5-103 is mostly used for comparatively slow transmission media with RS232 and RS485 interfaces. Connection via optical fiber is also covered by the standard. The transmission speed in general is specified with a maximum of 19200 Baud.

IEC 60870-5-104 [T-104]

IEC 60870-5-104 [T-104] protocol is a standard for tele-control equipment and systems with coded bit serial data transmission in TCP/IP based networks for monitoring and controlling geographically widespread processes. It is an extension of IEC 101 protocol suitable for networked circumstances with the changes in transport, network, link and physical layer services to suit the complete network access. The standard uses an open TCP/IP interface network to have connectivity to the Local Area Network (LAN) and routers with different facility used to connect to the Wide Area Network (WAN). Within TCP/IP various network types can be utilized including X.25, Frame Relay, ATM, ISDN, Ethernet and serial point to point (X.21), Application layer of IEC 104 is preserved same as that of IEC 101 with some of the data types and facilities which are not used. There are two separate link layers defined in the standard, which is suitable for data transfer over Ethernet and serial line Point-to-Point Protocol (PPP). The control field data of IEC104 contains various types of mechanisms for effective handling of network data synchronization.

Unfortunately, by design itself the security of IEC 104 is problematic, same as many of the other contemporary SCADA protocols developed. IEC Technical Committee(TC) 57 have published a security standard IEC 62351, which implements end-to-end encryption which would prevent such attacks as replay, man-in-the-middle and packet injection. However due to the increase in complexity and cost, vendors are reluctant to include this security features on their ICS networks.

Protocol Architecture of IEC 60870-5

Protocol Architecture of IEC 60870 is based on Enhanced Performance Architecture (EPA) model. The EPA model has three layers viz. Physical, Data Link and Application layers. An user layer is added to the top of the EPA model to provide the interoperability between equipements in a tele-control system. This four layer model is used for T-101, and T-103 companion standards. For companion standard T-104, which is the network adaptation, some additional layers are included from the OSI model. These are network and transport layers that are essential for the networked architecture. This networked architecture is useful for the transportation of data and messages over the network. Thus a non-networked version is used for T-101, T-103, and the networked version for T-104, as shown in Figure 8.4. It may be noted that the lower four layers of T-104 are now the TCP/IP suite for networking applications.

OSI model	T-101, T-103 (EPA with user defined process functions)	T-104-EPA with network and transport with user defined process functions
	User defined process application functions	User defined process application functions
Application layer	Application layer(ASDUs)	Application layer(ASDUs)
Presentation layer		
Session layer		
Transport layer		TCP/IP transport and network protocol suite
Network layer		TCP/IP transport and network protocol suite
Data link layer	Data link transmission procedures and frame formats	TCP/IP transport and network protocol suite
Physical layer	Physical interface specification	

Figure 8.4: Communication layers of IEC 60870-5

ATTACKS ON IEC 60870-5

SCADA StrangeLove is an independent group of cyber-security engineers founded in 2012, focused exclusively on security assessment of ICS and SCADA. They could successfully prove detection of an IEC 60870 device on a SCADA network. They also released python scripts which can identify and return the common address of an IEC 60870 device. The common address is an address used for all data contained within the IEC 60870-5 packet, used to identify the physical device. With the help of these existing scripts it is possible to scan an ICS/DCS network for any specific IEC 60870 hosts. Once investigation became successful, the scripts could be used to detect possible targets for a Man in the Middle (MITM) attack. Further improperly terminated VPN running on IEC 60870-5 protocols is highly susceptible to DoS attacks, hence end node security issue has to be sorted out with utmost care, else can be catastrophic.

IEC 61850

Several protocols exist for electrical substation automation, which include many proprietary protocols with custom communication links. Interoperation of devices from different vendors is a need of the hour in power system automation. IEC 61850 – Communication Networks and Systems in Substations – is the first global standard for the power utility industry, which provides a framework that will ease the integration and interoperability of intelligent devices in the substation. This in turn, will ultimately result in significant improvements in performance of substation systems while lowering the cost of substation construction and implementation. Further, the potential of IEC 61850 that in the future it is expected that it can be applied right across the power system spectrum. The standard document is structured as shown in Table 8.1.

Part	Title
IEC 61850 - 1	Introduction & Overview
IEC 61850 - 2	Glossary
IEC 61850 - 3	General Requirements
IEC 61850 - 4	System and project management
IEC 61850 - 5	Communication requirements for functions and device models
IEC 61850 - 6	Configuration description language for communication in electrical substations related to IEDs
IEC 61850 - 7	Basic communication structure for substation and feeder equipment
IEC 61850 - 7-1	Principles and models
IEC 61850 - 7-2	Abstract communication service interface (ACSI)
IEC 61850 - 7-3	Common data classes
IEC 61850 - 7-4	Compatible logical node classes and data classes
IEC61850 – 8	Specific communication service mapping (SCSM)
IEC 61850 - 8-1	Mappings to MMS (ISO 9506-1 and ISO 9506-2)
IEC 61850 - 9	Specific Communication Service Mapping (SCSM)

Continued...

IEC 61850 - 9-1	Sampled values over serial unidirectional multidrop point to point link
IEC 61850 - 9-2	Sampled values over ISO/IEC 8802-3
IEC 61850 - 10	Conformance testing

Table 8.1: Structure of the IEC 61850 Standard

By the scope of the specification, it quickly becomes evident that the specification for IEC 61850 is beyond that of a typical communications protocol specification. Using it's object-oriented hierarchical data model approach with high-level standardized semantics, IEC 61850 enables the abstract definition of data items and services. All application functions, including the data interfaces to the primary equipment, are broken down into the smallest feasible pieces, which may communicate with each other and be implemented separately in dedicated IEDs. The a need for a robust interoperable standard to serve the power system SCADA has been attended by a group of about 60 members from different countries worked in three IEC working groups from 1995 and created IEC 61850 which accomplished the following objectives.

1. A single protocol for complete substation automation considering all different data transfer requirement,

2. Definition of basic services required to data transfer,

3. Provides high inter-operability between systems from different vendors,

4. A common method/format for storing complete data, and

5. Defines complete testing required for the equipment which conforms to the standard.

IEC 61850 is a layered architecture standard with full OSI layers that separates the functionality required for electric utility applications from the lower level networking tasks. The layered architecture illustrating the separation of functions is shown in Figure 8.5.

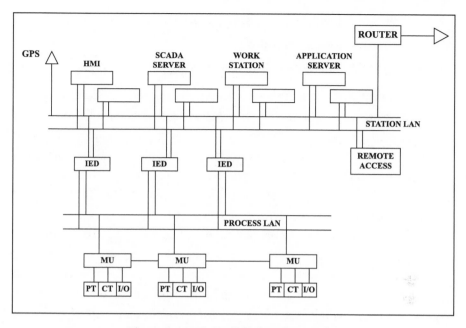

Figure 8.5: IEC 61850 Substation Model

IEC 61850 is an object oriented substation automation standard which defines how to describe the devices in an electrical substation and how to exchange the information about these devices. The information model of IEC 61850 is based on two main levels of modelling. The breakdown of physical device into logical device, and the breakdown of logical device into logical nodes, data objects and data attribute. The approach of IEC 61850 is to decompose the application function into the smallest entities which are used to exchange information.

While implementing the PSS, the data exchange between the process level devices and substation is necessary. In order to achieve this all participating devices must be compatible with this protocol. As the IEC 61850 standard has been developed with a clear vision to fully incorporate the IED interoperability, irrespective that the IEDs belong to different vendors. In fact the IEC 61850 compliance of devices takes the substation automation to a next level. IEC 61850 offers three types of communication models.

1. Client/server type communication services model,

2. A publisher subscriber model, and

3. Sample Value model for multicast measurement values.

Generic Object Oriented Substation Events (GOOSE): Client server communication is preferred for managing the process level equipments at substation because of its low latency. Generic Object Oriented Substation Events (GOOSE) is a controlled model mechanism in which any format of data like Status Values (SVs) is grouped into a data set and transmitted within a time period of 4 milliseconds. In GOOSE the critical commands of a power system such as a trip or interlocking are directly mapped to the link layer. The message structure of GOOSE supports the exchange of a wide range of possible common data organized by a dataset. Being the GOOSE message a multicast, it is received by all the IEDs which have been connected and configured to subscribe it. GOOSE message usually carries the information of a status change and time of the last status change. In other words, GOOSE time stamped events from IEDs are appropriately communicated to the subscribers. The message frame consists of the destination or source Media Access Control (MAC), addresses, tag protocol identifies, length, two reserved fields and application protocol data unit. Another feature of the GOOSE message is that it repeats until the subscriber receives it.

Main features of IEC 61850 are described below:

1. Data Modelling – Primary process objects as well as protection and control functionality in the substation is modelled into different standard logical nodes which can be grouped under different logical devices. There are logical nodes for data/functions related to the logical device (LLN0) and physical device (LPHD).

2. Reporting Schemes – There are various reporting schemes (BRCB & URCB) for reporting data from server through a server-client relationship which can be triggered based on pre-defined trigger conditions.

3. Fast Transfer of events – Generic Substation Events (GSE) are defined for fast transfer of event data for a peer-to-peer

communication mode. This is again subdivided into GOOSE & GSSE.

4. Setting Groups – The setting group control Blocks (SGCB) are defined to handle the setting groups so that user can switch to any active group according to the requirement.

5. Sampled Data Transfer — Schemes are also defined to handle transfer of sampled values using Sampled Value Control blocks (SVCB)

6. Commands – Various command types are also supported by IEC 61850 which include direct & select before operate (SBO) commands with normal and enhanced securities.

7. Data Storage – Substation Configuration Language (SCL) is defined for complete storage of configured data of the substation in a specific format.

Reduced implementation time in application development and integration, reduced cost of wiring, ease of equipment upgrade and application migration to new technologies, wider selection of equipment that will easily integrate, separation of application modelling from physical implementation, better availability of engineering tools due to standardization naming semantics, use of standardized models allows flexibility in current and future physical technology implementations are the major benefits of using IEC 61850. The significant benefits in various areas are described below.

1. Eliminate Procurement Ambiguity: Not only can SCL be used to configure devices and power systems, SCL can also be used to precisely define user requirement for substations and devices. Using SCL a user can specify exactly and unambiguously what is expected to be provided in each device that is not subject to misinterpretation by suppliers

2. Lower Installation Cost: IEC 61850 enables devices to quickly exchange data and status using GOOSE and GSSE over the station LAN without having to wire separate links for each relay. This significantly reduces wiring costs by more fully utilizing the

station LAN bandwidth for these signals and construction costs by reducing the need for trenching, ducts, conduit, etc.

3. Lower Transducer Costs: Rather than requiring separate transducers for each device needing a particular signal, a single merging unit supporting SMV can deliver these signals to many devices using a single transducer lowering transducer, wiring, calibration, and maintenance costs.

4. Lower Commissioning Costs: The cost to configure and commission devices is drastically reduced because

5. IEC 61850 devices don't require as much manual configuration as legacy devices. Client applications no longer need to manually configure for each point they need to access because they can retrieve the points list directly from the device or import it via an SCL file. Many applications require nothing more than setting up a network address in order to establish communications. Most manual configuration is eliminated drastically reducing errors and rework.

6. Lower Equipment Migration Costs: Because IEC61850 defines more of the externally visible aspects of the devices besides just the encoding of data on the wire, the cost for equipment migrations is minimized. Behavioural differences from one brand of device to another is minimized and, in some cases, completely eliminated. All devices share the same naming conventions minimizing the reconfiguration of client applications when those devices are changed.

7. Lower Extension Costs: Because IEC 61850 devices don't have to be configured to expose data, new extensions are easily added into the substation without having to reconfigure devices to expose data that was previously not accessed. Adding devices and applications into an existing IEC 61850 system can be done with only a minimal impact, if any, on any of the existing equipment.

8. Lower Integration Costs: By utilizing the same networking technology that is being widely used across the utility enterprise the cost to integrate substation data into the enterprise is

substantially reduced. Rather than installing costly RTUs that have to be manually configured and maintained for each point of data needed In control center and engineering office application, IEC 61850 networks are capable of delivering data without separate communications front-ends or reconfiguring devices.

9. Implement New Capabilities: The advanced services and unique features of IEC 61850 enables new capabilities that are simply not possible with most legacy protocols. Wide area protection schemes that would normally be cost prohibitive become much more feasible. Because devices are already connected to the substation LAN, the incremental cost for accessing or sharing more device data becomes insignificant enabling new and innovative applications that would be too costly to produce otherwise.

It is definite that all these benefits of IEC 61850 will make the protocol of choice for utilities and will migrate to this network solutions for the substations.

Challenges

Because IEC 61850 is a relatively new standard, the general availability of products that enable the user to easily engineer and implement a working system at this point in time is somewhat limited, although at least at the level of all other communication protocols. This is rapidly changing and will continue to accelerate as product developers gain expertise and experience. Initial interoperability demonstrations and projects uncovered differences in interpretation of standards by developers; as these differences are discovered, the developers are modifying their products and providing input for revision of the standard to help avoid these issues in the future. Initially, users will encounter learning curve challenges in gaining familiarity with the new techniques and terminology. However, because of the multi-vendor support of this standard, the amount of training overall will be reduced due to the commonality of data models and communications techniques between vendors. IEC 61850 depends heavily on Ethernet networks which will require better understanding by utility engineers of network design issues affecting reliability and communications volume. Fortunately this skill is widely available within other utility departments and through network service consultants. As project teams are put together to implement an IEC 61850 based solution, care should be taken to ensure that inappropriate networking resource is assigned.

Comparison of DNP3 and IEC-61850 GOOSE

IEC 61850 is not just a communication protocol as it not only defines how the data is transmitted and received but also describes how data is executed and stored. This makes data model of IEC61850 very different to the OSI reference model. This difference in the data model requires IEC61850 to work over a real set of communication protocols such as DNP3 or IEC T[101/3/4], requiring the data model of IEC 61850 to be mapped on to one of the above mentioned protocols. It's more advantageous if used only within a substation and its specification states that connection to the remote control centers such as remote MCC is beyond its scope. The use of IEC 61850 would be most appropriate if it is used in a substation environment where a number of IEDs interact with the SCADA master. In fact it is referred to as substation protocol.

Attacks on IEC 61850 Protocol

Though IEC 61850 based automated substations can provide various advantages over traditional substations, the power distribution utilities are very much cautious about its implementation due to security concerns. Security Engineers have identified a number of security vulnerabilities and flaws in the IEC 61850 protocol such as the lack of encryption used in the GOOSE messages, lack of Intrusion Detection System (IDS) implementation in IEC 61850 networks, and no firewall implementation inside IEC 61850 substation network. If these vulnerabilities are deviously exploited, a number of security attacks can be launched on IEC 61850 substation network.

One of the vulnerabilities within the GOOSE communication of IEC 61850 that can be exploited is by sending GOOSE frames containing higher status numbers. It prevents genuine GOOSE frames from being processed. This effectively causes a hijacking of the communication. This attack could be used to implement a Denial of Service (DoS) attack. This weakness in GOOSE can be exploited to insert spoofed messages with incorrect data between each valid message. This can be used to demonstrate using Scapy, which is a Python program that enables the user to sniff, dissect, forge, and send network packets. This attack is possible due to unencrypted and unauthenticated nature of the GOOSE message.

ICCP TASE 2 (IEC 60870-6)

The Inter Control Center Communications Protocol (ICCP or IEC 60870-6/TASE.2) is the protocol used by various power utilities throughout the world to provide data exchange over Wide Area Networks (WANs) between utility control centers, power pools, regional control centers, and independent power producers. In fact today ICCP is the international standard adopted by IEC as ICCP Telecontrol Application Service Element 2 (TASE2) and is an essential protocol in Power System Automation. Usually a typical national power grid includes a hierarchy of control centers to manage the generation, transmission, and distribution of power throughout the grid. The grid is controlled by one or more hierarchical control centers, which are responsible for scheduling of power generation to meet customer demand, and for managing major network outages and faults.

ICCP Functionalities

The basic functionality of the ICCP is to establish an appropriate link between the other control centres by managing and configuring it for proper information exchange. Generally ICCP establish link with the following control centers in a point to point communication as shown in Figure 8.6.

1. Generation control centers, responsible for managing the operation of generating plants such as coal-fired, natural gas, nuclear, solar, wind, etc. and for adjusting the power generated according to the requirements of the system control center,

2. Transmission control centers, responsible for the transmission of power from generating stations to network distributors, and

3. Distribution control centers, responsible for the distribution of power from the transmission networks to individual consumers.

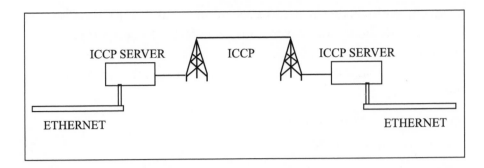

Figure 8.6: ICCP Communication

Protocol Architecture of ICCP TASE 2

At present, the ICCP TASE 2 protocol is the internationally recognized standard for communications between electrical utility control centers. ICCP uses the Manufacturing Messaging Specification (MMS) for the messaging service needed by ICCP. It is based on client/server principles. Consequently data transfers initiated with a request from one control center (client) to another control center (server). Control centers may be both clients and servers. ICCP TASE 2 operates at the application layer in the OSI model. Any physical interfaces transport and network services that fit this model are supported. However TCP/IP over Ethernet seems to be the most common. ICCP may operate over a single point-to-point link between two control centers. The logical connections or *associations* between control centers are completely general. A client can establish association with more than one server and a client can also establish more than one association with the same server. Multiple associations with same server can be established at different levels of Quality of Service (QoS) so that high priority real-time data is not delayed by lower priority or non-real-time data transfers.

Implementation Issues and Interoperability

ICCP is a standard real-time data exchange protocol. It provides numerous features for the delivery of data, monitoring of values, program control and device control. All the protocol specifics needed to ensure interoperability between different vendor's ICCP products have been included in the specifications. The ICCP specifications, however, do not attempt to specify other areas that will need to be implemented in an ICCP software product but that do not affect interoperability. These areas are referred to as local implementation issues in the specification. Some of the local implementation issues in the specification are listed below.

1. The API through which local applications interface to ICCP to send or receive data,

2. A user interface to ICCP for user management of ICCP data links,

3. Management functions for controlling and monitoring ICCP data links,

4. Failover schemes where redundant ICCP servers are required to meet stringent availability requirements, such as those typically experienced in an EMS/SCADA system environment, and

5. How data, programs or devices will be controlled or managed in the local SCADA/EMS to respond to requests received via an ICCP data link.

The wide acceptance of ICCP by the utility industry has resulted in several ICCP products are available on the market. Extensive interoperability testing between products of some of the major vendors has been a feature of ICCP protocol development. An ICCP purchaser must define functionality required in terms of conformance blocks and the objects within those blocks. Application profiles for the ICCP client and server conformances must match if the link is to operate successfully. Interoperability among ICCP of different vendors for the power grid is crucial for achieving the benefits of standardization such as application evolution, open architecture and scalability, plug and play capability of components and services, reliability and service orientation.

Security Concerns

- Like Modbus, ICCP represents several security concerns. ICCP is susceptible to spoofing, session hijacking, and any number of attacks made possible because of:

- Lack of authentication and encryption. ICCP does not mandate authentication or encryption, most often deferring these services to lower protocol layers. Although Secure ICCP does exist, it is not ubiquitously deployed. Explicitly defined trust relationships. The exploitation of bilateral tables could directly compromise security of ICCP servers and clients.

- Accessibility. ICCP is a Wide Area Protocol making it highly accessible and susceptible to many attacks including DoS attacks.

The limited security mechanisms within ICCP are configured on the ICCP Master station, meaning that the successful breach of the Master through a Man-in- the-Middle (MITM) or other attack opens the entire communication session up to manipulation.

8.4 SECURE COMMUNICATION (sCOMMUNICATION)

The main difference between DCS networks and IT networks is mainly the control part and which is not at all a surprise. As an example a compromised power system SCADA is an unacceptable threat to the reliability of the Bulk Electric System (BES). All software can be hacked, including firewalls, hence best-practices and unconditional security standards are recommended. Obviously ICCP communication meets all of these requirements, it does not provide authentication or encryption. These services are normally provided by lower protocol layers. ICCP uses bilateral tables to control access. A bilateral table represents the agreement between two control centers connected with an ICCP link. The agreement identifies data elements and objects that can be accessed via the link and the level of access permitted. Once an ICCP link is established, the contents of the bilateral tables in the server and client provide complete control over what is accessible to each party. There must be matching entries in the server and client tables to provide access to data and objects.

8.5 SELECTING THE RIGHT PROTOCOL FOR SCADA

There are so many protocols available as both proprietary and open, many factors are to be considered when choosing the protocol for SCADA. The following points are useful while designing the SCADA.

1. Determine the system area with which the SCADA may become concerned, e.g.

- the protocol from a SCADA master control station to the SCADA RTUs,
- a protocol from substation IEDs to an RTU or a PLC, or a LAN in the substation.

2. As the technology is changing so fast that the timing of utility installation can have a great impact on the protocol which is selected. Hence the installation period must be determined most appropriately.

If new IEDs are implemented in the substation and scheduled to be in service within six months, protocols may be selected accordingly as Modbus and Modbus Plus are suitable at present in Indian scenario. But if the period of installation and intended applications is for a long time, then consider IEC 61850 and UCA2 MMS as the protocol.

If the timeframe is around one year, make protocol choices from implementing agency that acts as the industry initiatives and incorporates this technology into their product's migration paths. This helps to protect the investment from becoming obsolete by allowing incremental upgrades to new technologies.

In the design phase, protocol choices differ with the application areas. Different application areas are in different stages of development. An awareness of development stages will help to determine realistic plans and schedules for specific projects. Earlier when SCADA were designed, information and system security was not a priority. Most of the SCADA were designed as proprietary, stand-alone systems, and their security resulted from their physical and logical isolation and controlled access to them.

With the advancement of Information and Communication Technology (ICT), SCADA and DCS began to accept open standards and advanced networking technologies especially the internet technology. Suppliers acquired the capability to implement Web-based applications to perform monitoring, control, and remote diagnostics. Obviously this introduces control system cyber-vulnerabilities. In addition to traditional IT vulnerabilities, SCADA specific vulnerabilities become the real threat which triggers unique cyber-security requirements to protect ICS against these SCADA specific attacks and vulnerabilities. Further it is a fact that present day technology may become obsolete tomorrow as the pace of the technological advancement is so fast, it seems the time between the present and the future is shrinking. Hence it is most important that one must evaluate not only the vendor's or implementation agency's present products but also their future product development and implementation strategies.

8.6 SECURITY STANDARDS

There are hundreds of cyber-security standards and regulations imposed by governments and industry, which provide everything from best practices recommendations to hard requirements that are enforced through penalties and fines. Common standards include the North American Electric Reliability Corporation's (NERC's) Critical Infrastructure Protection (CIP) Reliability Standards, ICS security recommendations published by NIST in Special Publication 800-82. International standards include ISA-99/IEC 62443 and ISO/IEC 27002. There are many specific compliance controls within these standards and efforts to maintain compliance with one or more of these regulations can be challenging and complex. These practices often agree with each other to a certain degree, although there are subtle differences among the various standards and regulations that can prove valuable when securing an industrial network.

NERC CIP

The NERC CIP reliability standard identifies security measures for protecting critical infrastructure with the goal of ensuring the reliability of the bulk power system. Compliance is mandatory for any power generation facility, and fines for noncompliance can be steep. The CIP reliability standards consist of mainly nine sections, each with its own requirements and measures. They are Sabotage Reporting, Critical Cyber Asset identification, Security Management Controls, Personnel & Training, Electronic Security Perimeter(s), Physical Security of Critical Cyber Assets, Systems Security Management, Incident Reporting and Response Planning, and Recovery Plans for Critical Cyber Assets. Critical Infrastructure Protection (CIP) standards are made up of nearly 40 rules and almost 100 sub-requirements are today most preferred security standard in power system automation. These provisions are critical for ensuring that electric systems are prepared for mitigating the cyber threats. Understanding certain definitions such as Critical *Assets and Responsible Entities* are better to conceive the concepts well.

Assets, Critical Assets, Cyber Assets, and Critical Cyber Assets: An asset is a unique device that is used within an industrial control system. Assets are often computers, but also include network switches and routers, firewalls, printers, alarm systems, Human–Machine Interfaces (HMIs), Programmable Logic Controllers (PLCs), Remote Terminal Units (RTUs), and the various relays, actuators, sensors, and other devices that make up a typical control loop. NERC CIP defines a *cyber-asset* as any device connected via a routable protocol, which limits the role of a *cyber-asset* to those devices communicating on a routable LAN. A *critical cyber-asset*, again as defined by NERC, is a cyber-asset whose operation can impact the bulk energy system.

Responsible Entities: They are defined as reliability coordinators, balancing authorities, interchange authorities, transmission service providers, transmission owners, transmission operators, generator owners, generator operators; load servicing entities and NERC/regional entities. All responsible entities are required to adhere to standards as defined by NERC.

The set of standards the NERC CIP standards covers mainly the Electronic Security Perimeter (ESP) and the protection of critical cyber-assets, personnel and employee training, security management and disaster recovery planning which are briefly described below.

CIP-002-5.1a-Cyber-Security-BES Cyber System Categorization

This standard requires the security engineer of the utility to identify and categorize BES cyber systems and their associated BES cyber assets for the application of cyber-security requirements commensurate with the adverse impact that loss, compromise, or misuse of those BES cyber systems could have on the reliable operation of the BES. Identification and categorization of BES cyber systems support appropriate protection against compromises that could lead to mal-operation or instability in the BES. During this time the security engineer will identify each critical asset, categorize the asset, prioritize how the asset coincides with compromise or loss and, ultimately, highlight the overall relationship or operating dependency the asset has to the facility. This is helpful when submitting to the NERC Compliance Registry (NCR), and it also aids in creating compliance monitoring objectives.

CIP-003-6-Cyber-Security-Security Management Controls

This standard requires to specify consistent and sustainable security management controls that establish responsibility and accountability to protect Bulk Electric Supply (BES) cyber systems against compromise that could lead to mal-operation or instability. This necessitates consistent and sustainable security management controls be enacted by an organization to protect all identified critical cyber assets from compromise, mal-operation or instability. Cyber-security policy, leadership, exceptions, information protection, access control, change control and configuration management are all included in CIP-003-6, while adherence to sub-requirements may vary by organization, criticality of assets and impact rating.

CIP-004-6-Cyber-Security-Personnel & Training

This standard requires minimizing of risk against compromise that could lead to mal-operation or instability in the BES from individuals accessing BES cyber systems by requiring an appropriate level of personnel risk assessment, training, and security awareness in support of protecting BES Cyber Systems. This necessitates that all personnel with authorized access to critical cyber assets have an adequate degree of personnel screenings and risk assessments, employee training and security awareness programs. Power utility also needs to maintain a list of credentialed access lists, including service providers and contractors. Moreover, CIP-004-6 also requires the organization to document, review and update such training and programs on an annual basis.

CIP-005-5-Cyber-Security-Electronic Security Perimeter(s)

This standard requires to manage electronic access to BES cyber systems by specifying a controlled Electronic Security Perimeter in support of protecting BES cyber systems against compromise that could lead to mal-operation or instability in the BES. This standard primarily focuses on the perimeter and efforts to address vulnerabilities encountered during remote access. The perimeter that houses all critical cyber assets should be protected and any and all access points be secured. Key components to this include, but are not limited to, the following: remote session encryption, multi-factor authentication, anti-malware updates, patch updates and using extensible authentication protocol (EAP) to limit access based upon roles.

CIP-006-6-Cyber-Security-Physical Security of BES Cyber Systems

This standard requires managing physical access to BES cyber systems by specifying a physical security plan in support of protecting BES cyber systems against compromise that could lead to mal-operation or instability in the BES.

This standard emphasizes the physical security perimeter and tasks the responsible entity with implementing a physical security program. The goal is to address the physical security zone and create preventative controls aimed at protecting and controlling access to cyber assets based upon risk-based security zones. A physical security plan, protection of physical access control systems, protection of electronic access control systems, physical access controls, physical access monitoring, physical access logging, log retention access, and maintenance and testing are all requirements of the security program for CIP-006-6.

CIP-007-6-Cyber-Security-System Security Management

This standard requires managing system security by specifying select technical, operational, and procedural requirements in support of protecting BES cyber systems against compromise that could lead to mal-operation or instability in the BES. This requires that create, implement and maintain processes and procedures for securing systems for both critical and non-critical cyber assets. This also means documenting security measures, including records of test procedures, ports and services, security patch management and malicious software prevention.

CIP-008-5-Cyber-Security-Incident Reporting and Response Planning

This standard requires mitigation of the risk to the reliable operation of the BES as the result of a cyber-security incident by specifying incident response requirements. Security incidents related to any critical cyber assets must be identified, classified, responded to and reported in a manner deemed appropriate by NERC. Utility has to create an incident response plan that should include the actions, roles and responsibilities of those involved, as well as details of how incidents should be handled and reported to governing bodies. This plan will need to be updated annually and tested for applicability.

CIP-009-6-Cyber-Security-Recovery Plans for BES Cyber Systems

This standard requires that recover reliability functions performed by BES cyber systems by specifying recovery plan requirements in support of the continued stability, operability, and reliability of the BES. Utility critical cyber assets must have recovery plans that align with their energy utilizes organization and adhere to disaster recovery best practices. A recovery plan, change control, backup and restoration processes and testing or backup media are all requirements of CIP-009-6.

CIP-010-2-Cyber-Security-Configuration Change Management and Vulnerability Assessment

This standard requires preventing and detecting unauthorized changes to BES cyber systems by specifying configuration change management and vulnerability assessment requirements in support of protecting BES Cyber Systems from compromise that could lead to mal-operation or instability in the BES.

CIP-011-2-Cyber-Security-Information Protection

This standard requires to prevent unauthorized access to BES cyber system Information by specifying information protection requirements in support of protecting BES cyber systems against compromise that could lead to mal-operation or instability in the BES.

CIP-014-2-Cyber-Security-Physical Security

This standard requires to identify and protect transmission stations and transmission substations, and their associated primary control centers that if rendered inoperable or damaged as a result of a physical attack, could result in instability, uncontrolled separation, or cascading within an interconnection.

➤ Achieving NERC CIP Compliance:

Compliance is the act of conforming to or adhering to rules, policies, regulations, standards, or requirements. Compliance is an important concern to security governance. On a personnel level, compliance is related to whether individual employees follow company policy and perform their job tasks in accordance to defined procedures. Many organizations rely on employee compliance in order to maintain high levels of quality, consistency, efficiency, and cost savings. If employees do not maintain compliance, it could cost the organization in terms of profit, market share, recognition, and reputation. Employees need to be trained in regard to what they need to do, only then can they be held accountable for violations or lacking compliance.

As NERC CIP is becoming mandatory in power system automation as presently no other equivalent standards are available or developed. Achieving NERC CIP compliance is a complex process, needs in-depth knowledge of ICS and ICT. To be NERC CIP compliant, bulk power supply operators must ensure that they've enacted the measures contained in all of the enforceable CIP standards. The steps below outline what an operator would need to do to ensure they're compliance with NERC's program.

Step 1: Categorization

The very first step in achieving NERC CIP compliance is categorizing an organization's assets. CIP-002 outlines the system used to determine which assets are critical. This allows bulk power suppliers to determine what risks pose the most immediate threats to their systems and so rationalize their security operations.

Step 2: Management and Training

The next steps outlined by the CIP are the management of security (CIP-003) and the training of personnel (CIP-004). CIP-003 requires the creation and maintenance of a security plan, which should outline the measures and processes for the other security measures contained in the other standards. For example, CIP-003 requires operators to create procedures for training personnel according to CIP-004, and to maintain documents pertaining to those procedures. CIP-003 recommends review of the security processes once every 15 months. CIP-004 includes requirements about keeping staff up to code, such as going through quarterly reviews of security practices.

Step 3: Creating and Managing Perimeters

In order to achieve NERC CIP compliance, operators must also implement the requirements of CIP-005 and 006. CIP-005's recommendations focus on creating electronic security perimeters, including creating access limitations for both inbound and outbound network traffic, and the use of measures such as password protection, encryption, and firewalls. CIP-006 moves security into the real world, setting out requirements for ensuring physical security, such as limiting unescorted access to the assets. Measures might include requiring someone to sign in and sign out when accessing the facility. CIP-007 provides information on managing system security. Items covered include keeping lists of listening ports, configuring firewalls, and documenting ports, as well as patch installation and management.

Step 4: Reporting and Recovering from Incidents

CIP-008 and 009 deal with what happens after an incident occurs: how to report it and implement recovery plans. CIP-008 emphasizes the need to adhere to a reporting procedure for incidents, and requires operators to have clear response procedures in place. The plans must be tested once every 15 months. CIP-009 outlines the requirements for recovery plans, which must set forth criteria for triggering a response and the roles and responsibilities of responders, among other things.

Step 5: Changing Environments

CIP-010 addresses change management and vulnerabilities. Operators are required to develop baseline configurations for system assets and use those to monitor and implement changes to the system. They must also document software and patches that are installed on the system. Vulnerability assessments are required once every 15 months.

Step 6: Protecting Data and Physical Assets

Keeping operators' assets, both digital and physical, safe is the goal of the CIP. CIP-011 lays out standards for protecting information and the new CIP-014 addresses the need for physical security. CIP-011 includes requirements for ensuring the staffs to know how to recognize and handle sensitive system information, and for protecting such information. CIP-014 discusses the need to perform vulnerability and risk assessments for the physical operating environment.

The current set of NERC's standards which almost cover all cyber issues of a Bulk Electric System (BES) is flexible and acceptable. Presently it is observed that the power utilities move towards an active consideration of NERC CIP versions 5 & 6 system security, needs rather than just compliance but an effective implementation especially after the cyber-attack on Ukraine power sector. It is largely due to the concerns that some owner/operators are not designating their bulk electric power facilities as *cyber-assets*, leaving potential holes in power system cyber-security.

Cyber Assets in NERC CIP

The NERC's comprehensive document, Security Guideline for the Electricity Sector: Identifying Critical Cyber Assets. Help toward creating a list of Critical Cyber Assets, which are the devices, software, and data described in the NERC glossary as essential to the reliable operation of Critical Assets. The security of the critical assets is essential for the operability of the Bulk Electric System.

The guideline lays out five basic steps for how to define a cyber-security asset:

1. Identify Cyber Assets Associated with a Critical Asset: A responsible entity should inventory and evaluate cyber assets in order to identify those that might impact any of their critical assets. Cyber assets to consider include, but are not limited to:

   - Control systems
   - Data acquisition systems
   - Networking equipment
   - Hardware platforms for virtual machines or storage
   - Secondary or supporting systems such as virus scanners, HVAC systems, and uninterruptible power supplies (UPS)

2. Group Cyber Assets: In order to simplify the process of cyber-security asset definition, group the cyber assets according to various functions and characteristics. One category might include cyber assets that communicate with a particular software. Other examples would be groups based on functions that support specific critical assets.

3. Determine Cyber Assets Which are Essential: Evaluate an asset's impact on critical assets according to the following criteria:

   - Is it essential to the reliable operation of a critical asset?
   - Does it display, transfer, or contain information necessary for real-time operational decisions?
   - Would its loss, degradation, or compromise affect the reliability or operability of the bulk power system?

4. Identify Cyber Assets with Qualifying Connectivity: According to standard CIP-002 R3, cyber assets that meet any of the following requirements are critical:

   - It uses a routable protocol to communicate outside the Electronic Security Perimeter (ESP).
   - It uses a routable protocol within a Control Center.
   - It is dial-up accessible.

5. Compile the List of Critical Cyber Assets: Once evaluated cyber assets and determined which of those are essential to the security

of critical assets, one must document them in a list in order to comply with NERC-CIP standards.

ISA 99/IEC 62443

ISA/IEC-62443 is a series of industrial automation and control system standards, technical reports, and related information that define procedures for implementing electronically secure Industrial Automation and Control Systems (IACS). This guidance applies to end-users (i.e. asset owner), system integrators, security practitioners, and control systems manufacturers responsible for manufacturing, designing, implementing, or managing industrial automation and control systems. All ISA work products are now numbered using the convention ISA-62443-x-y and previous ISA99 nomenclature is maintained for continuity purposes only. Corresponding IEC documents are referenced as IEC 62443-x-y. The approved IEC and ISA versions are generally identical for all functional purposes.

The IEC 62443 standard rests on four pillars.

1. Pillar 1 comprises all documents related to the philosophy of the standard and its underlying concepts, terms and methods.

2. Pillar 2 outlines an IT security management system for industrial automation and control systems with the requisite requirements.

3. Pillar 3 presents technical specifications to serve as design guidance for industrial automation and control systems (IACS); an IACS is an IT system made up of various components such as SCADA applications, PLCs, field buses, actuators and sensors.

4. Pillar 4 contains design and development requirements for control system components.

Communication Security

ACC: Achilles Communications Certification. The certification process assesses the network robustness of industrial devices and certifies that they meet a comprehensive set of requirements. Wurldtech offers two levels of ACC:

- Level 1: An established industry benchmark for the deployment of robust industrial devices recognized by the major automation vendors and operators.

- Level 2: Expansions of Level 1 Certification by employing more tests and more monitor pass/fail requirements

One way to get to into networked embedded device is through communication protocol and Communication between nodes is one of most important aspect of making an embedded device secure. Major security threats for a communication system are:

1. Spoofing – Impersonating as Master and communicating to salve device

2. Data Integrity – Assurance the data sent by master is same received by slave

Level 2 Certification is the successor to Level 1. It employs more tests, Denial of Service tests at higher link rates, and more pass/fail requirements. The tests and pass/fail requirements for Level 2 are a superset of Level 1, so a device that achieves Level 2 certification also meets the requirements for Level 1.

Spoofing

As industrial protocols have no authentication mechanism on their own, it is very much possible that an intruder's message, from outside the company firewall, can be sent directly to a process controller. The Corporate Firewall does not check for specific protocol messages. The possible defense techniques would be to have additional firewalls that have rules to drop malformed messages or allow access to change only few parameters and drop requests to access/change other parameters. Figure 8.7 shows it as *Control Firewall*, these devices check each packet passing through it. These can only restrict the intruder's activity, but will not prevent if intruder message falls within rules set on control firewall. So truly speaking, defense against spoofing is still not yet there for most industrial protocols.

Data Integrity

As in safety critical applications, implementing a safety layer on top of communication layer guarantees the integrity of message. The safety layer is developed on both the transmitter and receiver message as shown in diagram below.

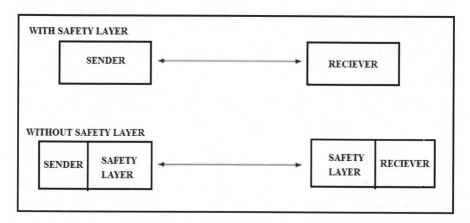

Figure 8.7: Data integrity in IEC 62443

All ISA-62443 standards and technical reports are organized into four general categories called

1. General,

2. Policies and Procedures,

3. System, and

4. Component.

1. The first (top) category includes common or foundational information such as concepts, models and terminology. Also included are work products that describe security metrics and security life cycles for IACS.

2. The second category of work products targets the Asset Owner. These address various aspects of creating and maintaining an effective IACS security program.

3. The third category includes work products that describe system design guidance and requirements for the secure integration

of control systems. Core in this is the zone and conduit design model.

4. The fourth category includes work products that describe the specific product development and technical requirements of control system products. This is primarily intended for control product vendors, but can be used by integrator and asset owners for to assist in the procurement of secure products.

The planned and published ISA-62443 documents are as follows:

Group 1: General

- **ISA-62443-1-1 (IEC/TS 62443-1-1)** (formerly referred to as ISA-99 Part 1 was originally published as ISA standard ANSI/ISA-99.00.01-2007, as well as an IEC technical specification IEC/TS 62443-1-1. The ISA99 committee is currently revising it to make it align with other documents in the series, and to clarify normative content.

- **ISA-TR62443-1-2 (IEC 62443-1-2)** is a master glossary of terms used by the ISA99 committee. This document is a working draft, but the content is available on the ISA99 committee Wiki.

- **ISA-62443-1-3 (IEC 62443-1-3)** identifies a set of compliance metrics for IACS security. This document is currently under development and the committee will be releasing a draft for comment in 2013.

- **ISA-62443-1-4 (IEC/TS 62443-1-4)** defines the IACS security life cycle and use case. This work product has been proposed as part of the series, but as of January 2013 development had not yet started.

Group 2: Policy and Procedure

- **ISA-62443-2-1 (IEC 62443-2-1)** (formerly referred to as ANSI/ISA 99.02.01-2009 or ISA-99 Part 2 addresses how to establish an IACS security program. This standard is approved and published the IEC as IEC 62443-2-1. It now being revised to permit closer alignment with the ISO 27000 series of standards.

- **ISA-62443-2-2 (IEC 62443-2-2)** addresses how to operate an IACS security program. This standard is currently under development.

- **ISA-TR62443-2-3 (IEC/TR 62443-2-3)** is a technical report on the subject of patch management in IACS environments. This report is currently under development.

ISA-62443-2-4 (IEC 62443-2-4) focuses on the certification of IACS supplier security policies and practices. This document was adopted from the WIB organization and is now a working product of the IEC TC65/WG10 committee. The proposed ISA version will be a U.S. national publication of the IEC standard.

Group 3: System Integrator

- **ISA-TR62443-3-1 (IEC/TR 62443-3-1)** is a technical report on the subject of suitable technologies for IACS security. This report is approved and published as ANSI/ISA-TR99.00.01-2007 and is now being revised.

- **ISA-62443-3-2 (IEC 62443-3-2)** addresses how to define security assurance levels using the zones and conduits concept. This standard is currently under development.

- **ISA-62443-3-3 (IEC 62443-3-3)** defines detailed technical requirements for IACS security. This standard has been published as ANSI/ISA-62443-3-3 (99.03.03)-2013. It was previously numbered as ISA-99.03.03.

Group 4: Component Provider

- **ISA-62443-4-1 (IEC 62443-4-1)** addresses the requirements for the development of secure IACS products and solutions. This standard is currently under development.

- **ISA-62443-4-2 (IEC 62443-4-2)** series address detailed technical requirements for IACS components level. This standard is currently under development.

➤ **Compliance Procedure**

The procedure to get an embedded device compliant is very much similar to getting a device safety certified. The very first step is to have a certified system/product development process. Though it is not a must to have a mature process, it is an advantage in obtaining the IEC 62443 certification. Compliance to CMMI (Capability Maturity Model Integration), level 3 certification and above quality standards is good benchmark of a mature process.

The device needs to be designed considering the requirements as specified in ISA99/IEC62443. The processes and design of device have to be approved by an Assessor. The Assessor is usually from an external organization that has track record of certifying compliance to ISA99. Testing the device based on set of test procedures usually carry out in an accredited lab such as Achilles Test Platform.

> **Organization certifying embedded devices**

There are two well recognized organizations certifying embedded devices on cyber-security viz. Wurldtech and ISASecure. The choice between the two certification bodies would be purely based on specific project teams or cost or comfort level or previous project experiences.

1. Wurldtech, a GE company, offers the Achilles certification for devices. There are 2 levels of certification viz. level 1 and level 2. Level 2 requires more number of tests to be passed. Wurldtech does not publicly state the requirements that need to pass to obtain the certification rather they recommend the use of Achilles Test Platform during the development stage to test the embedded device.

2. ISASecure, an association of Industrial control system users and manufacturers. ISASecure's EDSA (Embedded Device Security Assurance) certification is intended for embedded devices. ISA Secure EDSA certification comprises of,

   - certifying the processes,
   - the design of embedded device and
   - passing the conformance testing.

The ISA Secure have come out with their own specifications on all 3 above mentioned steps and publicly available on their website. It is largely based on IEC 62443 standards and also some specifications from NERC and NIST. There are 3 levels of EDSA certification with level 3 being the stringent.

One thing to be noted is both the organizations offer their own named certification – Achilles certification or ISA Secure EDA certification and do not explicitly certify complying to ISA 99/IEC 62443. The choice between the 2 certification bodies would be purely based on specific project teams or cost or comfort level or previous project experiences.

NIST SP 800-53

NIST sets the security standards for agencies and implementers. It's structured as a set of security guidelines, designed to prevent major security issues that are making the headlines nearly every day. It is a non-regulatory agency of the U.S. Commerce Department, tasked with researching and establishing standards across all federal agencies. NIST SP 800-53 defines the standards and guidelines for federal agencies to architect and manage their information security systems. It was established to provide guidance for the protection of agency's and citizen's private data. In many cases, complying with NIST guidelines and recommendations will help federal agencies ensure compliance with other regulations, such as the Health Insurance Portability and Accountability Act (HIPAA), Federal Information Security Management Act (FISMA), or Sarbanes-Oxley Act (SOX). NIST guidelines are often developed to help agencies meet specific regulatory compliance requirements. NIST has outlined the following nine steps toward FISMA compliance.

- Categorize the data and information you need to protect
- Develop a baseline for the minimum controls required to protect that information
- Conduct risk assessments to refine your baseline controls
- Document your baseline controls in a written security plan
- Roll out security controls to your information systems
- Once implemented, monitor performance to measure the efficacy of security controls

- Determine agency-level risk based on your assessment of security controls
- Authorize the information system for processing
- Continuously monitor your security controls

NIST's 800 series documents provide best practices and information of general interest to information security. All 800 series documents concern information security and should be used as references where applicable. Of particular relevance to industrial network security is SP 800-53 (Recommended Security Controls for Federal Information Systems), which defines many aspects of information security procedures and technologies, and SP 800-82 (Guide to Supervisory Control and Data Acquisition [SCADA] and Industrial Control Systems Security), which discusses industrial control system security specifically. Although of the entire SP800-53 is applicable to the protection of critical infrastructures, the technical aspects defined under SP 800-53 as Access Control, Security Assessment and Authorization, Configuration Management, Identification and Authentication, Risk Assessment, System and Communications Protection, and System and Information Integrity are directly applicable to industrial networks. SP 800-82 details control system architectures, protocols, vulnerabilities, and security controls.

CEA GUIDELINES TO CYBER-SECURITY IN POWER SECTOR IN INDIA

The objective of the CEA guidelines to cyber-security in power sector are:

a. Creating cyber security awareness,

b. Creating a secure cyber ecosystem,

c. Creating a cyber-assurance framework,

d. Strengthening the regulatory framework,

e. Creating mechanisms for security threat early warning, vulnerability management and response to security threats,

f. Securing remote operations and services,

g. Protection and resilience of critical information infrastructure,

h. Reducing cyber supply chain risks,

i. Encouraging use of open standards,

j. Promotion of research and development in cyber security,

k. Human resource development in the domain of Cyber Security,

l. Developing effective public private partnerships,

m. Information sharing and cooperation

n. Operationalization of the National Cyber Security Policy

The Guidelines on Cyber Security are in the form of Articles mentioned below, requires mandatory Compliance by all Responsible Entities.

Article 1. Cyber-security policy

Article 2. Appointment of CISO.

Article 3. Identification of Critical Information Infrastructure (CII).

Article 4. Electronic Security Perimeter

Article 5. Cyber-security Requirements

Article 6. Cyber Risk Assessment and Mitigation Plan

Article 7. Phasing out of Legacy System

Article 8. Cyber-security Training.

Article 9. Cyber Supply Chain Risk Management

Article 10. Cyber-security Incident Report and Response Plan

Article 11. Cyber Crisis Management Plan(C-CMP)

Article 12. Sabotage Reporting

Article 13. Security and Testing of Cyber Assets

Article 14. Cyber-security Audit

Summary

This chapter begins with the evolution of communication protocols and then move on to explain the various communication protocols used today such as DNP3, Modbus, Profibus, IEC 60870, IEC 61850, and ICCP TASE 2 (IEC 60870-6). Then move on to explaining various security standards presently existing in the industrial sector and their selection requirements. IEC 62443, NIST 800, NERC CIP, CEA guidelines and ISO 27001 standards are briefly explained. The compliance procedure for IEC 62443 and NERC CIP are also described as they are most pertinent today.

Investigations and Litigations of Cybercrimes in CII

9.1 INTRODUCTION

Cybercrime investigation is the process of investigating, analyzing and recovering critical forensic digital data from the networks involved in the attack – this could be the Internet and/or a local network--in order to identify the authors of the digital crime and their true intentions. This chapter describes the drawbacks, constrains and requirements of the present law enforcement system.

9.2 CYBERCRIME

Cybercrime is any criminal activity that involves a computer, networked device or a network to carry out a wide range of malicious activities, including the illegal interception of data, system interferences that compromise network integrity and availability, and copyright infringements. While most cybercrimes are carried out in order to generate profit for the cybercriminals, some cybercrimes are carried out against computers or devices directly to damage or disable them. Some cybercrimes do both – i.e., target computers to infect them with a computer virus, which is then spread to other machines and, sometimes, entire networks. Cybercrime has been divided into three categories:

1. crimes in which the computing device is the target – for example, to gain network access;

2. crimes in which the computer is used as a weapon – for example, to launch a denial of Service; and

3. crimes in which the computer is used as an accessory to a crime – for example, using a computer to store illegally obtained data.

The necessity of internet connectivity has enabled an increase in the volume and pace of cybercrime activities because the criminal no longer needs to be physically present when committing a crime. The internet's speed, convenience, anonymity and lack of borders make computer-based variations of financial crimes – such as ransomware, fraud and money laundering, as well as crimes such as stalking and bullying – easier to carry out. Cybercriminal activity may be carried out by individuals or groups with relatively little technical skill, Or by highly organized global criminal groups that may include skilled developers and others with relevant expertise. To further reduce the chances of detection and prosecution, cybercriminals often choose to operate in countries with weak or non-existent cybercrime laws.

Cybercrimes generally do not occur in a vacuum; they are, in many ways, distributed in nature. That is, cybercriminals typically rely on other actors to complete the crime such as selling the developed malware code, selling the illegal pharmaceuticals using the dark web, etc. Cybercriminals use various attack vectors to carry out their cyber-attacks and are constantly seeking new methods and techniques for achieving their goals, while avoiding detection and arrest. Computer crimes are generally classified as one of the following types:

1. Military and intelligence attacks
2. Business attacks
3. Financial attacks
4. Terrorist attacks
5. Grudge attacks
6. Thrill attacks

It is important to understand the differences among the categories of computer crime to best understand how to protect a system and react when an attack occurs. The type and amount of evidence left by an attacker is often dependent on their expertise. This evidence can help to determine the attacker's actions and intended target. Among these attacks, CI attacks may be the result of a *Terrorist attack or a Thrill attack*.

9.3 TERRORIST ATTACKS

Terrorist attacks are a reality in modern society. The increasing reliance on information systems makes them more and more attractive to terrorists. Such attacks differ from military and intelligence attacks. The purpose of a terrorist attack is to disrupt normal life and instil fear, whereas a military or intelligence attack is designed to extract secret information. Intelligence gathering generally precedes any type of terrorist attack. The very systems that are victims of a terrorist attack were probably compromised in an earlier attack to collect intelligence. The more diligent in detecting attacks of any type, the better prepared to intervene before more serious attacks occur. Possible targets of a computer terrorist attack could be systems that regulate power plants or control telecommunications or power distribution. Many such control and regulatory systems are computerized and vulnerable to terrorist action. In fact, the possibility exists of a simultaneous physical and computerized terrorist attack. Our ability to respond to such an attack would be greatly diminished if the physical attack were simultaneously launched with a computer attack designed to knock out power and communications. Most large power and communications companies have dedicated a security staff to ensure the security of their systems, but many smaller businesses that have systems connected to the Internet are more vulnerable to attacks. One must diligently monitor their systems to identify any attacks and then respond swiftly when an attack is discovered.

Thrill Attacks

Thrill attacks are the attacks launched only for the fun of it. Attackers who lack the ability to devise their own attacks will often download programs that do their work for them. These attackers are often called *script kiddies* because they run only other people's programs, or scripts, to launch an attack. The main motivation behind these attacks is the high of successfully breaking into a system. If you are the victim of a thrill attack, the most common fate one will suffer is a service interruption. Although an attacker of this type may destroy data, the main motivation is to compromise a system and perhaps use it to launch an attack against another victim.

Incident Handling

When an incident occurs, one must handle it in a manner that is outlined in their security policy and consistent with local laws and regulations. The first step in handling an incident properly is recognizing when it occurs. Better one should understand the following two terms related to incident handling.

Event Any occurrence that takes place during a certain period of time

Incident An event that has a negative outcome affecting the confidentiality, integrity, or availability of an organization's data. The most common reason incidents are not reported is that most of the occasions they are never identified. One could have many security policy violations occurring each day, but if one don't have a way of identifying them, they will never know. Therefore, the security policy should identify and list all possible violations and ways to detect them. It's also important to update the security policy as new types of violations and attacks emerge.

9.4 INCIDENT RESPONSE PROCESS

Many organizations use a three-step incident response process, consisting of the following phases:

1. Detection and identification
2. Response and reporting
3. Recovery and remediation

9.5 COMPLEXITIES IN CYBERCRIME

Hacking, cracking, and attacking have only increased over the years and will not stop anytime soon. Several issues deal with why these activities have not been properly stopped or even curbed. These include proper identification of the attackers, the necessary level of protection for networks, and successful prosecution once an attacker is captured.

Most attackers are never caught because they spoof their addresses and identities and use methods to cover their footsteps. Many attackers break into networks, take whatever resources they were after, and clean the logs that tracked their movements and activities. Because of this, many companies do not even know they have been violated. Even if an attacker's activities trigger an intrusion detection system (IDS) alert, it does not usually find the true identity of the individual, though it does alert the company that a specific vulnerability was exploited.

Attackers commonly hop through several systems before attacking their victim so that tracking them down will be more difficult. Many of these criminals use innocent people's computers to carry out the crimes for them. The attacker will install malicious software on a computer using many types of methods: e-mail attachments, a user downloading a Trojan horse from a web site, exploiting a vulnerability, and so on. Once the software is loaded, it stays dormant until the attacker tells it what systems to attack and when. These compromised systems are called *zombies*, the software installed on them are called *bots*, and when an attacker has several compromised systems, this is known as a *botnet*. The botnet can be used to carry out DDoS attacks, transfer spam or pornography, or do whatever the attacker programs the bot software to do.

Within the United States, local law enforcement departments, the FBI, and the Secret Service are called upon to investigate a range of computer crimes. Although each of these entities works to train its people to identify and track computer criminals, collectively they are very far behind the times in their skills and tools, and are outnumbered by the number of hackers actively attacking networks. Because the attackers use tools that are automated, they can perform several serious attacks in a short timeframe.

When law enforcement is called in, its efforts are usually more manual—checking logs, interviewing people, investigating hard drives, scanning for vulnerabilities, and setting up traps in case the attacker comes back. Each agency can spare only a small number of people for computer crimes, and generally they are behind in their expertise compared to many hackers. Because of this, most attackers are never found, much less prosecuted. This in no way means all attackers get away with their misdeeds. Law enforcement is continually improving its tactics, and individuals are being prosecuted every month.

Really only a handful of laws deal specifically with computer crimes, making it more challenging to successfully prosecute the attackers who are caught. Many companies that are victims of an attack usually just want to ensure that the vulnerability the attacker exploited is fixed, instead of spending the time and money to go after and prosecute the attacker

9.6 CYBER LAW FOR CYBER TERRORISM

The traditional concepts and methods of terrorism have taken new dimensions especially with the amalgamation of ICT in Critical Infrastructure of a Nation, which are more destructive and deadly in nature. In the age of information technology the terrorists have acquired an expertise to produce the most deadly combination of weapons and technology, which if not properly safeguarded in due course of time, will take its own toll. The damage so produced would be devastating and irreversible in nature. In short, Nations are facing the worst form of terrorism popularly known as *Cyber Terrorism*. The expression *cyber terrorism* includes an intentional negative and harmful use of the information technology for producing destructive and harmful effects to the property, whether tangible or intangible, of others.

The nature of *cyberspace* is such that new methods and technologies are invented occasionally; hence it is not advisable to put the definition in a straightjacket formula or pigeons hole. In fact, the first effort of the Courts should be to interpret the definition as liberally as possible so that the menace of cyber terrorism can be tackled stringently and with a punitive hand. The law dealing with cyber terrorism is, however, not adequate to meet the precarious intentions of these cyber terrorists and requires a rejuvenation in the light and context of the latest developments all over the world.

Thus, a cyber-terrorist can collapse the economic structure of a country from a place with which a Nation may not have any reciprocal arrangements, including an extradition treaty. The only safeguard in such a situation is to use the latest technology to counter these problems. Thus, a good combination of the latest security technology and a law dealing with cyber terrorism is the need of the hour.

Any ICT infrastructure is effective till the authorities are capable of securing and protecting it. It must be appreciated that the ICT infrastructure of a nation can exist only to the extent it can be protected from internal and external online attacks. This *need* becomes a *compulsion* if a law fixes both civil and criminal liability to the authorities for failure to act diligently. Both the citizens and companies are required to establish a sound and secure ICT infrastructure to escape the accusation of lack of *due diligence.*

9.7 CYBER TERRORISM-PREVENTION IS BETTER THAN CURE

The vast majority of successful cyber-attacks continue to exploit inadequate (or vulnerable) implementation of basic technical and management disciplines-a lack of fundamental cyber hygiene. It is better to have a prevention strategy rather curing mechanism as a catastrophic CI attack is mostly non-curable.

How it is possible? The investigation agencies have to meticulously dissect the previous CI attacks occurred and a proper inferences have to be drawn out to design and implement an appropriate mitigation strategy. Above all the courts which deal with cyber terrorism must have not only techno savvy judges, rather constantly updating techno-conscious judges as in US. Else the investigation reports, FIRs, etc. will be garlands in the hands of monkeys. A careful examination reveals that this is the outcome in most of the cyber terrorism litigations globally.

U.S is the nation which faces maximum number of industrial cyber-attacks especially to their critical infrastructure. Colonial Pipeline ransomware attack, Crashed Ohio Nuke Plant Network by Slammer Worm, Taum Sauk Hydroelectric Power Station Failure, Cyber Incident on Georgia Nuclear Power Plant, Penetration of Electricity Grid of US by Spies, etc. are some them. The US power sector has prevented millions of cyber-attacks in 2020-that takes 24/7 commitment.

Presently FBI is the lead federal agency for investigating cyber-attacks and intrusions and also predestined as their number one priority to protect the United States from terrorist attacks. They are committed to remaining agile in its approach to the terrorism threat, which has continued to evolve since the September 11, 2001 terror attacks.

The Bureau works closely with its partners to neutralize terrorist cells and operatives here in the United States, to help dismantle extremist networks worldwide, and to cut off financing and other forms of support provided to foreign terrorist organizations. The FBI's cyber strategy is to impose risk and consequences on cyber adversaries. Their goal is to change the behaviour of criminals and nation-states who believe they can compromise U.S. networks, steal financial and intellectual property, and put critical infrastructure at risk without facing risk themselves. To do this, they use their unique mix of authorities, capabilities, and partnerships to impose consequences against their cyber adversaries. Whether through developing innovative investigative techniques, using cutting-edge analytic tools, or forging new partnerships in our communities, the FBI continues to adapt to meet the challenges posed by the evolving cyber threat.

- The FBI has specially trained cyber squads in all their field offices, working hand-in-hand with inter-agency task force partners.

- The rapid-response Cyber Action Team can deploy across the country within hours to respond to major incidents.

- With cyber assistant legal attachés in embassies across the globe, the FBI works closely with their international counterparts to seek justice for victims of malicious cyber activity.

- The Internet Crime Complaint Center (IC3) collects reports of Internet crime from the public. Using such complaints, the IC3's Recovery Asset Team has assisted in freezing hundreds of thousands of dollars for victims of cybercrime.

- CyWatch is the FBI's 24/7 operations center and watch floor, providing around-the-clock support to track incidents and communicate with field offices across the country.

It is important for people to protect themselves both online and in-person, and to report any suspicious activity they encounter by:

- Remain aware of their surroundings.

- Refrain from oversharing personal information.

Say something if see something. The insular nature of today's violent extremists makes them difficult for law enforcement to identify and disrupt before an attack. Many times, a person's family or friends may be the first to notice a concerning change in behaviour that may indicate a person is mobilizing to violence.

9.8 A TECHNO-LEGAL ISSUE AND FUTILE INVESTIGATIONS

To most of the investigation agencies and law enforcement agencies of different nations, cyber-terrorism investigation is a paradox as it is hard to conceive the high tech crime details. For instance, in 2021 there was a cyber-attack on Mumbai power grid. Initially it has been thought as a power failure by the supply utility and by the government authorities. But the private agencies who are engaged with the power system automation expressed concern of a cyber-attack as they could observe the nature of cascading failure of BES from Mumbai to Pune. Following this comments an enquiry has been conducted and 14 Trojans and 8 GB unaccounted data has been found in the server of the State Load Dispatch Center (SLDC) installed from a foreign server. Even then investigation agencies could not conclusively found how these Trojans attack the energy management system to disrupt the power supply. Most important fact is that the investigation agencies failed to find how the Trojans have been infiltrated and installed in the server of SLDC. Even the competent cyber-experts of Government agencies are fumbling to find the exact cause, obviously it is not at all a surprise that attempts of usual crime detecting agencies become futile, unless they team up with an appropriate domain experts. Hence cyber-attacks on CI are exclusively a high tech techno-legal issue and has to be investigated by team comprising domain experts and legal experts in addition to cops. Today cyber-terrorism investigation in many countries are initiated with appropriate public-private participation.

In US, the cyber-attacks on CI are investigated by teams comprising techno savvy police officers and domain experts in the respective fields. Unfortunately, there is no enabling provision in most of the other nation's legal system which empowers a domain expert to be formally part of the evidence gathering team. In the absence of such a provision, the prosecution is susceptible to charges of evidence tampering in case a domain expert is involved by any agency, as the Criminal Procedure Code authorizes only the police to collect evidence. The following technical experts are usually be the part of such investigations in US.

Critical Infrastructure Protection

1. Senior Emerging Technology Security Researcher

2. Senior Director, Critical Infrastructure Protection

3. Senior Critical Infrastructure Analyst

4. Operational Technology Specialist

5. Senior Application Security Engineer

Critical Infrastructure Threat Management

1. Third Party Cyber Risk Program Manager

2. Cyber Sr. Strategic Analyst

3. Cyber Strategic Analyst

4. Cyber Technical Analyst

5. Counter Threat Automation Engineer (Content Engineer)

6. Counter Threat Automation Engineer (Developer)

7. Counter Threat Automation - Associate Developer

8. CERT Specialist

The cyber-terrorism issues need to be investigated by team comprising appropriate technical experts, legal experts and techno savvy police officers. The minimum domain expertise requirements for the team investigating critical infrastructure cyber-terrorism issues are listed below.

I. **Knowledge Set Requirements**

1. Deep understanding of computer networking and industrial networking concepts and protocols.

2. Knowledge of electronic devices used in ICS control room, industrial process, access control devices, digital cameras, memory cards, modems, hard drives, network components, printers, copiers, storage devices, etc.

3. Knowledge of Defense-in-Depth architecture and policies of Critical Infrastructure Protection(CIP),

4. Knowledge of Security Operations Center(SOC) and its functions,

5. Knowledge of SCADA, ICS and modern automation devices used especially PLC, RTU, DCU, MU, WSN, BCU etc.,

6. Knowledge of communication protocols deployed such as IEC 101, 102, 104, IEC 61850, DNP3, Modbus, Profibus, etc.,

7. Knowledge of security standards such as ISA 99/IEC 62443, NERC CIP, NIST SP-800-53, ISO/IEC 27001 etc.,

8. Knowledge of defining Electronic Security Perimeter (ESP) especially in power sector automation,

9. Knowledge of cyber threats and vulnerabilities to automated critical infrastructure, SCADA systems and deployment of IDS, IPS and Firewalls.

10. Knowledge of industrial network perimeter security,

11. Knowledge of system and application security threats and vulnerabilities,

12. Knowledge of insider threat investigations, reporting, investigative tools, laws and regulations,

13. Knowledge of physical and physiological behaviors of employees that may indicate suspicious or abnormal activity,

14. Knowledge of crisis management protocols, processes and techniques,

15. Knowledge of IT laws prevailing in the country, regulations, policies and ethics related to cyber security,

16. Knowledge of cyber security principles and privacy principles,

17. Knowledge of crisis management protocols, processes and techniques, and

18. Knowledge of covert communication techniques

II. **Legal Procedure Requirements**

1. Knowledge for processes for seizing and preserving digital evidence without delay, proper testing and certifications from approved Labs.

2. Knowledge of legal governance related to admissibility of digital evidences,

3. Knowledge of processes for collecting, packaging, transporting and storing electronic evidence while maintaining chain of custody,

4. Knowledge of types and collection of persistent data,

5. Knowledge of electronic evident law,

6. Knowledge of legal rules of evidence and court procedures, and

7. Knowledge of judicial process, including the presentation of facts and evidence.

III. **Skill Set Requirements**

1. Skill in preserving evidence integrity according to standard operating procedures or national standards,

2. Skill in collecting, processing, packaging, transporting and storing electronic evidence to avoid alteration, loss, physical damage or destruction of data,

3. Skill in using scientific rules and methods to solve problems, and

4. Skill in evaluating the trustworthiness of the supplier and product.

IV. **Abilities Required**

1. Ability to find and navigate the dark web using the TOR network to locate markets and forums.

2. Ability to examine digital media on multiple operating system platforms.

9.9 ISSUES WITH DIGITAL EVIDENCE COLLECTION

Collecting digital evidence is a tricky process and should be attempted only by professional forensic technicians. The International Organization on Computer Evidence (IOCE) outlines six principles to guide digital evidence technicians as they perform media analysis, network analysis, and software analysis in the pursuit of forensically recovered evidence: When dealing with digital evidence, all of the general forensic and procedural principles must be applied.

Upon seizing digital evidence, actions taken should not change that evidence. When it is necessary for a person to access original digital evidence, that person should be trained for the purpose. All activity relating to the seizure, access, storage, or transfer of digital evidence must be fully documented, preserved, and available for review.

An individual is responsible for all actions taken with respect to digital evidence while the digital evidence is in their possession. Any agency that is responsible for seizing, accessing, storing, or transferring digital evidence is responsible for compliance with these principles.

As one conduct forensic evidence collection, it is important to preserve the original evidence. Therefore, when analysing digital evidence, it's best to work with a copy of the actual evidence whenever possible. For instance, when conducting an investigation into the contents of a hard drive, make an image of that drive, seal the original drive in an evidence bag, and then use the disk image for the investigation.

Media Analysis

Media analysis, a branch of computer forensic analysis, involves the identification and extraction of information from storage media. This may include the following: Magnetic media (e.g., hard disks, tapes) Optical media (e.g., CDs, DVDs, Blu-ray discs) Memory (e.g., RAM, solid state storage) Techniques used for media analysis may include the recovery of deleted files from unallocated sectors of the physical disk, the live analysis of storage media connected to a computer system (especially useful when examining encrypted media), and the static analysis of forensic images of storage media.

Network Analysis

Forensic investigators are also often interested in the activity that took place over the network during a security incident. This is often difficult to reconstruct due to the volatility of network data-if it isn't deliberately recorded at the time it occurs, it generally is not preserved. Network forensic analysis, therefore, often depends on either prior knowledge that an incident is underway or the use of pre-existing security controls that log network activity.

These include:

> Intrusion detection and prevention system logs

> Network flow data captured by a flow monitoring system

> Packet captures deliberately collected during an incident

> Logs from firewalls and other network security devices

The task of the network forensic analyst is to collect and correlate information from these disparate sources and produce as comprehensive a picture of network activity as possible.

Software Analysis

Forensic analysts may also be called on to conduct forensic reviews of applications or the activity that takes place within a running application. In some cases, when malicious insiders are suspected, the forensic analyst may be asked to conduct a review of software code, looking for back doors, logic bombs, or other security vulnerabilities. In other cases, forensic analysis may be asked to review and interpret the log files from application or database servers, seeking other signs of malicious activity, such as SQL injection attacks, privilege escalations, or other application attacks.

Hardware/Embedded Device Analysis

Finally, forensic analysts often must review the contents of hardware and embedded devices. This may include a review of Personal computers, Smartphones, Tablet computers, embedded computers in cars, security systems, and other devices. Analysts conducting these reviews must have specialized knowledge of the systems under review. This often requires calling in expert consultants who are familiar with the memory, storage systems, and operating systems of such devices. Because of the complex interactions between software, hardware, and storage, the discipline of hardware analysis requires skills in both media analysis and software analysis.

Investigation Process

When someone initiate a computer security investigation, he should first assemble a team of competent analysts to assist with the investigation. This team should operate under the organization's existing incident response policy and be given a charter that clearly outlines the scope of the investigation, the authority, roles, and responsibilities of the investigators and any rules of engagement that they must follow while conducting the investigation. These rules of engagement define and guide the actions that investigators are authorized to take at different phases of the investigation, such as calling in law enforcement, interrogating suspects, collecting evidence, and disrupting system access.

Calling in Law Enforcement

One of the first decisions that must be made in an investigation is whether law enforcement authorities should be called in. This is a relatively complicated decision that should involve senior management officials. There are many factors in favour of calling in the experts.

9.10 GATHERING DIGITAL EVIDENCE

It is common to confiscate equipment, software, or data to perform a proper investigation. The manner in which the evidence is confiscated is important. The confiscation of evidence must be carried out in a proper fashion. There are three basic alternatives. First, the person who owns the evidence could *voluntarily surrender* it. This method is generally appropriate only when the attacker is not the owner. Few guilty parties willingly surrender evidence they know will incriminate them. Less experienced attackers may believe they have successfully covered their tracks and voluntarily surrender important evidence. A good forensic investigator can extract much covered-up information from a computer. In most cases, asking for evidence from a suspected attacker just alerts the suspect that you are close to taking legal action.

Second, you could get a court to issue a *subpoena*, or court order, that compels an individual or organization to surrender evidence and then have the subpoena served by law enforcement. Again, this course of action provides sufficient notice for someone to alter the evidence and render it useless in court. The last option is a *search warrant*. This option should be used only when you must have access to evidence without tipping off the evidence's owner or other personnel. You must have a strong suspicion with credible reasoning to convince a judge to pursue this course of action. You should consider the following sources of data when determining what evidence to gather.

1. Computer systems involved in the incident,

2. Logs from security systems such as intrusion detection, file integrity monitoring, and firewalls,

3. Logs from network devices Physical access logs, and

4. Other relevant sources of information specific to the incident under investigation.

In fact these digital evidence collection is a highly skilled job and badly need domain experts. Just imagine that an investigation team which has proven track record in crime investigation other than cybercrimes has been assigned to investigate a cybercrime of stealing an iPhone belongs to an OT cyber-security engineer having a memory of 64GB data stored which includes PII and critical information of attack surfaces/vectors of a CI of a Nation. What would be the outcome?

As the gravity of the incident of stealing the iPhones and storage elements containing critical data and intellectual property, the following minimum procedures which have to be followed by the investigation officer. The collection of computer evidence is a very complex and technology oriented task, it require highly skilled people. Else evidence can be ruined forever. Hence if the investigating officer to take expert opinion from domain expert for a proper investigation.

Comprehend the motive, opportunity, and means (MOM) very urgently. The theft is no longer restricted to physical constraints as the assets include intangible objects that can also be stolen or disclosed via technological means. The evidence life cycle which include the identification and collection of the evidence and its storage, preservation, transportation, presentation in court, and return to the owner, must be carried out quickly with due diligence as possible as the impact/risk in the OT security can be devastating.

In relation to the iPhones it has to be kept in the following conditions.

Whether device is ON or OFF

if ON, then:

1. Leave the iPhones ON,
2. Photograph the device
3. Note down serial number etc,
4. Label and collect all the cables.
5. If possible keep device charged. (If Device goes off, it may not turn back on, or it may be password protected and difficult to crack at the time of forensic analysis).
6. Seize the phone in a Faraday's Bag (that protects phone from external signals) and/or any other anti-static bag.
7. The suspects should not be allowed to work on the iPhones.

As the evidence in this computer crime comes straight from iPhones, the data are held as electronic voltages, which are represented as binary bits. Some data can be held on memory sticks and some data may be held in the memory of the system itself. This type of evidence is intangible in that it is not made up of objects one can hold, see, and easily understand. Hence requested to carry out the investigation with due diligence. o Also requested follow when gathering and extracting evidence as the iPhones and external hard disk have been confiscated, the first thing the computer forensics team may make an image of the storage/memory. The investigation team may work from this image instead of the original hard drive so it stays in a pristine state and the evidence on the drive is not accidentally corrupted or modified.

The iPhones may carry personally identifiable information (PII) and can be used to uniquely identify, contact, or locate a single person or can be used with other sources to uniquely identify a single individual. This type of data are under privacy laws and regulation protection requirements.

Suppose the investigation team which has no domain expert was able to seize the iPhone, definitely they were quite unaware of the procedures and definitely the evidence would have been lost as they treat the iPhone simply as a material object. Their incapability of comprehending the logical evidence stored in the device, which is the vital object will be lost due to the lack of due diligence. This is the actual situations happening to most of the cybercrimes and the real culprits simply escapes. Suppose what would be the result if the data breaching has been occurred, and the critical information of attack surfaces/vectors of a CI of a Nation reaches the cyber terrorists. A sabotage on the Critical Infrastructure by the cyber terrorists. Who will responsible for this sabotage? Absolutely no doubt, the investigation authorities are responsible for failure to act diligently if a cyber-law exists in that Nation to counter cyber terrorism. Hence without the assistance of an appropriate domain expert, investigation of a cyber-attack on a CI can be hardly fruitful. Similarly when dealing with investigation of CI crimes, one may be thoroughly familiar with the ICS, SCADA components and ICS networks and architecture. Else the investigation will certainly futile.

9.11 UPDATING CYBER LAWS IN CYBER TERRORISM

Critical infrastructure protection is an issue with almost all nations today, and local law enforcement will have to contend in the future. With the adoption of open SCADA protocols, it is now possible to attack these infrastructures with far less preparation and expense than in the past. State and local law enforcement agencies are frequently the recipient of threats against critical infrastructure components and, many times, are the first responders to attacks on them. Of particular concern is the gap between training and technologies available to and used by law enforcement, especially State and local agencies and the advanced technologies used by persons and groups committing electronic crimes.

Effective, uniform laws and regulations that keep pace with electronic crime need to be formulated, circulated and applied at the Federal and State levels from time to time. As the computer use is growing in an exponential manner, so is the cybercrimes. Deterring and punishing these offenders requires a legal structure that will support early detection and successful prosecutions. Examples of emerging trends include the increased reliance of criminals and terrorists on encryption technologies and obvious efforts to cloak the identity and location of offenders. Currently, there is no effective legal mechanism to require that subpoenas generated in one State be enforced in another.

Clearly, the laws defining computer offenses, as well as the legal methods needed to properly investigate current electronic crimes, have lagging behind technological and social changes. Hence need cooperation with the high-tech industry and the crime solvers need the industry's full support and cooperation to control electronic crime. Industry support is needed to develop and maintain trusted relationships and cooperative agreements to help sponsor training, join task forces, and share equipment for the examination of electronic evidence. These cooperative relationships can also encourage the reporting of electronic crime.

A study on global cyber-terrorism confirms the need for industry and government to work together to address the growing problem of computer intrusions and cybercrime in general. Only by sharing information about incidents, and threats, and exploited vulnerabilities can we begin to stem the rising tide of illegal activity on networks and protect our nation's critical infrastructure from destructive cyber-attacks. Many technology firms have their own information security units that, among other responsibilities, detect and investigate electronic crime. Increased cooperation between industry and government provides the best opportunity to control electronic crime and protect the Nation's critical infrastructure, which heavily relies upon computer technology. The most important aspect of these challenges is the time sensitivity. Hence there is a need to maximize investments in new or expanded tools, training, onsite assistance, and research to prevent cybercrime and cyber terrorism.

Summary

At present, the advanced cybercrimes posing significant challenges to the existing legal system, because technology is moving at an exponential rate. Legislators, judges, law enforcement, and lawyers are behind the eight ball because of their constraint to keep up with technological advancements in the digital world and the complexity of the problems involved. Law enforcement needs to know how to capture a cybercriminal, properly seize and control/(capture) evidence, and hand over those evidences to the prosecutorial and defense teams. Both teams must understand what truthfully took place in a cybercrime, how it was carried out, and what legal precedents to use to prove their points in court. Many times, investigating police officers, judges and juries are confused by the technology, terms, and concepts used in these types of trials, and laws are not written fast enough to properly punish the guilty cybercriminals. Law enforcement, the court system, and the legal community are definitely experiencing growth pains as they are being pulled into the technology of the 21st century. It is an absolute truth and real fact is that most of the present system of cyber-terrorism investigations usually attempt to hide their incompetency of existing Cyber Laws and technical unawareness by fabricating concocted versions for evading/referring the investigation which lead the culprits always escaping or find a safe exit from the charges framed.

Abbreviations

ADO	Advanced Distribution Operation
ADU	Application Data Unit
AER	All Electronic Range
AES	Advanced Encryption Standard
AH	Authentication Header
AMI	Advanced Metering Infrastructure
AMR	Automatic Meter Reading
ANSI	American National Standard Institute
AP	Access Point
API	Application Programming Interface
APT	Advanced Persistent Threat
ARP	Address Resolution Protocol
ASAI	Average System Availability Index
ASCII	American Standard Code for Information Interchange
ASD	Adjustable Speed Drives
ASEAN	Association of Southeast Asian Nations
ATM	Asynchronous Transfer Mode
BCMAC	Block Chaining Message Authentication Code
BES	Bulk Electric System
BGP	Border Gateway Protocol
BPLC	Broadband Power Line Communication
CATV	Coaxial Cable TV

CCA	CCA Centre for Cyber Assessment
CCF	Common Cause Failure
CDMA	Code Division Multiple Access
CEA	Central Electricity Authority
CERC	Centre Electricity Regulatory Commission
CERT	Computer Emergency Response Team
CERT-In	CERT-In Indian Computer Emergency Response Team
CESG	Communications-Electronics Security Group
CFE	Communication Front End
CIAC	Critical Infrastructure Advisory Council
CII	Critical Information Infrastructure
CIIP	Critical Information Infrastructure Protection
CIP	Critical Infrastructure Protection
CIR	Critical Infrastructure Resilience
CISO	Chief Information Security Officer
CIWIN	Critical Infrastructure Warning Information Network
CMF	Common Mode Failure
COTS	Commercial off-the Shelf
CPNI	Centre for the Protection of National Infrastructure
CSMA/CD	Carrier Sense Multiple Access/Collision Detection
CSOC	Cyber Security Operations Centre
CTSA	Counter Terrorism Security Advisor
DCS	Distributed Control Systems
DCU	Data Control Unit
DER	Distributed Energy Resources
DMS	Distributed Management System
DMZ	De Militarized Zone
DNP	Distribution Network Protocol

DNS	Domain Name Servers
DOS	Denial Of Service
DDoS	Distributed Denial of Service
DP	Distributed Power
DPSCI	Documented Power System Cyber Incidents
DST	Decision Support Tools
EAP	External Access Point
EBCDIC	Extended Binary Coded Decimal Interchange Mode
ECB	Electronic Code Block
ECI	European Critical Infrastructures
ENISA	European Union Agency for Network and Information
ENS	End Node Security
EP3R	European Public-Private Partnership for Resilience
EPA	Enhanced Power Architecture
EPCIP	European Programme for Critical Infrastructure
ESP	Electronic Security perimeter
ESZ	Enterprise Security Zone
ETDR	Endpoint Threat Detection and Response
EU	European Union
FDDI	Fiber Distributed Data Interface
FDMA	Frequency Division Multiple Access
FEP	Front End Processor
FES	Flywheel Energy Storage
FMS	Fieldbus Message Specification
FOCS	Fibre Optical Current Sensor
FTP	File Transfer Protocol
FTS	Fault Tolerant System
FTTH	Fibre To The Home

FTTP	Fibre Transmission Transfer Protocol
GCHQ	Government Communications Headquarters
GIF	Graphic Interchange Format
GII	Global Information Infrastructure
GMPLS	Generalizes Multi-Protocol Label Switching
GoI	GoI Government of India
GOOSE	General Object Oriented Substation Event
GPS	Global Positioning System
GRE	General Routing Encapsulation
GSM	Global System For Mobile Communication
HA	High Availability
HASR	High Availability Seamless Redundancy
HDLC	High Level Data Link Control
HHU	Hand-Held Unit
HMAC	Hash-based Message Authentication Code
HMI	Human Machine Interfaces
HSIN-CI	Homeland Security Information Network-Critical
HTTP	Hypertext Transfer Protocol
ICCP	Intercontrol Centre Communication Protocol
ICMP	Internet Control Message Protocol
ICONS	Industry Consultation on National Security
ICS	Industrial Control System
ICT	Information and Communication
IDS	Intrusion Detection System
IEC	International Electrotechnical Commission
IED	Intelligent Electronic Device
IEEE	Institute Of Electrical and Electronics Engineering
IGMP	Internet Group Management Protocol

IMAP	Internet Message Access Protocol
IP	Internet Protocol
IP FRR	IP Fast Reroute
IPS	Intrusion Prevention System
IPSec	Internet Protocol Security
IPX	Internetwork Packet Exchange
ISA	International Society for Automation
ISD	Information Security Division
ISDN	Integrated Service Digital Network
ISIS	Islamic State of Iraq and Syria
ISMS	Information Security Management System
ISO	International Organisation for Standards
IT	Information Technologies
L2TP	Layer 2 Tunnelling Protocol
LAN	Local Area Networks
LDMS	Local Data Monitoring System
LDP	Label Distribution Protocol
LLC	Logical Link Control
LSP	Label Switched Path
LTE	Long Term Evaluation
MAC	Media Access Control
MAU	Multistation Access Unit
MBP	Manchester Bus Powered
MCC	Master Control Centre
MDMS	Meter Data Management
MITM	Man In The Middle attack
MMS	Manufacturing Messaging Specification
MPLS	Multi-Protocol Label Switching

MU	Merging Unit
NAS	Network Access Server
NATO	North Atlantic Treaty Organization
NCIIPC	National Critical Information Infrastructure Protection Centre
NCSC	National Cyber Security Centre
NERC	North American Electric Reliability Corporation
NFS	Network File System
NIC	Network Interface Card
NIC	National Informatics Centre
NII	National Information Infrastructure
NIPP	National Infrastructure Protection Plan
NIS	Network and Information Security
NIST	National Institute For Standard and Technology
NLDC	National Load Dispatch Centre
NNTP	Network News Transport Protocol
O&M	Operation and Maintenance
OAREC	Optimal and Automatic Residential Energy Consumption
OCSIA	Office of Cyber Security and Information Assurance
OCSP	Online Certificate Status Protocol
OECD	Organisation for Economic Co-operation and
OEM	OEM Original Equipment Manufacturer
OFB	Output Feedback
OFDMA	Orthogonal frequency division multiple access
OS	Operating System
OSI	Open System Interconnection
OSPF	Open Shortest Path First
OT	Operational Technology
PAC	Programmable Automation Controller

PC	Personal Computer
PCI	Peripheral Component Interconnect
PCMCIA	Personal Computer Memory Card International Association
PDF	Portable Document Format
PDU	Protocol Data Unit
PKI	Public Key Infrastructure
PLC	Programmable Logic Controller
PLCC	Power Line Carrier Communication
POP3	Post Office Protocol version 3
PPA	Profibus Process Automation
PPP	Point-To-Point Protocol
PPTP	Point To Point Tunnelling Protocol
PSS	Power System SCADA
PSTN	Public Switched Telephone Network
QR	Quick Removing
RAS	Remote Access Server
REA	Rural Electric Association
RLDC	Regional Load Dispatch Centres
ROW	Right Of Way
RSVP	Resource Reservation Protocol
RTOS	Real Time Operating System
RTU	Remote Terminal Unit
SCADA	Supervisory Control And Data Acquisition
SDO	Standard and Specification Development Organization
SERC	State Electricity Regulatory Commission
SIEM	Security Information and Event Management
SLA	Service Level Agreement
SLDC	State Load Dispatch Centre

SM	Smart Meter
SMTP	Simple Mail Transfer Protocol
SNMP	Simple Network Management Protocol
SQL	Sructured Query Language
TC	Technical Committee
TCP	Transmission Control Protocol
TCP/IP	Transmission Control Protocol/Internet Protocol
TDM	Time Division Multiplexing
TDMA	Time Division Multiple Access
TFTP	Trivial File Transfer Protocol
TIFF	Tagged Image File Format
TISN	Trusted Information Sharing Network
TLS	Transport Layer Security
UDP	User Data Protocol
UN	United Nation
USB	Universal Serial Bus
UTP	Unshielded Twisted Pair
VPN	Virtual Private Network
WAN	Wide Area Network
WG	Working Group
WWW	World Wide Web
ZDA	Zero Dynamic Attack
ZDV	Zero Day Vulnerability

Index

Made in the USA
Monee, IL
20 November 2023

46970163R00206